Scott Foresman - Addison Wesley
MIDDLE SCHOOL MATH

Assessment Sourcebook

Course 3

Scott Foresman - Addison Wesley

Editorial Offices: Menlo Park, California • Glenview, Illinois
Sales Offices: Reading, Massachusetts • Atlanta, Georgia • Glenview, Illinois
Carrollton, Texas • Menlo Park, California

http://www.sf.aw.com

ISBN 0–201–31300–6

Printed in the United States of America

1 2 3 4 5 6 7 8 9 10 – ML – 02 01 00 99 98 97

Table of Contents for Assessment Sourcebook

Table of Contents for Assessment Sourcebook *(continued)*

Assessing Student Performance in Mathematics

"Instead of assuming that the purpose of assessment is to rank students on a particular trait, the new approach assumes that high public expectations can be set that every student can strive for and achieve . . ."

—*NCTM Assessment Standards for School Mathematics*

Linking Assessment and Instruction

Recommendations made by the National Council of Teachers of Mathematics stress the importance of linking assessment and instruction methods. As teachers employ more diverse methods of instruction, such as hands-on activities, open-ended investigations, and long-term projects, they also need to employ diverse methods of assessment. As we make the goal of mathematics the acquisition of dynamic processes, we strive for methods of assessment that further our goals. Authentic assessment tools require critical thinking and problem solving, not merely mastery of facts and procedures.

Because instruction and its assessment are closely linked, methods of evaluation need to change as instructional methods change. New forms of assessment provide a more authentic way of evaluating the depth of our students' knowledge of mathematics rather than their ability to memorize facts and procedures. These alternative methods of assessment offer the opportunity for students to display how they approach problem situations, collect and organize information, formulate and test conjectures, and communicate their mathematical insights.

An authentic assessment program contains tasks that are appropriate to the topics students are learning and that provide outcomes that are valuable to the students. Such an assessment program allows for such highly individual factors as a school's curriculum objectives, a teacher's style of instruction, and a student's maturity level. Each individual teacher determines the assessment best suited to the needs of his or her students.

To help teachers select the most appropriate evaluation tools for their classrooms, the Assessment Sourcebook provides the following materials.

Informal Assessment Forms
- Student-completed forms for Math Logs (journals), Student Surveys, Self-evaluations, Portfolio Guides, and more
- Teacher-completed forms for Ongoing Assessment in Problem Solving, Observation, Cooperative Learning, as well as forms for assessing projects and portfolios

Formal Assessment Instruments
- Free-response chapter tests that cover every objective in the student text chapter; parallel forms (A and B) of this test are provided.
- Multiple-choice test for each chapter
- Alternative chapter assessment (Performance Assessment) comprised of several open-ended questions. Each test is accompanied by its own Evaluation Guide.
- Mixed-response chapter tests that include a short performance task
- Mixed-response cumulative chapter test that prepares students for standardized tests and includes items for current chapter objectives along with items covering concepts from previous chapters
- Item Analysis Management Forms that teachers can use to evaluate student comprehension of each chapter objective
- Class record forms

"Assessment should be a means of fostering growth toward high expectations."

—*NCTM Assessment Standards for School Mathematics*

Guidelines for Developing an Authentic Assessment Program

Developing an authentic program of assessment is an ongoing process. Some assessment instruments will seem perfectly suited to the teacher and his or her students from the start. Others may be effective only after the teacher has had a chance to experiment with and refine them. Still others may be inappropriate for a given class or instructional situation. The following are some guidelines that may be helpful when choosing the types of assessment for a particular program.

Use an assessment form that serves your purposes.

- For the teacher, assessment yields feedback on the appropriateness of instructional methods and offers some clues as to how the content or pace of instruction could be modified.
- For the students, assessment should not only identify areas for improvement, but should also affirm their successes.
- Traditional forms of assessment yield a tangible score.

Make the assessment process a positive experience for students.

- Use a variety of assessment techniques.
- Provide opportunities for students to demonstrate their mathematical capabilities in an atmosphere that allows maximum performance.
- Emphasize what students *do* know and *can* do, not what they do not know and cannot do.
- Motivate students to achieve by using tasks that reflect the value of their efforts.

Use performance assessment to focus on higher-order thinking skills.

- Performance assessment provides a picture of the student as a critical thinker and problem solver.
- Performance assessment helps to identify *how* the student does mathematics, not just what answer he or she gets.

Provide assessment activities that resemble day-to-day tasks.

- Use activities similar to instructional activities to do assessment.
- Use assessment activities to further instruction.
- Give students the immediate and detailed feedback they need to further the learning process.
- Encourage students to explore how the mathematics they are learning applies to everyday life.

Include each student as a partner in the assessment process.

- Encourage students to reflect on what they have done.
- Encourage students to share their goals.

Making and Using an Assessment Portfolio

For students and teachers alike, portfolios are exciting records of progress. In mathematics, the process of making a portfolio and adding materials to it on an ongoing basis is an extremely effective method for learning and assessment. A math portfolio can contain student work, including projects, reports, drawings, reflections, and formal assessment instruments.

As students review their portfolios, they observe concrete evidence of their growth in skills and confidence. For many students, seeing progress is believing.

> *"Large pieces of work like performance tasks, projects, and portfolios provide opportunities for students to demonstrate growth in mathematical power."*
>
> —NCTM Assessment Standards for School Mathematics

Getting Started

There are many procedures that students and teachers can use to make and use portfolios. It might be helpful to use a two-stage approach for keeping student portfolios. In this approach, students use a Work Portfolio, which contains the work they have completed in a period of a few weeks. At designated times, the teacher and student can evaluate the Work Portfolio and transfer materials to the Assessment Portfolio.

At the beginning of the school year, you will want to do the following:

- Provide two file folders for each student.
- Have students label one folder *Work Portfolio* and the other *Assessment Portfolio*.

About the Work Portfolio

The *Work Portfolio* is for "work in progress" and recently completed materials. The student should have access to it on a day-to-day basis and should keep in it all class work, group work, homework, and projects for the current period, including student assessment forms such as *My Math Log*.

- You can periodically review students' *Work Portfolios* to verify that students are completing assignments on time.
- You can write notes to students, commenting on individual items in their *Work Portfolios*.
- Every two to six weeks students should review their *Work Portfolios* to determine which materials they would like to transfer to their *Assessment Portfolios*. (See below.)
- After transferring selected items to the *Assessment Portfolio*, students complete the *Portfolio Guide* forms and take home all items remaining in the *Work Portfolio*.

About the Assessment Portfolio

- The *Assessment Portfolio* contains materials that will help students and teachers evaluate progress over the course of a time interval such as a marking period or a school year. Some of the materials included in the *Assessment Portfolio* will be chosen by students and some may be chosen by teachers.

You may find it helpful to schedule Portfolio conferences with individual students. In that way, you can work with students to evaluate materials. The following questions may help guide students and teachers as they evaluate materials for the Assessment Portfolios:

- Does an item illustrate the student's ways of thinking about mathematical processes?
- Does an item show a baseline—a starting point for a given year?
- Does an item show progress, or growth in understanding, over time?

- Is an item an example of how mathematics connects with experiences outside the classroom?
- Does the item show positive attitudes toward mathematics?
- Does the item show problem-solving processes?

The following list includes some, but not all, of the materials you and your students may want to include in their Assessment Portfolios.

- Student-selected items from the Work Portfolio
- Letter from the student about the work included in the Assessment Portfolio
- Math autobiography
- Other work selected by you and the student, including math surveys, formal assessments, and informal assessments such as interviews and observations.

> *"The opportunity to share mathematical ideas through portfolios can mark a real turning point in student attitudes."*
>
> —NCTM Mathematical Assessment

Evaluating a Portfolio

When you need to evaluate student Assessment Portfolios, you may want to use the following tips:

- Keep in mind that portfolio evaluation is a matter of ongoing discussion.
- Set aside time to discuss the Assessment Portfolio with the student.
- Use the Assessment Portfolio when discussing the student's progress with his or her family.
- Use it as a basis for identifying strengths and weaknesses and for setting group and individual goals for the next period.
- Consider developing your own rubrics or other criteria for evaluating portfolios.

Table of Contents for Assessment Forms

Assessment Forms

Using Assessment Forms

This sourcebook provides eight forms that students can use as aids to self-assessment. Use one or more depending upon students' needs.

Form	Purpose	Suggested Uses
My Math Log	To write about experiences in mathematics	Keep a daily math journal which lets students reflect on how mathematics relates to daily life.
Student Survey	To check student attitudes toward various math activities	Periodically monitor the change in student attitudes toward math.
Group Learning Self-Evaluation	To evaluate student interaction with members of groups	Complete at the conclusion of group projects.
Group Work Log	To keep records of group assignments	Monitor and evaluate group assignments.
Checklist for Problem-Solving Guidelines	To organize problem-solving efforts Follows the steps given in the Student Edition	Monitor student use of the problem-solving process.
Student Self-Assessment	To encourage student awareness of independent work	Monitor student progress in working independently.
Portfolio Guide	To describe the contents of student's portfolio	Update when student places materials in his or her *Assessment Portfolio*.
My Math Experiences	To summarize attitudes toward and achievements in mathematics	Complete at the end of instructional periods.

Using Teacher-Completed Forms

Eight assessment forms are provided in this sourcebook to help you keep a record of authentic but informal assessments. Some forms are for use with individual students while others are for use with groups of students.

Form	Purpose	Suggested Uses
Assessing Performance in Problem Solving	To assess individual students in a problem-solving situation	Describe the level of student performance. Modify instruction to meet individual needs.
Ongoing Assessment: Problem Solving	To assess groups of students in problem-solving situations	Assess the entire class. Assess small groups over time.
Ongoing Assessment: Observation	To observe and assess several students at one time	Provide a mathematical profile of the entire class. Identify common strengths and weaknesses. Modify pace or content. Determine appropriate groupings.
Ongoing Assessment: Cooperative Learning	To assess student abilities to work constructively in groups	Assess one or more cooperative groups.
Individual Assessment Through Observation	To determine the student's thought processes, performance, and attitudes	Record observation of a student in the classroom.
Overall Student Assessment	To summarize each student's overall performance	Evaluate student performance over an entire instructional period.
Project/Presentation Checklist	To evaluate oral presentations or extended projects	Prepare students and evaluate presentations or projects.
Portfolio Assessment	To evaluate individual portfolios	Periodically evaluate contents of portfolio. Help students assess process of creating a portfolio.

My Math Log

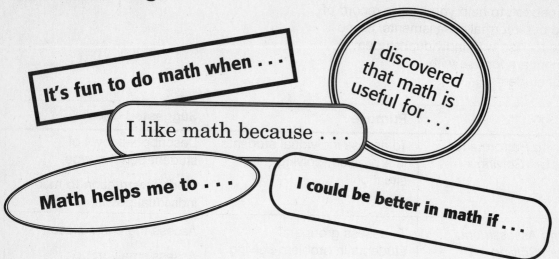

Use this sheet to help you write about math.

You may use the phrases above to help you get started.

You may use the space at the bottom for math drawings or sample problems.

_____

_____

_____

_____

_____

_____

_____

Name _____

Date _____

Student Survey

For each statement, record a ✔ to tell how you feel.

	Most of the time	Some of the time	Hardly ever
I am good in math.			
I need help on most problems.			
I see how math is used in real life.			
I understand word problems.			
I can solve most problems.			
I like to try new strategies.			
I give up easily.			
I keep an organized notebook.			
I think math is fun.			

Describe a project you would like the class to work on.

_____

_____

What is your favorite kind of math? Explain why.

_____

_____

List some activities outside of school where you have used math.

_____

_____

Name _____

Date _____

Group Learning Self-Evaluation

Group Members: _____

_____

Read each statement and rate your group 4 if you agree with the statement, 3 if you somewhat agree, 2 if you somewhat disagree, or 1 if you disagree. Use NA, not applicable, if the statement does not apply in this situation. Circle one response for each description of your group.

Members of the group . . .	agree	somewhat agree	somewhat disagree	disagree	not applicable
performed their assigned roles.	4	3	2	1	NA
understood the purpose of the assignment.	4	3	2	1	NA
understood the solution to the assignment.	4	3	2	1	NA
listened to each other's ideas.	4	3	2	1	NA
gave feedback to those who contributed ideas.	4	3	2	1	NA
stayed on task.	4	3	2	1	NA
assisted in preparing the work that was collected.	4	3	2	1	NA
had their assignment from the previous day.	4	3	2	1	NA
expressed their ideas to the group.	4	3	2	1	NA
were willing to compromise when needed.	4	3	2	1	NA
_____	4	3	2	1	NA

By working in a group, I _____

_____

_____

Name _____

Date _____

Group Work Log

Group Members: _____

_____

List the date, assignment, and page numbers for each group assignment. Describe how the group worked together to arrive at a group solution for the assignment. Mention any techniques that you found helpful in completing the assignment.

Date	Assignment	Description of Group's Work

Name _____

Date _____

Checklist for Problem-Solving Guidelines

Put a ✔ in the box after you answer each question or complete each part.

━ Understand ━

☐ What do you know? _____

_____

_____

☐ What do you need to find? _____

_____

━ Plan ━

☐ Decide how you will find the solution. _____

_____

☐ Have you solved a similar problem? _____

☐ What strategies will you use? _____

_____

☐ Estimate the solution. _____

_____

━ Solve ━

☐ Use your plan. Show your solution.

☐ What is the solution? Give a complete sentence.

_____

━ Look Back ━

☐ Did you answer the question? _____

☐ Does your answer make sense? _____

Name _____

Date _____

Student Self-Assessment

Assignment: _____

Write about what you did.

What were you trying to learn? _____

_____

_____

How did you start your work? _____

_____

_____

What materials did you need? _____

_____

What did you learn? _____

_____

_____

Check the sentences that describe your work.

_____ I made a plan before I began my work.

_____ I was able to do the work.

_____ I did not understand the directions.

_____ I followed the directions but got the wrong answer.

_____ I found a different way to do this assignment.

_____ I could explain how to do this to someone else.

_____ The work was easier than I thought it would be.

_____ The work was harder than I thought it would be.

_____ Other: _____

_____

Portfolio Guide

Put check marks in the table below to describe your portfolio.

	Required by my teacher	Planned by me	Included
Table of contents			
Letter of explanation			
Corrected homework			
Corrected tests			
Numbers			
Number operations			
Measurement			
Graphing			
Geometry/shapes			
Patterns			
Fractions/mixed numbers			
Decimals			
Ratios, proportions, percents			
Mental math/estimation			
Probability			
Statistics			
Algebra			
Connections to science			
Connections to reading/literature			
Connections to social studies/history			
Connections to geography			
Connections to my life			
Essay on math			
Photos/sketches related to math			
Project			
Favorite problems			
Picture of work with manipulatives			
Journal entry			
Group work			
Paragraph: How this portfolio has been helpful			

Name ______________________________

Date ____________________

Math Experiences

My Math Experiences

Math that interests me: ______________________________

____

____

____

____

My math goals: ______________________________

____

____

____

____

Math skills I have mastered: ______________________________

____

____

____

____

Math skills I need to work on: ______________________________

____

____

Math awards I have received: ______________________________

____

____

____

____

Assessing Performance in Problem Solving

Student _____ Date _____

Put a check in the column that accurately describes the student's work.

	Frequently	Sometimes	Never
Understand			
Reads the problem carefully	_____	_____	_____
Studies any tables or graphs	_____	_____	_____
Can restate the problem in own words	_____	_____	_____
Can identify given information	_____	_____	_____
Can identify the question to be answered	_____	_____	_____
Plan			
Chooses an appropriate solution strategy	_____	_____	_____
Estimates the answer	_____	_____	_____
Solve			
Works systematically	_____	_____	_____
Shows solution in an organized fashion	_____	_____	_____
Computes correctly	_____	_____	_____
Gives answer in a sentence, with correct units	_____	_____	_____
Look Back			
Checks reasonableness of answer	_____	_____	_____
Tries other ways to solve the problem	_____	_____	_____
Attitude			
Shows a willingness to try the problem	_____	_____	_____
Demonstrates self-confidence	_____	_____	_____
Perseveres in problem-solving attempts	_____	_____	_____

Other Comments

Ongoing Assessment: Problem Solving

Date ______________________

Rate each item with a
+ if excellent
✔ if satisfactory
– if needs improvement
NA if not applicable

	Reads problem carefully	Studies any tables or graphs	Can restate problem in own words	Can identify given information	Can identify question to be answered	Chooses appropriate strategy	Estimates what the answer should be	Works systematically	Shows solution in organized fashion	Computes correctly	States answer in sentence giving correct units	Checks that the answer is reasonable	Tries other ways to solve problem
1.													
2.													
3.													
4.													
5.													
6.													
7.													
8.													
9.													
10.													
11.													
12.													
13.													
14.													
15.													
16.													
17.													
18.													
19.													
20.													
21.													
22.													
23.													
24.													
25.													
26.													
27.													
28.													

Ongoing Assessment: Observation

Date ______________________________

Rate each item with a
+ if excellent
✔ if satisfactory
− if needs improvement
NA if not applicable

	Demonstrates knowledge of skills	Understands concepts	Works neatly and systematically	Works well with others	Displays a positive attitude	Considers and uses ideas of others	Shows patience and perseverance	Asks for help when needed	Uses time productively	Tries alternate approaches			
1.													
2.													
3.													
4.													
5.													
6.													
7.													
8.													
9.													
10.													
11.													
12.													
13.													
14.													
15.													
16.													
17.													
18.													
19.													
20.													
21.													
22.													
23.													
24.													
25.													
26.													
27.													
28.													

Ongoing Assessment: Cooperative Learning

Date ______________________

Rate each item with a
- \+ if excellent
- ✔ if satisfactory
- – if needs improvement
- NA if not applicable

	Performs assigned role	Stays on task	Demonstrates problem-solving ability	Works systematically	Works with others in the group	Tutors and helps others	Considers and uses ideas of others	Speaks quietly	Expresses ideas to others	Initiates questions	Has a positive attitude	Shows patience and perseverance	Disagrees without being disagreeable
1.													
2.													
3.													
4.													
5.													
6.													
7.													
8.													
9.													
10.													
11.													
12.													
13.													
14.													
15.													
16.													
17.													
18.													
19.													
20.													
21.													
22.													
23.													
24.													
25.													
26.													
27.													
28.													

Individual Assessment Through Observation

Student _____   Date _____

	Frequently	Sometimes	Never
Understanding			
Demonstrates knowledge of skills	_____	_____	_____
Understands concepts	_____	_____	_____
Selects appropriate solution strategies	_____	_____	_____
Solves problems accurately	_____	_____	_____
Work Habits			
Works in an organized manner	_____	_____	_____
Works neatly	_____	_____	_____
Gets work in on time	_____	_____	_____
Works well with others	_____	_____	_____
Uses time productively	_____	_____	_____
Asks for help when needed	_____	_____	_____
Confidence			
Initiates questions	_____	_____	_____
Displays a positive attitude	_____	_____	_____
Helps others	_____	_____	_____
Flexibility			
Tries alternate approaches	_____	_____	_____
Considers and uses ideas of others	_____	_____	_____
Uses mental math and estimation	_____	_____	_____
Uses calculators and other technology	_____	_____	_____
Perseverance			
Shows patience and perseverance	_____	_____	_____
Works systematically	_____	_____	_____
Is willing to try	_____	_____	_____
Checks work without being told	_____	_____	_____
Other			
_____	_____	_____	_____
_____	_____	_____	_____

© Scott Foresman Addison Wesley 8

Overall Student Assessment

Date ______________________

Rate each item with a
+ if excellent
✔ if satisfactory
– if needs improvement
NA if not applicable

	Problem Solving	Cooperative Learning	Math Writing	Class Work	Homework	Participation in Discussion	Quiz Scores	Test Scores					
1.													
2.													
3.													
4.													
5.													
6.													
7.													
8.													
9.													
10.													
11.													
12.													
13.													
14.													
15.													
16.													
17.													
18.													
19.													
20.													
21.													
22.													
23.													
24.													
25.													
26.													
27.													
28.													

Project/Presentation Checklist

This form can be used to evaluate an oral or written student project made by one student or a group of students. This checklist also can be used to discuss successful methods for making presentations, or given to students to help guide them in planning their projects such as mathematical art, scientific experiments, data gathering for charts and graphs, computer demonstrations, skits, or oral and written research projects.

Student(s) _____

Project _____

The Project

> Rate each item with a
> + if excellent
> ✔ if satisfactory
> − if needs improvement
> NA if not applicable

_____ Demonstrates a mathematical concept properly

_____ Communicates math ideas clearly

_____ Shows a connection to another subject

_____ Shows time spent in planning and preparation

_____ Is original and/or creative

_____ Is colorful and neat

_____ Stimulates further investigation of the topic

_____ Includes a written report

_____ Lists resources used

_____ Shows delegation of tasks among group members

The Oral Presentation

_____ Demonstrates a knowledge of the mathematical concept

_____ Is organized, and includes an introduction, main section, and conclusion

_____ Uses audio-visual props where appropriate

_____ Speaks clearly and paces presentation at proper speed

_____ Answers questions and stimulates further interest in the topic

_____ Demonstrates a positive problem-solving attitude

_____ Mentions resources used

© Scott Foresman Addison Wesley 8

Portfolio Assessment

Student _____   Date _____

	Required	Included	Comments
Table of Contents			
Letter from student • Explanation of contents • Criteria for selection			
Excerpt from Journal			
Working solution to an open-ended question			
Photo or sketch of problem worked with manipulatives			
Mathematical connections • Problems that work with more than one chapter • Problems that work with more than one area of math			
Subject-area connections • Problems that show connections with health, science, art, literature, data collection, social science, history, or geography			
Quiz, test, or homework; corrected or revised homework			
Projects			
Paragraph from student • How making a portfolio has been helpful			

© Scott Foresman Addison Wesley 8

Table of Contents for Tests and Quizzes

Tests and Quizzes

Using the Quizzes and Chapter Tests Forms A, B, C, E, F

Assessment should be compatible with styles of learning and teaching. The *Assessment Sourcebook* offers several options for formal assessment. As teachers, you set the instructional styles for your classroom. The various forms of chapter tests help you incorporate assessment into whatever instructional styles you choose.

Teachers use written tests for many purposes. Particularly when a test is objective-referenced, it can be an efficient method of diagnosing the scope of a student's mathematical understanding. Tests can also provide valuable instructional feedback. And, of course, grades are a traditional instrument for reporting student achievement to parents, administrators, and the community. You may wish to have students show their work for all test forms. When space is limited for this on the test page, ask that they include an additional sheet of paper with their work shown.

Quizzes (one per section)
There is a 1-page quiz for each section of the Student Edition. It covers each objective from the section.

Chapter Test Forms A and B (free response)
Each test covers all of the objectives of the chapter in the Student Edition in a free-response format. Forms A and B are essentially parallel to each other. You can use forms A and B together as pre- or post-tests. If you administer Form A and the test results show that students need additional instruction for particular objectives, you can reteach the objectives and then administer Form B.

The Item Analysis for Individual Assessment (in the Management Forms section of this *Assessment Sourcebook*) correlates these test items to objectives from the course, and it provides review options that you may use as needed.

While free-response tests are generally designed for written responses, they may also be used orally with individual students. An oral response approach might be especially helpful with students having special needs and with students who have limited proficiency in English.

Chapter Test Form C (multiple choice)
Form C is a 4–6 page multiple-choice test, which includes items that test every chapter objective. Because Test C is longer than Tests A and B, there are more items per objective. Even though Test C has a multiple-choice format, students taking these tests are not limited to performing calculations. Items, including word problems, are designed to assess understanding of concepts. In many school districts, students are required to take standardized tests. Using Test Form C provides students with practice in responding to multiple-choice questions, which are often used in standardized tests. You may want to have students use the Answer Form for Multiple-Choice Tests provided on page 292.

The Item Analysis for Individual Assessment (in the Management Forms section of this *Assessment Sourcebook*) correlates these test items to objectives from the course, and it provides review options that you may use as needed.

Chapter Test Form D (performance test)
This form is a 1-page performance test. The use of this form and its accompanying Evaluation Guide is discussed on page 29 of this *Assessment Sourcebook*.

Chapter Test Form E (mixed response)
This test is a 2–3 page mixed-response test, which includes free-response and multiple-choice items. At the end of each Test Form E, there is a performance task, which requires students to apply mathematical concepts in a real-life application. Because Test Form E includes varied types of test items, you are able to use one test to evaluate understanding for students with varied learning and assessment styles.

The Item Analysis for Individual Assessment (in the Management Forms section of this *Assessment Sourcebook*) correlates these test items to objectives from the course, and it provides review options that you may use as needed.

Chapter Test Form F (cumulative chapter test)

This 2–4 page test is a mixed-response test designed to prepare students for standardized tests. About two-thirds of the test covers all of the objectives from the chapter at hand. The rest of the test covers important objectives from previous chapters. The test items are both free response and multiple choice.

There are three sections on each test. The first section, *Computation*, includes exercises designed to assess student ability to perform calculations. The second section, *Concepts*, assesses student understanding of mathematical ideas. The third section, *Applications*, provides opportunities for students to apply what they have learned in class to real-world situations.

The Item Analysis for Individual Assessment (in the Management Forms section of this *Assessment Sourcebook*) correlates these test items to objectives from the course, and it provides review options that you may use as needed.

Evaluating the Quizzes and Chapter Tests Forms A, B, C, E, and F

For Test Forms A and B, answers are displayed on reduced facsimiles of student pages. These answers begin on page 296. Answers for the Quizzes and Chapter Test Forms C, E, and F begin on page 308. While many numerical answers are straightforward, it is important to keep in mind that a student may not use the exact wording given for problems requiring written explanation. Also, it is a good idea to refer to students' work and grant partial credit if the work is correct, but the answer is not. A Percent Table for Scoring is found on page 345 of this *Assessment Sourcebook*.

Using Chapter Test Form D (Performance Assessment)

> "Possessing mathematical power includes being able, and predisposed, to apply mathematical understanding in new situations, as well as having the confidence to do so."
>
> —NCTM Assessment Standards for School Mathematics

Students often wonder aloud when they will ever need to use a particular concept or skill. By using long term projects and performance tasks, teachers respond to students' need for meaningful learning experiences. As teachers expand their use of projects and other authentic tasks for teaching mathematics, performance assessment becomes a logical choice for assessing student understanding of mathematics.

For each chapter, the *Assessment Sourcebook* provides Test Form D, which is a performance assessment. Many of these tests provide information about a realistic situation and ask students to use new information along with their mathematics power to solve problems. Most of the problems are open ended, with an emphasis on finding meaningful solutions rather than calculating one and only one correct response.

The mathematical tasks included in Test Form D allow students to demonstrate a broad spectrum of abilities. By using performance assessment, you can evaluate how students:

- reason through problems
- make and test conjectures
- use number sense to predict reasonable answers
- utilize alternative strategies.

Performance tests also give you a way to assess student qualities of imagination, creativity, and perseverance.

Administering Chapter Test Form D

Managing performance-assessment projects may be more difficult than managing other types of assessment. The following tips may help you with classroom management during performance assessment administration.

- Consider having students work in groups to complete a performance assessment.
- Move among students as they work to collect anecdotal information during the test. Ask questions that will give you information about thought processes.
- Spend time at the beginning of the test to be sure all students understand the purpose.
- You may wish to share the evaluation standards on the Evaluation Guide with students before they begin work.

Evaluating Chapter Test Form D

The *Assessment Sourcebook* provides a 1-page **Evaluation Guide** on the reverse side of each Test Form D. This page includes teacher notes that identify the mathematical concepts and skills involved in performing the assessment task.

For each test, a set of task-specific evaluation standards helps you evaluate student work. These standards identify four levels of performance. Specific standards were created using the following characteristics of student performance as general guidelines.

Level 4: Accomplishes and extends the task; displays in-depth understanding; communicates effectively and completely.

Level 3: Substantially completes the task; displays minor flaws in understanding or technique; communicates successfully.

Level 2: Partially completes the task; displays one or more major errors in understanding or technique; communicates unclear and/or incomplete information.

Level 1: Makes an attempt; gives little evidence of understanding; communicates little relevant information.

Because performance assessments are open-ended, student responses may be as varied and individual as the students themselves. For that reason, you may find it helpful to use these general standards as well as the task-specific standards when evaluating student performance.

By providing students with information about the standards, you can make each of them an integral part of his or her own assessment.

Using the Inventory Test and Quarterly Tests

Inventory Test

A four-page Inventory Test helps assess student skill levels at the beginning of the school year. The Item Analysis for Individual Assessment (in the Management Forms section of this *Assessment Sourcebook*) correlates these test items to objectives from the course, and it provides review options that you may use as needed.

Evaluating the Inventory Test

Answers for the Inventory Test are given on page 308. A Percent Table for Scoring is found on page 345 of this *Assessment Sourcebook*.

Quarterly Tests

Four Quarterly Tests (cumulative tests covering chapters 1–3, 1–6, 1–9, and 1–12 respectively) help maintain ongoing assessment of student mastery of the course objectives. The Item Analysis for Individual Assessment (in the Management Forms section of this *Assessment Sourcebook*) correlates these test items to objectives from the course, and it provides review options that you may use as needed.

Evaluating the Quarterly Tests

Answers for the Quarterly Tests are given sequentially after the answers for Test Form F for Chapters 3, 6, 9, and 12, respectively. A Percent Table for Scoring is found on page 345 of this *Assessment Sourcebook*.

Give the letter of the correct answer.

1. The data value 92 is represented in a stem-and-leaf diagram.   1. _____
   How is it displayed?

   A 9 is the stem and 2 is the leaf.
   B 2 is the stem and 9 is the leaf.
   C 92 is the stem and 0 is the leaf.
   D 2 is the stem and 90 is the leaf.

2. Consider the data 8, 8, 2, 3, 10, 6, 5. Which of the following is 6?   2. _____

   A Mean and median   **B** Mean   **C** Median   **D** Mode

3. Which statement is true about two sets of data whose   3. _____
   scatterplot shows a positive relationship?

   A One set of data increases as the other decreases.
   B The sets of data increase together.
   C The sets neither increase or decrease together.
   D Not here

4. Evaluate $6 + 5 \cdot 0 - 12$.   4. _____

   A 50   **B** 104   **C** 44   **D** 5

5. Which expression shows 3 times the sum of a number n and 5?   5. _____

   A $3n + 5$ **B** $3(n + 5)$ **C** $5 + 3n$ **D** $3(5 - n)$

6. A rectangle has an area of 32 square inches. What is the height   6. _____
   of the rectangle if its base is 4 inches?

   A 24 inches   **B** 16 inches   **C** 8 inches   **D** Not here

7. Round 7.956792 to the nearest ten thousandth.   7. _____

   A 7.9568   **B** 7.96   **C** 17.95679   **D** 7.957

8. Find the product $2\frac{1}{4} \times 1\frac{1}{3} \times 3\frac{2}{5}$.   8. _____

   A $6\frac{1}{30}$ **B** $8\frac{2}{5}$ **C** $5\frac{1}{2}$ **D** $10\frac{1}{5}$

9. Write 3.617×10^8 in standard form.   9. _____

   A 361,700,000,000   **B** 36,170,000
   C 361,700,000   **D** 0.00000003617

10. Solve the equation $x - \dfrac{4}{7} = \dfrac{5}{14}$.

10. _____

   A $x = \dfrac{5}{14}$ **B** $x = \dfrac{11}{14}$ **C** $x = \dfrac{3}{49}$ **D** $x = \dfrac{13}{14}$

11. Find the difference $6\dfrac{1}{3} - 1\dfrac{4}{9}$.

11. _____

   A $7\dfrac{7}{9}$ **B** $5\dfrac{7}{9}$ **C** $4\dfrac{2}{3}$ **D** $4\dfrac{8}{9}$

12. A gear rotates every $3\dfrac{1}{2}$ seconds. How many times does it rotate in 28 seconds?

12. _____

   A 98 times   **B** 8 times   **C** 11 times   **D** $31\dfrac{1}{2}$ times

13. What is the sum of the angle measures in a hexagon?

13. _____

   A 720°   **B** 360°   **C** 900°   **D** 540°

14. Between which two consecutive whole numbers is $\sqrt{130}$?

14. _____

   A 10 and 11   **B** 11 and 12   **C** 12 and 13   **D** 13 and 14

15. Which of these sets of lengths can be the lengths of the sides of a right triangle?

15. _____

   A 5 inches, 6 inches, 7 inches   **B** 6 inches, 9 inches, 12 inches
   C 6 inches, 8 inches, 10 inches   **D** Not here

16. Which of the following is $3.60 for 5 cans written as a unit rate?

16. _____

   A $\dfrac{\$0.50}{1 \text{ can}}$ **B** $\dfrac{\$1}{2 \text{ cans}}$ **C** $\dfrac{\$5.00}{10 \text{ cans}}$ **D** $\dfrac{\$0.72}{1 \text{ can}}$

17. Which proportion is made up of ratios equivalent to $\dfrac{5}{8}$?

17. _____

   A $\dfrac{20}{26} = \dfrac{10}{13}$ **B** $\dfrac{3}{4} = \dfrac{9}{12}$ **C** $\dfrac{10}{16} = \dfrac{20}{32}$ **D** $\dfrac{1}{2} = \dfrac{6}{12}$

18. Solve the proportion $\dfrac{7}{12} = \dfrac{x}{18}$.

18. _____

   A $x = 1\dfrac{1}{2}$ **B** $x = 10\dfrac{1}{2}$ **C** $x = 15$ **D** $x = 105$

19. Two cities are 150 miles apart. How far apart will they appear on a map with the scale 1 inch = 25 miles?

19. _____

   A 6 inches   **B** 60 inches   **C** 150 inches   **D** Not here

Continued

20. Carla left school at 3:30 P.M. and walked to the park at a rate of   **20.** _____
5 mi/hr. If the park is 2.5 mi from the school, what time did she arrive?

   A 4:05 P.M.   **B** 3:35 P.M.   **C** 3:32 P.M.   **D** 4:00 P.M.

21. Which of these rates is slower than 60 miles per hour?   **21.** _____

   A 0.5 mile in 30 seconds   **B** 2.5 miles in 2 minutes
   C 18 miles in 15 minutes   **D** 50 feet per second

22. Jan's coin collection has gone up 50% in value since last year.   **22.** _____
If it was worth $200 last year, how much is it worth now?

   A $400   **B** $300   **C** $50   **D** $150

23. If sales tax is 8%, how much tax is charged on a $150 coat?   **23.** _____

   A $1.20   **B** $8.00   **C** $12.00   **D** $80.00

24. 6.3 is what percent of 90?   **24.** _____

   A 1.70%   **B** 7%   **C** 70%   **D** 170%

25. Which quadrant contains $(-2, -3)$?   **25.** _____

   A I   **B** II   **C** III   **D** IV

26. Which statement is true?   **26.** _____

   A The product of two negative integers is greater than either integer.
   B The product of two positive integers is less than either integer.
   C The product of two negative integers is less than either integer.
   D Not here

27. Find the sum $-6 + -5$.   **27.** _____

   A -11 **B** -30 **C** 30   **D** -1

28. Which equation shows the relationship between the variables   **28.** _____
in the table below?

x	1	2	3	4
y	-4	-8	-12	-16

   A $y = x - 4$ **B** $y = -4x$ **C** $y = \dfrac{x}{-4}$ **D** $y = x + 4$

29. Solve the equation $m + (-15) = 12$.   29. _____

A $m = -3$ B $m = -27$ C $m = 3$ D $m = 27$

30. Solve the equation $6x - 5 = 19$.   30. _____

A $x = 4$ B $x = 3$ C $x = -4$ D $x = 20$

31. How many faces, edges, and vertices does a triangular   31. _____
prism have?

A 5 faces, 8 edges, 5 vertices
B 4 faces, 6 edges, 4 vertices
C 6 faces, 12 edges, 8 vertices
D 5 faces, 9 edges, 6 vertices

32. Maria has a box with a volume of 3168 in^3. If the area of the   32. _____
base of the box is 288 in^2, what is its height?

A 11 in.   B 912,384 in.   C 12 in.   D 2880 in.

33. A circle graph shows that the Tigers won 60% of the games   33. _____
they played. What is the measure of the sector showing the wins?

A 320°   B 60°   C 216°   D 144°

34. What is the exact area of a circle whose radius is 6 cm?   34. _____

A 9π cm^2 B 36π cm^2 C 6π cm^2 D $\dfrac{198}{7}$ cm^2

35. How many different 4-digit numbers can be made from   35. _____
the digits 1–7 if no digits are repeated?

A 28   B 35   C 840   D 5040

36. How many different ways can a student choose 2 books from   36. _____
a shelf containing 3 books?

A 9   B 6   C 4   D 3

37. Which of these odds means the same thing as a probability of 25%? 37. _____

A 1:1   B 1:2   C 2:1   D 1:3

38. A spinner is divided into five congruent sections, labeled 1–5.   38. _____
What is the probability of spinning a 1 and then a 2?

A $\dfrac{1}{25}$ B $\dfrac{1}{10}$ C $\dfrac{1}{2}$ D $\dfrac{1}{5}$

1. Create a line plot to represent the survey data.

1.

Main Use of the Home Computer			
Work	4	Homework	2
Budget	5	Games	3

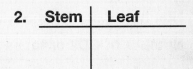

2. Create a stem-and-leaf diagram to represent the data.
56, 47, 48, 52, 49, 55, 52, 50, 48, 51

2.

Stem	Leaf

3. The January high temperatures for two weeks in
Mickey's hometown are 20, 23, 42, 37, 33, 32, 12,
9, 5, 6, 4, 11, 15, 23. Find the mean, the median, and
the mode of the temperatures.

3. _____

4. Create a box-and-whisker plot for the data in Item 3.

4.

5. According to the line
graph, in which month
was Fred's weight the
least? The greatest?

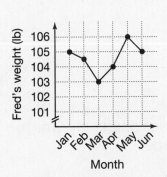

Month

5. _____

6. According to the
bar graph, what
percent of students
prefer oranges?

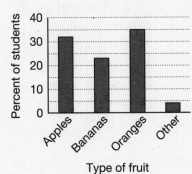

Type of fruit

6. _____

7. Test Prep What is the median of the data?
16, 13, 11, 16, 10, 17, 15

A 14 **B** 15 **C** 16 **D** 17

7. _____

Name _____

Date _____ Score _____

1. Jan asked her classmates in the After-School Chorus if they enjoy singing. State the population of her survey and whether or not the sample is random.

1. _____
   _____

Jeb took a survey about how many CDs and tapes his classmates bought in May. In 2 and 3, use Jeb's data.

Number of students buying	2	4	7	6	3	1
Number of CDs or tapes purchased	0–1	2–3	4–5	6–7	8–9	Over 10

2. Display the data in a line plot.

3. Display the data in a histogram.

4. A scatterplot compared test grades and study time. What type of trend would you expect?

4. _____

5. A scatterplot compared times for a race and time spent conditioning. What type of trend would you expect?

5. _____

6. Tell what type of company might ask this question in a survey: Which do you purchase most often, apple juice, orange juice, or tomato juice?

6. _____
   _____

7. **Test Prep** What is the best sample for a survey on preferred types of movies among teens?

7. _____

   A People leaving a movie
   B Teens leaving the school grounds
   C Parents who go to movies
   D Members of the school hiking club

In 1–4, use the chart below, which lists how much four students spent on entertainment each month for 9 months during the school year.

Student	Sept	Oct	Nov	Dec	Jan	Feb	Mar	Apr	May
Irene	$14.00	$10.95	$ 8.95	$15.50	$11.95	$12.30	$25.00	$ 9.65	$10.25
Deepak	$ 7.00	$12.75	$ 5.80	$ 7.00	$16.40	$ 9.95	$ 8.30	$11.75	$ 7.00
Kim	$ 6.50	$ 8.10	$ 7.35	$ 5.25	$ 8.40	$ 6.25	$ 7.75	$ 9.00	$11.10
Stan	$12.35	$10.15	$ 8.05	$11.95	$ 7.85	$ 9.75	$ 8.50	$10.00	$ 9.20

1. Find the mean, the median, and the mode of Deepak's monthly entertainment costs.

1. _____

_____

2. Make a box-and-whisker plot for all of Irene's monthly entertainment costs.

3. Construct a bar graph comparing the four monthly entertainment costs for February.

4. Draw a line graph that shows all of Stan's monthly entertainment costs.

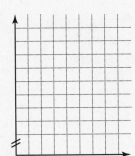

5. At a small, local airport, Beverly asked 75 people eating in the cafeteria if they like to fly. Did Beverly take a random sample for her survey?

_____

Name _____

6. Make a stem-and-leaf diagram for these biology
test scores: 83, 67, 91, 85, 88, 78, 85, 95, 89, 85, 82

6. Stem | Leaf
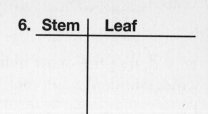

7. Jake recorded his weekly math test scores and the
number of hours he studied for each test: 78–2 hours,
89–4 hours, 82–3 hours, 91–4.5 hours, 87–3.5 hours,
94–4 hours. Construct a scatterplot of Jake's data.

7.

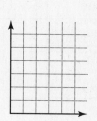

8. Draw a possible trend line in the scatterplot in
Item 7. Is the trend line positive or negative?

8. _____

9. The table shows the results Nanci recorded
when she asked several people the name
of their favorite local restaurant. Complete
the table by giving the frequency for each
restaurant.

10. Display the results
of Nanci's survey
as a line plot.

Restaurant	Tally	Frequency
Matt's Grill	ЖℍI	
Oak St. Cafe	ЖℍIII	
Oregano Palace	ЖℍII	
Sunny Side Up	IIII	

←——————————→

11. Geoff asked many of his classmates the following
three questions:
- What is your least favorite meal in the cafeteria?
- What is your favorite meal in the cafeteria?
- Rate the cafeteria food in general on a scale
  of 1 to 5, with 5 being the best score.

a. What is the population of his survey?

_____

b. What could be a possible purpose for his survey?

_____

In 1–4, use the chart below, which lists how much time four students spent exercising or playing a sport for one week.

Student	Sun	Mon	Tues	Wed	Thurs	Fri	Sat
Paul	120 min	58 min	48 min	105 min	75 min	37 min	32 min
Suzanne	0 min	0 min	45 min	10 min	0 min	18 min	41 min
Mario	151 min	18 min	32 min	15 min	43 min	16 min	115 min
Elizabeth	12 min	15 min	12 min	15 min	12 min	15 min	41 min

1. Find the mean, the median, and the mode of Elizabeth's exercise times.

1. _____

_____

2. Make a box-and-whisker plot for Suzanne's exercise times.

2.

3. Construct a bar graph comparing the four students' exercise times on Saturday.

3.

4. Construct a line graph of Mario's exercise time during the school week.

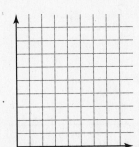

5. At a mall, Terry asked shoppers what kind of pet (or pets) they own. Did Terry take a random sample for his survey?

_____

6. Make a stem-and-leaf diagram for these basketball scores: 78, 84, 99, 91, 85, 79, 83, 90, 101, 95

6.

Stem	Leaf

7. Patrick had his sister record the number of wrong notes he hit during 10-minute intervals as he practiced his piano recital piece: 1st interval–21 notes, 2nd interval–15 notes, 3rd interval–12 notes, 4th interval–9 notes, 5th interval–5 notes, 6th interval–3 notes. Construct a scatterplot of Patrick's data.

7.

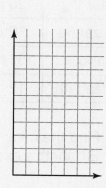

8. Draw a possible trend line in the scatterplot in Item 7. Is the trend positive or negative?

8. _____

9. The table shows Lauren's results when she recorded how many people ordered the lunch specials at her family's restaurant. Complete the table by giving the frequency for each special.

10. Display Lauren's results as a line plot.

Special	Tally	Frequency
"Spag" & Sauce	II	
Tofu Cakes	IIII	
Vegetable Bake	JHf	
Very Veggie Salad	III	

<— — — — — — — — — —>

11. Kate asked many of her relatives the following three questions:
- What month is best for you to travel?
- Where should a reunion be held?
- What activities do you enjoy?

a. What is the population of her survey?

_____

b. What could be a probable purpose for her survey?

_____

Name _____

Date _____   Score _____

Give the letter of the correct answer.
In 1 and 2, use the line plot.

Favorite Color of Sweater

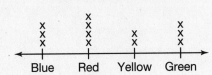

Blue   Red   Yellow   Green

1. Which color sweater is most popular?

   A Blue   **B** Red   **C** Yellow   **D** Green

1. _____

2. How many people in all voted for their favorite sweater color?

   A 3   **B** 4   **C** 12   **D** 3423

2. _____

3. Below is a stem-and-leaf diagram showing the scores on a test. How many students scored 98?

Stem	Leaf
7	8 9
8	0 3 8 8 9
9	2 2 5 8 9

   A 1   **B** 2   **C** 3   **D** 4

3. _____

4. Which stem-and-leaf diagram shows the following data?
12, 12, 16, 16, 17, 22

A
Stem	Leaf
2	1 1 2
6	1 1
7	1

B
Stem	Leaf
1	2 1 2
1	6 1 6
1	7

C
Stem	Leaf
1	2 2
1	6 7
2	2

D Not here

4. _____

In 5–7, use the following data:
2.2, 2.7, 3.5, 3.9, 4.0, 4.6, 4.8, 5.0, 5.0, 5.3

5. What is the mean of the data?

   A 4.1   **B** 4.2   **C** 4.3   **D** 5.0

5. _____

Continued **41**

6. What is the median of the data?

   A 4.1   **B** 4.2   **C** 4.3   **D** 5.0

6. _____

7. What is the mode of the data?

   A 4.1   **B** 4.2   **C** 4.3   **D** 5.0

7. _____

In 8–10, use the box-and-whisker plot.

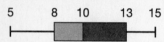

8. What is the range of this data?

   A 5–8   **B** 8–13   **C** 13–15   **D** 5–15

8. _____

9. Which set of numbers gives the 1st, 2nd, and 3rd quartiles?

   A 5, 8, 10   **B** 8, 10, 13   **C** 10, 13, 15   **D** 5, 10, 15

9. _____

10. Which set of data would you give this box-and-whisker plot?

   A 5, 6, 10, 10, 11, 15, 15   **B** 5, 8, 10, 10, 12, 14, 15
   C 5, 8, 10, 10, 10, 13, 15   **D** 5, 7, 9, 10, 13, 14, 15

10. _____

In 11 and 12, use the bar graph.

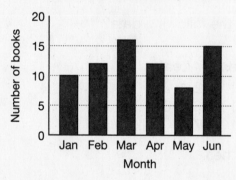

Number of Books Read per Month

11. In which month were the fewest books read?

   A Jan   **B** Mar   **C** May   **D** June

11. _____

12. In which two months were the same number of books read?

   A Jan and Feb   **B** Feb and Apr
   C Mar and May   **D** Mar and June

12. _____

Continued

Name _____

In 13 and 14, use the line graph.

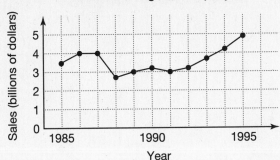

Annual Earnings of Company X

13. Between which successive years did the sales per year stay the same?

    A 1986–1987   **B** 1989–1991
    C 1990–1991   **D** 1990–1992

13. _____

14. Which two time periods showed a drop in sales?

    A 1985–1986, 1989–1990   **B** 1986–1987, 1989–1991
    C 1987–1988, 1990–1991   **D** 1988–1990, 1991–1995

14. _____

15. Barry wants to conduct a survey to find out whether people would rather spend money on entertainment or sports activities. Which would be the best place to conduct the survey?

    A Theater lobby   **B** Bowling alley
    C Campground   **D** Grocery store

15. _____

16. SuperSno wants to test market its bright-colored snow gloves. Which population would be best to test market the gloves?

    A New York, NY   **B** Los Angeles, CA
    C Miami, FL   **D** Houston, TX

16. _____

17. Which term means "the number of times a data value occurs"?

    A Median   **B** Mean   **C** Frequency   **D** Quartile

17. _____

18. How are data grouped in a histogram?

    A Using line graphs   **B** With tally marks
    C By equal intervals   **D** With a trend line

18. _____

In 19 and 20, use the scatterplot.

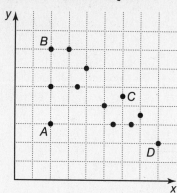

19. Which term best describes the trend shown?

19. _____

   A Positive   **B** Negative   **C** Frequent   **D** No trend

20. Which point does *not* fit the trend?

20. _____

   A Point *A*   **B** Point *B*   **C** Point *C*   **D** Point *D*

21. Cynthia wants to know what kind of used car appeals to first-time car owners. Who should be the population of her survey?

21. _____

   A Eighth-grade girls   **B** High school seniors
   C All licensed drivers   **D** Parents of her friends

22. Kathy asked the following four questions in a survey about how people stay fit. Which question is least important to her survey?

22. _____

   A What sports do you play?
   B How often do you work out?
   C How long do you work out?
   D Where do you buy your equipment/shoes?

23. These are the numbers of games won by each National League baseball team in a recent season: 96, 88, 80, 71, 67, 88, 82, 81, 76, 73, 91, 90, 83, 68. Find the median number of games won.

23. _____

   A 81   **B** 81.5   **C** 82   **D** Not here

Continued

24. Baseball teams play the same number of games each year, and in the past, National League teams have played all their games against other National League teams. In this situation, how would you expect the mean number of games won by National League teams to change?

24. _____

   A Increase   **B** Decrease
   C No change **D** Cannot be predicted

25. Which is *not* a good way to display the number of games won by teams in one season?

25. _____

   A Scatterplot   **B** Bar graph   **C** Line plot   **D** Histogram

26. Which of the statements is true?

26. _____

   A A more representative sample gives survey results that are more accurate for the population as a whole.

   B A larger sample is more representative.

   C You can choose a good sample without knowing any characteristics of the population.

   D Not here

Name _____

Date _____ Score _____

Chapter 1 Test
Form
D

You will need graph paper and a ruler.

You are on a committee to help choose a mascot and school colors for your school, Main North Middle School. The committee sent a questionnaire to all 275 members of the 8th grade. The survey results follow.

1. Which is your choice for a new mascot?

Animal	179
Historical figure	65
Local landmark	27
Other _____	4

2. Should the mascot and the school colors look good together?

Yes	237
It doesn't matter	38

3. Which is your choice for the initial letter of the type of mascot?

M as in Main	126
N as in North	17
It doesn't matter	132

4. What are your 4 favorite colors?

Black	41	Maroon	50
Blue	237	Pink	29
Bright Red	225	Turquoise	61
Forest Green	226	White	72
Kelly Green	58	Yellow	101

a. Explain whether or not your sample is a good sample. If it is not, explain how you could make it better.

b. Which would best help you show your school's mascot preferences—stem-and-leaf diagram, box-and-whisker plot, bar graph, histogram, or scatterplot? Explain.

c. Represent this data using the graph you chose in **b.**

The committee decides to choose an animal mascot. They use the results from a new survey to help them choose.

Animal	Freq	Animal	Freq	Animal	Freq
Armadillo	12	Cougar	50	Mustang	153
Bear	33	Eagle	46	Piranha	11
Blue Jay	15	Malamute	7	Tiger	23
Cardinal	176	Marlin	10	Wolf	14

d. Which animal would you choose for the mascot if your decision were based on the mode of the sample above?

© Scott Foresman Addison Wesley 8

Teacher Notes

Concepts and Skills This activity requires students to:

- determine if a sample for a survey is a good sample.
- choose the best way to organize data.
- organize data from two surveys.
- make a graph using data from a survey.
- find the mean and mode of data.

Guiding Questions

- Why do the results for favorite color add to 1100 instead of 275?
- Why were three animal names beginning with M included in the 2nd survey?

Answers

a. No; the size is good, but it is not representative of the entire school; survey many students from each grade.

b. A bar graph is the best choice. A bar graph is the best to show frequency.

c.

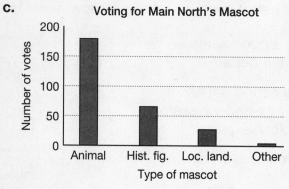

Voting for Main North's Mascot

d. Cardinal

Extension

Assuming the survey results are representative of the school, have students choose a mascot and school colors based on the surveys. Have them prepare a poster announcing the final choice. Have them include an explanation of why the sample size was good; how each survey question was used to choose the mascot and colors; the graph they prepared; and how statistics were used to choose the mascot from the animals listed in the second survey.

Evaluation

Level	Standard to be achieved for performance of specified level
4	The student demonstrates a clear understanding of how to organize and represent data by using graphs and measures of central tendency. The graph made by the student is thorough, having accurate scales, labeling, and appropriate name. All calculations are accurate and complete.
3	The student demonstrates a fundamental understanding of how to organize and represent data by using graphs and measures of central tendency. The graph made by the student is fairly well organized and easy to read, but may have some inaccuracies in the scales or labeling. Calculation of the mean and mode is done but may contain some minor errors.
2	The student demonstrates some understanding of how to organize and represent data by using graphs and measures of central tendency, but is easily confused without assistance. The graph made by the student is not well organized, and may have inaccuracies in the scales and sloppiness in labeling, as well as incorrect plotting of data. Calculation of the mean and mode is attempted but is incorrect.
1	The student demonstrates little if any understanding of how to organize and represent data by using graphs and measures of central tendency, and requires much assistance. The graph may be attempted by the student but is missing several critical items and contains incorrectly plotted data. Calculation of the mean and mode may be attempted but not completed.

In 1 and 2, use the line plot.

Hours Volunteered

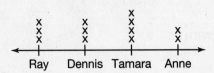

Ray   Dennis Tamara Anne

1. Who volunteered the most hours?   **1.** _____

   A Ray   **B** Dennis   **C** Tamara   **D** Anne

2. How many hours were volunteered by the boys?   **2.** _____
   The girls?

**In 3 and 4, use the stem-and-leaf diagram for
a set of quiz scores.**

Stem	Leaf
2	6 8 9
3	1 3 3 6
4	2 4 5 5 8

3. How many students scored 45 on the quiz?   **3.** _____

   A 0   **B** 1   **C** 2   **D** 5

4. How many students took the quiz?   **4.** _____

   A 10   **B** 12   **C** 15   **D** 48

**In 5–9, use the following data for Beth's bowling
scores: 110, 114, 138, 114, 117, 113, 123, 118,
115, 120**

5. What was Beth's mean score?   **5.** _____

6. What was her median score?   **6.** _____

7. Do her scores show a mode? If so, what is it?   **7.** _____

8. Draw a box-and-whisker plot for   **8.**
   Beth's bowling data.

9. What is the range of Beth's scores?   9. _____

10. Which graph is best for showing LuAnne's data from a   10. _____
survey about the brands of jeans her classmates prefer?

    A Bar graph   **B** Line graph
    C Scatterplot   **D** Stem-and-leaf diagram

11. What does a line graph usually show?   11. _____

    A Median values   **B** Changes over time
    C Frequency   **D** Measures of central tendency

12. What does a histogram usually show?   12. _____

    A Changes over age groups   **B** Changes over time
    C Frequency   **D** Measures of central tendency

13. Gail asked the parents of her classmates if they support a property
tax increase for education. Was her sample random? Explain.

_____

_____

14. A frequency table would best be used for which of these?   14. _____

    A Growth in height of a student over a year
    B School budget increases over a decade
    C Numbers of students in different after-school clubs
    D The mean score on the last mathematics exam

15. What kind of trend is shown by the scatterplot?   15. _____

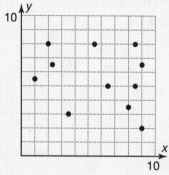

       Continued

© Scott Foresman Addison Wesley 8

16. Alex wants to know which athletic shoe is preferred by
8th-grade boys. Which is the best sample for a survey?

16. _____

   A His friends
   B All students in the lunchroom
   C All customers in an athletic-shoe store
   D All the boys in his 8th-grade class

17. Performance Task You have been asked to design T-shirts for
your Teen Theater club. You will need a survey for design input.

   a. Whom will you survey?

   _____

   b. What will your questions deal with?

   _____

   c. How will you organize the survey results? Explain.

   _____

   _____

— Computation —

In 1–3, use the following data listing scores on an English test: 92, 83, 78, 85, 88, 95, 82, 90, 87, 88, 89, 91

1. Find the mean score of the data.

1. _____

2. Find the median score of the data.

2. _____

3. Do the scores show a mode? If so, what is it?

3. _____

4. Fill in the frequencies in the table.

Favorite Class	Tally	Frequency
Art	JHT III	
Biology	JHT II	
English	JHT JHT I	
Foreign Language	JHT IIII	
Music	JHT JHT II	
Mathematics	JHT III	
Social Studies	JHT II	

In 5–7, find each answer.

5. 428 − 397

5. _____

6. 113 + 2897

6. _____

7. 63 × 25

7. _____

— Concepts —

8. What is (are) the mode(s) in the stem-and-leaf diagram?

8. _____

Stem	Leaf
0	1 5 5 6 8
1	1 2 3 7
2	2 3 3 6 9

Name _____

In 9 and 10, use the box-and-whisker plot.

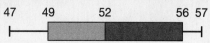

47   49   52   56 57

9. Which number is the median?

   A 47   **B** 49   **C** 52   **D** 56

9. _____

10. Which numbers are the lower and upper quartiles?

   A 47, 57   **B** 49, 56   **C** 47, 52   **D** 49, 57

10. _____

11. What does a bar graph usually show?

   A Changes over time   **B** Frequency
   C Measures of central tendency   **D** Trends in data

11. _____

12. Peter wants to graph data about his savings account activity over time. Which would be best for him to use?

   A Bar graph   **B** Line graph
   C Scatterplot   **D** Stem-and-leaf diagram

12. _____

13. Which is the most important thing to consider when choosing a population for a survey?

   A Who will be writing the survey
   B Who will be reading the survey
   C Whom the survey will represent
   D How the data will be represented

13. _____

In 14 and 15, order from least to greatest.

14. 768, 678, 876, 786

_____

15. 2001, 2100, 2010, 201

_____

Continued

▬ Applications ▬

16. Draw a line plot to show the days Suzie baby-sat
in October: Monday—1 day, Wednesday—1 day,
Friday—3 days, Saturday—4 days, Sunday—2 days

16.

⟵──────────────────⟶

**In 17 and 18, use Nelson's scatterplot comparing
fitness workouts and heart rates of his classmates.**

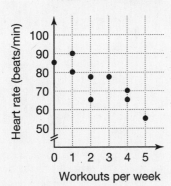

Heart Rate Workouts

17. Draw a trend line for the data.

18. Describe the trend line shown by the data.

18. _____

19. Paula is planning a survey to find out what her
classmates think about television news programs.
Which question would it be most important to
include in the survey?

19. _____

A How much time do you spend watching television?
B Do you discuss world events with your friends?
C Do TV news programs cover events that are important
to you?
D Do you enjoy reading the newspaper?

20. Joey included the following questions on his survey:
• What is your favorite sport to watch?
• How much time do you spend watching sports?
• How often (days) do you watch sports?

What is the probable purpose of his survey?

_____

1. Order the following altitudes from lowest to highest:
   -27 ft, -10 ft, 8 ft, -78 ft, 66 ft

   _____

2. Use >, <, or = to compare: $28 \ \square \ -59$ 2. _____

3. Find the absolute value of -1.   3. _____

4. Add $60 + (-37)$.   4. _____

5. David climbed steps to work out. Starting at the   5. _____
   ground floor, he went down 26 steps, then up
   28 steps, then down 14 steps, then up 13 steps.
   Find which step he ended up on by adding integers.

6. Subtract $78 - (-99)$.   6. _____

7. Subtract $-25 - (-7) - 7$.   7. _____

8. Multiply -5×4.   8. _____

9. Divide $\dfrac{36}{-3}$.   9. _____

10. There was a leak in the Smiths' outdoor garden hose.   10. _____
    From 9 A.M. Monday to 9 A.M. Tuesday, 36 gallons of
    water were lost. Give a rational number to express how
    much water was lost per hour. Give an integer to express
    how much more the Smiths will lose if the hose is
    not fixed until next Monday at 9 A.M.

11. Use the distributive property to rewrite $3(2 + 5)$.   11. _____

12. Which should be done first in the expression?   12. _____
    $6 + 12 \div (2 + 8) - 3$

13. Evaluate $\dfrac{(4 - 19)}{3 + 2}$.   13. _____

14. **Test Prep** Evaluate $33 \times (-6 - 4) + (-10)$.   14. _____

    A -340 **B** 340 **C** -320 **D** 320

Name _____

Date _____ Score _____

In 1–4, find the coordinates of each point.

1. *A*

2. *B*

3. *C*

4. *D*

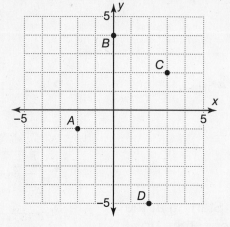

1. _____

2. _____

3. _____

4. _____

In 5–7, plot each point on the grid above.

5. *E* (−4, 1)

6. *F* (4, −3)

7. *G* (−2, −3)

8. Write 7^3 in standard form.

9. Evaluate $(-5)^4$.

10. Find the missing number in $3^{\square} = 81$.

11. Write 2.9×10^4 in standard notation.

12. Write 5.826×10^8 in standard notation.

13. Write 22 thousandths in scientific notation.

14. **Test Prep** Which of the following numbers is in scientific notation?

   A 0.3×10^8 **B** 86×10^{-2}
   C 10×10^3 **D** 9.1×10^{-6}

5. _____

6. _____

7. _____

8. _____

9. _____

10. _____

11. _____

12. _____

13. _____

14. _____

1. Order the following numbers from least to greatest: −4, 3, 2, 0, −1.

1. _____

In 2–5, use >, <, or = to compare the numbers in each pair.

2. 9 ☐ −9

2. _____

3. −5 ☐ −4

3. _____

4. $|-4|$ ☐ 4

4. _____

5. $|11|$ ☐ $|-13|$

5. _____

In 6–16, add or subtract.

6. 5 + (−1)

6. _____

7. −1 + 5

7. _____

8. 22 + (−14)

8. _____

9. −212 + 35

9. _____

10. −125 + (−75)

10. _____

11. 6 − 31

11. _____

12. −10 − 7

12. _____

13. −12 − (−4)

13. _____

14. −5 − (−15)

14. _____

15. 3 − (−11) + 17 + (−9) − 2

15. _____

16. −45 − 18 − (−18) − (−45)

16. _____

17. Jared hiked from 132 feet above sea level to 6 feet below sea level. Give an integer to express his change in elevation.

17. _____

In 18–20, multiply or divide.

18. -10×7

18. _____

19. $12(-2)$

19. _____

20. $-20 \div 4$

20. _____

In 21–24, evaluate.

21. $\dfrac{9(-4 + 6)}{3}$

21. _____

22. $2 \cdot 3 - (-12) \div 6$

22. _____

23. 8^2

23. _____

24. $(-3)^3$

24. _____

In 25 and 26, use the grid below.

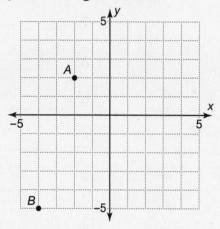

25. Find the coordinates of points A and B.

25. _____

26. Plot points C $(3, -1)$ and D $(0, 1)$.

26. _____

27. Saturn is about 1,430,000,000 km from the sun. Write this distance in scientific notation.

27. _____

28. Write 112,648 in scientific notation.

28. _____

29. Write 5.45×10^5 in standard notation.

29. _____

30. Write 9.01×10^{-4} in standard notation.

30. _____

1. Order the following numbers from least to greatest: 5, −7, −3, 2, 0

1. _____

In 2–5, use >, <, or = to compare the numbers in each pair.

2. 2 ☐ −2

2. _____

3. −24 ☐ −20

3. _____

4. |−1| ☐ 1

4. _____

5. |−7| ☐ |−4|

5. _____

In 6–16, add or subtract.

6. 17 + (−9)

6. _____

7. −9 + 17

7. _____

8. 18 + (−6)

8. _____

9. −363 + (−36)

9. _____

10. 99 + (− 55)

10. _____

11. −75 − 21

11. _____

12. −15 − (− 6)

12. _____

13. −30 − (− 19)

13. _____

14. −15 − (−6)

14. _____

15. 7 − (−4) + 28 + (−3) − 9

15. _____

16. −65 − 27 − (−27) − (−65)

16. _____

17. The temperature fell from 28 degrees above 0 to 5 degrees below 0. Give an integer to express the change in temperature.

17. _____

In 18–20, multiply or divide.

18. -12×3

18. _____

19. $15(-3)$

19. _____

20. $-75 \div 3$

20. _____

In 21–24, evaluate.

21. $\dfrac{4(-5 + 10)}{2}$

21. _____

22. $7 \cdot 6 - (-15) \div 5$

22. _____

23. 6^2

23. _____

24. $(-2)^5$

24. _____

In 25 and 26, use the grid below.

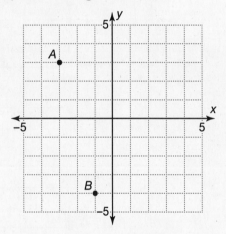

25. Find the coordinates of points A and B.

25. _____

26. Plot points C $(1, -2)$ and D $(4, 0)$.

26. _____

27. The star Antares is about 4,000,000,000,000,000 km from Earth. Write this number in scientific notation.

27. _____

28. Write 68,042 in scientific notation.

28. _____

29. Write 2.43×10^4 in standard notation.

29. _____

30. Write 8.34×10^{-5} in standard notation.

30. _____

Name _____

Date _____ Score _____

Give the letter of the correct answer.

In 1 and 2, order each set of integers from least to greatest.

1. $-19, 0, 17, 20, -21$

    A $-21, 20, -19, 17, 0$ **B** $-21, -19, 0, 17, 20$
    C $0, 17, -19, 20, -21$ **D** $0, 17, 20, -19, -21$

1. _____

2. $-5, -101, 88, 36, -77$

    A $-101, -77, -5, 36, 88$ **B** $-101, 88, -77, 36, -5$
    C $-5, 36, -77, 88, -101$ **D** Not here

2. _____

In 3–5, which of the following is true?

3. **A** $-7 > 4$ **B** $-4 < -6$ **C** $-5 < 3$ **D** $2 > 6$

3. _____

4. **A** $|-3| > |3|$ **B** $-5 > |1|$
    C $|6| = -6$ **D** $|-15| > 13$

4. _____

5. **A** $|1| > |-1|$ **B** $|6| < |-13|$
    C $|19| < |18|$ **D** $|-8| < |-3|$

5. _____

6. What integer is described by the following? The absolute value is 77 and the number is to the left of 0 on a number line.

    A $(-7)^2$ **B** 7   **C** -77 **D** Not here

6. _____

7. Write an addition problem for the model.

7. _____

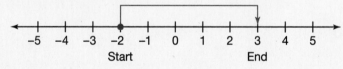

               Start   End

    A $5 + (-3) = 2$ **B** $-2 + 5 = 3$
    C $-2 + 3 = 5$ **D** $3 + (-5) = -2$

8. Add $65 + 68$.

    A 3   **B** -3 **C** 133   **D** -133

8. _____

9. Add $-23 + (-6)$.

    A 17   **B** -17 **C** 29   **D** -29

9. _____

10. Add $5 + 7 + (-5) + (-4)$.

    A -4 **B** 8 **C** -2 **D** 3

10. _____

11. Jay walked up the stairs to the 9th floor of a building, then down 10 flights, then up 8 flights, then down 5 flights. Find which floor he ended up on by adding integers.

    A 2 **B** 4 **C** 8 **D** Not here

11. _____

12. Subtract $37 - 49$.

    A 12 **B** -12 **C** 86 **D** -86

12. _____

13. Subtract $-144 - 158$.

    A 14 **B** -14 **C** 302 **D** -302

13. _____

14. Subtract $61 - (-18) - 5$.

    A 38 **B** 48 **C** 74 **D** 84

14. _____

15. Will saw the same shirt in two stores. In the first store, the shirt was $24 with a discount of $8. In the second store, the shirt was $22 with a discount of $5. What was the better buy for the shirt?

    A $14   **B** $16   **C** $17   **D** $19

15. _____

16. Multiply $4 \cdot -8$.

    A -2 **B** -4 **C** -12 **D** -32

16. _____

17. Divide $15 \div -3$.

    A -5 **B** -12 **C** -18 **D** -45

17. _____

18. Evaluate $12 \times 2 \div (-3)$.

    A $\dfrac{14}{-3}$ **B** -4 **C** -8 **D** Not here

18. _____

19. Tina makes $5 each time she mows her neighbor's lawn. If she mows the lawn 12 times during the summer, how much money will she make?

    A $5   **B** $12   **C** $17   **D** $60

19. _____

20. Evaluate $8 \div 4 + 9 \div 3 - 5$.   **20.** _____

    A -6 **B** -1.3 **C** 0 **D** 10

21. Evaluate $12 - 8 \div 2 + 6 \times 3$.   **21.** _____

    A 6 **B** 20 **C** 24 **D** Not here

22. Rewrite $-3(4 + 2)$ using the distributive property.   **22.** _____

    A $3 \times 4 + 3 \times 2$ **B** $-3 \times 4 + 3 \times 2$
    C $3 \times 4 + (-3 \times 2)$ **D** $-3 \times 4 + (-3 \times 2)$

In 23–25, give the point for each ordered pair.

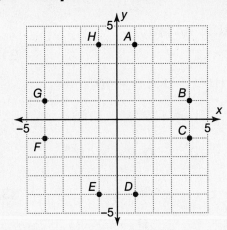

23. $(4, 1)$ **23.** _____

    A Point A **B** Point B **C** Point E **D** Point F

24. $(-1, 4)$

    A Point B **B** Point D **C** Point F **D** Point H **24.** _____

25. $(1, -4)$ **25.** _____

    A Point A **B** Point D **C** Point E **D** Point H

26. What is the exponential form of $-3 \bullet -3 \bullet -3 \bullet -3 \bullet -3$?   **26.** _____

    A 3^{-5} **B** $(-3)^5$ **C** 5^3 **D** 5^{-3}

27. Find the missing number.   **27.** _____
    $\square^3 = -8$

    A 2 **B** -2 **C** 24 **D** -24

28. Evaluate 4^3.

    A 0   **B** 4   **C** 16   **D** 64

28. _____

29. A shed shaped like a cube has a volume of 512 ft^3. Given that the volume of a cube is (length of one edge)^3, what is the length of one edge of the shed?

    A 8 ft   **B** 22.6 ft   **C** 64 ft   **D** Not here

29. _____

30. Sarah had 7 dogs. Each dog had 7 fleas. Each flea laid 7 eggs. How many eggs were there in all?

    A 7   **B** 7×3 **C** 7^2 **D** 7^3

30. _____

In 31–34, write each number in scientific notation.

31. 550,000

    A 5.5×10^5 **B** 55×10^4 **C** 5.5×10^7 **D** 5.5×10^8

31. _____

32. 24,000,000,000

    A 24×10^9 **B** 2.4×10^{10} **C** 2.4×10^{13} **D** 2.4×10^{24}

32. _____

33. 0.0012

    A 1.2×10^{-1} **B** 1.2×10^{-2} **C** 1.2×10^{-3} **D** 1.2×10^{-4}

33. _____

34. 0.0000000051

    A 5.1×10^{-8} **B** 5.1×10^{-9} **C** 51×10^{-10} **D** 5.1×10^{-51}

34. _____

In 35–38, write each number in standard notation.

35. 1.7×10^2

    A 0.17   **B** 17   **C** 170   **D** Not here

35. _____

36. 6.3×10^6

    A 630,000   **B** 6,300,000   **C** 63,000,000   **D** Not here

36. _____

37. 8.05×10^{-4}

    A 0.805   **B** 0.0805   **C** 0.00805   **D** Not here

37. _____

38. 7.72×10^{-10}

    A 0.0000000772   **B** 0.00000000772
    C 0.000000000772   **D** 0.0000000000772

38. _____

For an astronomy project, you plan to make a scale model of the solar system. You first collect data for your project. An *astronomical unit* (AU) is often used to describe distance in astronomy. It is the approximate distance from Earth to the sun.

Planet	Average Distance from Sun (km) in Standard Notation	Average Distance from Sun (km) in Scientific Notation	Average Distance from Sun (AU)
Mercury	58,000,000		0.39
Venus	107,500,000		0.72
Earth	149,600,000		1
Mars	227,900,000		
Jupiter	778,400,000		
Saturn	1,429,400,000		
Uranus	2,869,300,000		
Neptune	4,500,000,000		
Pluto	5,913,700,000		

a. Add to the table each distance from the sun in scientific notation.

b. Complete the last column of the table.

c. Compare the distances from Earth to its three closest neighbors. Which three planets are closest to Earth? In kilometers, what is the average distance of each from Earth?

d. List the planets in order from closest to Earth to farthest from Earth.

e. You compare the size of the planets. You find that the Great Red Spot on Jupiter, an oval-shaped atmospheric storm, is about 26,000 km by 14,000 km. Earth is spherical and about 12,750 km in diameter. If Earth and Jupiter were drawn on a sheet of paper and to scale, about how many Earths (side by side) would fit inside Jupiter's Great Red Spot?

f. You need to find a scale for your solar system. You try the scale 300,000,000 km to 1 cm; that is, every centimeter will stand for 300,000,000 km. With this scale, about how far will Earth be from the sun? About how far will Pluto be from the sun?

Teacher Notes

Concepts and Skills This activity requires students to:
- convert large numbers in the form of distances from standard notation to scientific notation.
- subtract integers in the form of distances.
- compare integers in the form of distances.
- divide integers to make comparisons and a scale.

Guiding Questions
- Why do you think astronomical units are often used in astronomy?
- In making a scale model of the solar system, what other consideration should you have besides the distance between planets?

Answers
a. Mercury: 5.8×10^7; Venus: 1.075×10^8; Earth: 1.496×10^8; Mars: 2.279×10^8; Jupiter: 7.784×10^8; Saturn: 1.4294×10^9; Uranus: 2.8693×10^9; Neptune: 4.5×10^9; Pluto: 5.9137×10^9

b. Mars: 1.52; Jupiter: 5.20; Saturn: 9.55; Uranus: 19.18; Neptune: 30.08; Pluto: 39.53

c. Mercury, Venus, Mars; 91,600,000 km (Mercury), 42,100,000 km (Venus), 78,300,000 km (Mars)

d. Venus, Mars, Mercury, Jupiter, Saturn, Uranus, Neptune, Pluto

e. 2

f. 0.5 cm; 19.7 cm

Extension
Think about what you learned about making a scale for planet distances in part **e**. Try to find a scale that works for the planets closest to the sun as well as those farthest from the sun. What is the main problem in making a scale model of the solar system? Pretend you are marking the planet distances outside. If Earth is one meter from the sun, how far away will Pluto be? You may also want to study the size of the sun and planets. How will representing size cause a problem with your scale model?

Evaluation

Level	Standard to be achieved for performance of specified level
4	The student demonstrates a clear understanding of and proficiency in converting large numbers from standard notation to scientific notation. Integers are compared successfully. All calculations, including those for the scale model, are accurate and complete.
3	The student demonstrates a fundamental understanding of and proficiency in converting large numbers from standard notation to scientific notation. Integers are compared successfully, although one may be out of order. All calculations, including those for the scale model, are complete but may contain minor errors.
2	The student demonstrates some understanding of and proficiency in converting large numbers from standard notation to scientific notation, but makes several errors or is in need of substantial assistance. An attempt to compare integers is made, although two or three may be out of order. Calculations, including those for the scale model, are attempted, but several are incorrect.
1	The student demonstrates little if any understanding of and proficiency in converting large numbers from standard notation to scientific notation, even with substantial assistance. No attempt to compare integers is made. Some calculations, including those for the scale model, may be attempted but are not completed, even with assistance.

1. Order from least to greatest: 0, 27, −21, 12, −11

2. Order from greatest to least: $|-13|$, $|0|$, $|5|$

In 3 and 4, which is true?

3. **A** $28 < 26$ **B** $-45 > -35$
   C $12 > -17$ **D** $0 < -4$

4. **A** $|-3| < |3|$ **B** $|2| > |-5|$
   C $|-4| = -4$ **D** $|-6| > |4|$

5. Add $-16 + (-33) + 7 + (-2) + 54$.

6. Dana made these deposits and withdrawals into her savings account: $12, $6, $5, −$2, $2, −$4. Give an integer to show the total change in the account.

7. Subtract $200 - (-100) - 59 - (-6) - 1$.

8. Sheila owed her brother $20. He told her he would subtract $5 of her debt if she washed his car and subtract $3 of her debt if she vacuumed it. Write an expression showing how much Sheila will owe her brother after washing and waxing his car one time.

9. Because of an incoming storm, the temperature dropped 21 degrees in 7 hours. Approximately how much did the temperature drop each hour?

10. Marc makes $32 every 4 weeks by doing yard work for families in his neighborhood. How much does he make in 1 week? How much will he make in 12 weeks?

11. Evaluate $72 \div 8 - 1 + 6 \cdot 2 - 20$.

12. Evaluate $2(7 - 4)^0 \times 5$.

1. _____

2. _____

3. _____

4. _____

5. _____

6. _____

7. _____

8. _____

9. _____

10. _____

11. _____

12. _____

13. Anna has $29.57 she can spend. She needs to buy three shirts at $6.95 each for work. If Anna goes to the store, buys the shirts, and receives $7.25 for a vest she returns, how much money will she have?

  A −$7.25 **B** $6.95 **C** $15.97 **D** $20.85

13. _____

In 14 and 15, give the point for each ordered pair.

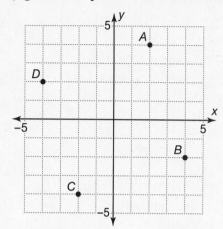

14. (−2, −4)

  A Point *A* **B** Point *B* **C** Point *C* **D** Point *D*

14. _____

15. (−4, 2)

  A Point *A* **B** Point *B* **C** Point *C* **D** Point *D*

15. _____

16. Chuck divided a square into 4 squares. He divided each of these squares into 4 squares. He then divided each of these squares into 4 squares. Express the number of smallest squares in terms of a power of 4.

16. _____

17. Express 4202 in scientific notation.

17. _____

18. Express 1.001×10^9 in standard notation.

  A 100,100,000   **B** 1,001,000,000
  C 1,010,000,000 **D** 10,010,000,000

18. _____

19. Express 0.0991 in scientific notation.

19. _____

Continued

20. Express 5.05×10^{-5} in standard notation.

20. _____

    A 0.000505   **B** 0.0000505
    C 0.00000505   **D** 0.00005505

21. Performance Task In biology class, Sidney recorded the size of 5 cells.

    a. Complete the table.

Cell	Size Standard Notation	Size Scientific Notation
A	0.0002 m	
B	0.00006 m	
C	0.00008 m	
D	0.0009 m	
E	0.0000026 m	

    b. Cell A is how many times as large as Cell C?

b. _____

A classmate says, "Cell A is the largest described in the table. It would never fit on a microscope slide that is only 2 centimeters wide." How could you respond to this statement? Compare the size of Cell A with the size of the microscope slide using scientific notation in your response.

_____

_____

_____

_____

_____

— Computation —

1. Multiply $4 \cdot -5 \cdot 2$.

A 8   **B** −20   **C** 10   **D** −40

1. _____

2. Divide $-63 \div -9$.

A $\frac{1}{7}$ **B** $\frac{-1}{7}$ **C** 7   **D** −7

2. _____

3. Evaluate 6^0.

3. _____

4. Evaluate 9^3.

4. _____

5. Write 52,010,916 in scientific notation.

5. _____

6. Write 0.0009922 in scientific notation.

6. _____

— Concepts —

7. Which of the following is true?

A $4 > -7$ **B** $-17 < -19$ **C** $0 < -8$ **D** $64 > 73$

7. _____

8. Which of the following is true?

A $16 < 15$ **B** $37 < -38$ **C** $-1 < 0$ **D** $-24 < -25$

8. _____

9. Rewrite $-6(5 + 3)$ using the distributive property.

9. _____

10. Follow the directions. Use the grid at the right.

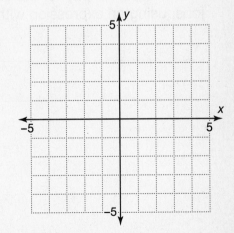

- Plot a point at $(-2, -3)$ and a point at $(-1, 2)$.
- Draw a segment from $(-2, -3)$ to $(-1, 2)$.
- Plot a point at $(0, 0)$ and draw a segment from $(-1, 2)$ to $(0, 0)$.
- Plot a point at $(1, 2)$ and draw a segment from $(0, 0)$ to $(1, 2)$.
- Plot a point at $(2, -3)$ and draw a segment from $(1, 2)$ to $(2, -3)$.

What letter did you make?

10. _____

11. Which is another way to write $(-2)^4$?

  A $-\dfrac{2}{4}$ **B** $4 \cdot 4$

  C $-2 \cdot 4$ **D** $-2 \cdot -2 \cdot -2 \cdot -2$

11. _____

12. To find out what type of car is preferred by drivers in your town, where should you take a survey?

  A At a used-car lot
  B At a sports-car dealership
  C At a large parking lot
  D At a car-repair garage

12. _____

— Applications —

13. At 6:00 P.M. it was 0°F. The temperature then fell 14° in 6 hours. Write an expression using absolute value that tells how much the temperature changed.

13. _____

14. Benji started at the center of town. He rode his bicycle 3 blocks north, then 6 blocks south, then 8 blocks north, and finally 5 blocks south. Where did he end up?

_____

15. Ralph wanted to buy a pair of skates for $43. The store owner said he would deduct $7 if Ralph helped take inventory, $2 if Ralph swept the storeroom, and $4 if Ralph made a new skating display. Tell how much Ralph will pay for the skates if he does all three jobs, using an expression with addition of integers.

_____

_____

Continued

In 16–19, Terrence recorded these gasoline prices:
$1.51, $1.56, $1.56, $1.55, $1.52, $1.54

16. What is the mean of the data?

16. _____

    A $1.54   **B** $1.545   **C** $1.55   **D** $1.56

17. What is the median of the data?

17. _____

    A $1.54   **B** $1.545   **C** $1.55   **D** $1.56

18. What is the mode of the data?

18. _____

    A $1.54   **B** $1.545   **C** $1.55   **D** $1.56

19. Draw a box-and-whisker plot below representing these data.

Evaluate each formula for the values given.

1. $C = (3.14)d$ for $d = 6$

2. $A = (3.14)r^2$ for $r = 3$

3. $P = 2l + 2w$ for $l = 18$ and $w = 11$

1. _____

2. _____

3. _____

In 4–6, evaluate each expression.

4. $4x - 21$ for $x = 9$

5. $x(3y - 1)$ for $x = 7$ and $y = 4$

6. $\dfrac{(a + b)}{2}$ for $a = 25$ and $b = 77$

4. _____

5. _____

6. _____

In 7–10, solve each equation.

7. $a - 7 = 11$

8. $6g = 54$

9. $x = 3(-1 + 8)$

10. $y = -\dfrac{72}{9}$

7. _____

8. _____

9. _____

10. _____

In 11–14, give an expression for each phrase.

11. A number c increased by 12

12. The product of 8 and a number z

13. Twice a number x subtracted from 10

14. The number of weeks in d days

11. _____

12. _____

13. _____

14. _____

15. Test Prep Which equation has $x = 6$ as its solution?

15. _____

    A $x + 1 = 5$ **B** $x - 5 = 1$ **C** $4x = 20$ **D** $\dfrac{x}{4} = 2$

In 1–8, solve each equation.

1. $h + 15 = 37$

2. $c - 4 = 21$

3. $6 = x + 20$

4. $\dfrac{b}{5} = 8$

5. $12n = -60$

6. $\dfrac{3}{4}y = 30$

7. $8x + 5 = 37$

8. $\dfrac{a}{2} - 18 = 12$

9. A catering company buys lunch meat for $3 a pound. How many pounds of lunch meat can be bought for $72?

10. If 8 is added to 7 times a number, the result is 50. Find the number.

1. _____

2. _____

3. _____

4. _____

5. _____

6. _____

7. _____

8. _____

9. _____

10. _____

In 11 and 12, solve and graph each inequality.

11. $7x - 3 \le 11$

11. _____

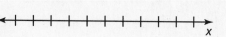

12. $5n + 23 > 3$

12. _____

13. Wilma has a part-time job that pays $5 per hour. How many hours must she work in a week to earn at least $40?

13. _____

14. LeRoy makes lawn ornaments to sell. He sells them for 3 times the cost of his materials. If he wants to sell an ornament for at most $15, what is the maximum cost of the materials?

14. _____

15. **Test Prep** Which of the inequalities shows that x is at least 5?

   A $x > 5$ **B** $x \ge 5$ **C** $x < 5$ **D** $x \le 5$

15. _____

In 1 and 2, decide if you would use $A = lw$, $l = \frac{A}{w}$, or $w = \frac{A}{l}$ to answer each question, where A is the area of a rectangle, l is its length, and w is its width. Then answer the questions.

1. A rectangle has a width of 10 and a length of 25. What is its area?

    1. _____

2. The area of a rectangle is 80. Its width is 4. What is the length?

    2. _____

3. Use the formula $P = 2l + 2w$ to find P when $l = 12$ and $w = 7$.

    3. _____

In 4 and 5, evaluate each expression.

4. $8x - 15$ for $x = 7$

    4. _____

5. $x(4 + 5y)$ for $x = 3$ and $y = 2.4$

    5. _____

6. The sum of the first n natural numbers can be found using the expression $\frac{n(n + 1)}{2}$. What is the sum of the first 40 natural numbers?

    6. _____

In 7–10, solve and check your solution.

7. $n + 7 = 16$

    7. _____

8. $5d = 45$

    8. _____

9. $x = -4(-2 + 4)$

    9. _____

10. $y = -\frac{27}{3}$

    10. _____

In 11–15, write an expression for each phrase.

11. Twice a number increased by 8

    11. _____

12. The quotient of 10 divided by 3 times a number

    12. _____

13. A number subtracted from 14

    13. _____

14. The number of sides in r rectangles

    14. _____

15. The number of yards in f feet

    15. _____

In 16–23, solve and check your solution.

16. $n + 10 = 18$

16. _____

17. $c - 12 = 7$

17. _____

18. $15 = x + 26$

18. _____

19. $\frac{n}{4} = 11$

19. _____

20. $7p = -105$

20. _____

21. $\frac{2}{5}y = 20$

21. _____

22. $6x - 11 = 13$

22. _____

23. $\frac{n}{8} + 10 = 21$

23. _____

24. A company sells its product for $16 per unit. How many units would have to be sold in order for the company to earn $528?

24. _____

25. If 15 is subtracted from 4 times a number, the result is 19. Find the number.

25. _____

In 26 and 27, solve the inequality. Graph the solution.

26. $2x - 3 < 5$

26. _____

27. $5z + 12 \geq 2$

27. _____

28. To pay for expenses, at least 500 copies of each issue of a school newspaper must be sold. If 450 copies go to subscribers, how many more copies must be sold so that the expenses are covered?

28. _____

In 1 and 2, decide if you would use $A = lw$, $l = \frac{A}{w}$, or $w = \frac{A}{l}$ to answer each question, where A is the area of a rectangle, l is its length, and w is its width. Then answer the questions.

1. A rectangle has a width of 6 and a length of 30. What is its area?

1. _____

2. The area of a rectangle is 60. Its length is 12. What is the width?

2. _____

3. Use the formula $V = lwh$ to find V when $l = 10$, $w = 5$, and $h = 6$.

3. _____

In 4 and 5, evaluate each expression.

4. $3x + 8$ for $x = 10$

4. _____

5. $x(22 - 5y)$ for $x = 3$ and $y = 2.2$

5. _____

6. The sum of the first n natural numbers can be found using the expression $\frac{n(n + 1)}{2}$. What is the sum of the first 20 natural numbers?

6. _____

In 7–10, solve and check your solution.

7. $x - 7 = 9$

7. _____

8. $8g = 56$

8. _____

9. $x = -6(-3 + 7)$

9. _____

10. $z = -\frac{44}{11}$

10. _____

In 11–15, write an expression for each phrase.

11. A number increased by 5

11. _____

12. The quotient of 4 times a number divided by 9

12. _____

13. 15 subtracted from twice a number

13. _____

14. The number of sides in h hexagons

14. _____

15. The number of years in m months

15. _____

Name _____

In 16–23, solve and check your solution.

16. $m - 7 = 15$ 16. _____

17. $t + 23 = 70$ 17. _____

18. $11 = y + 13$ 18. _____

19. $\dfrac{x}{6} = 12$ 19. _____

20. $9w = -81$ 20. _____

21. $\dfrac{3}{5}n = 12$ 21. _____

22. $8x - 7 = 25$ 22. _____

23. $\dfrac{n}{4} + 15 = 28$ 23. _____

24. A company sells its product for $12 per unit. How   24. _____
    many units would have to be sold in order for the
    company to earn $504?

25. If 10 is subtracted from 7 times a number, the result   25. _____
    is 39. Find the number.

**In 26 and 27, solve the inequality. Graph the
solution.**

26. $3x - 1 < 11$ 26. _____

27. $7z + 16 \geq 2$ 27. _____

28. Composina has at most $20 to spend at the camera   28. _____
    store. If she pays $10 to have some film developed,
    how many rolls of new film can she buy at $4 each?

Date _____   Score _____

1. If the formula $P = 2w + 2l$ is evaluated for $w = 6$ and $l = 8.5$, what is P?

   A 18.5   **B** 28.5   **C** 29   **D** 108.25

1. _____

2. Use the formula $d = rt$ to determine the distance traveled by a car at a rate of 50 mph for $5\frac{1}{2}$ hours.

   A 250 miles   **B** $55\frac{1}{2}$ miles

   C $250\frac{1}{2}$ miles   **D** 275 miles

2. _____

3. Use the formula $F = 1.8C + 32$ to determine the temperature in degrees Fahrenheit (F) when the temperature in degrees Celsius (C) is 20.

   A –6.7   **B** 1.8   **C** 32   **D** 68

3. _____

4. Find the value of the expression $48 - 3x$ when $x = 7$.

   A 38   **B** 27   **C** 315   **D** 11

4. _____

5. Find the value of the expression $x(3y - 2)$ when $x = 5$ and $y = 8$.

   A 110   **B** 90   **C** 118   **D** 27

5. _____

6. A large room has a wooden floor with a ceramic-tiled pattern in the center. Use the measurements to write an expression to find the area of the section of the floor that is wood.

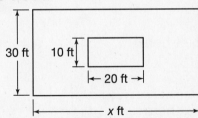

   A $20x - 200$ **B** $20x + 200$ **C** $30x - 200$ **D** $30x + 200$

6. _____

7. Solve $x = -4(12 - 3)$.

   A $x = 5$ **B** $x = -36$ **C** $x = -51$ **D** Not here

7. _____

8. Solve $m = -\dfrac{42}{7}$.

   A $m = -35$ **B** $m = 6$ **C** $m = -294$ **D** Not here

8. _____

Name _____

9. When a number cube is rolled r times, $n = \frac{1}{6}r$ represents the average number of times a certain number will occur. What is the average number of times you would get a 6 if the cube is rolled 50 times?

    A 1 time   **B** 6 times   **C** $6.\overline{6}$ times   **D** $8.\overline{3}$ times

9. _____

10. Give an algebraic expression for five less than twice a number x.

    A $2x - 5$ **B** $(x + 2) - 5$ **C** $5 - 2x$ **D** $2(x - 5)$

10. _____

11. Which phrase describes the expression $3(n + 8)$?

    A 8 more than 3 times a number
    B The sum of 3 times a number and 8
    C 3 times the sum of a number and 8
    D The product of 3 and 8 less than a number

11. _____

12. Give an expression for the number of sides in c octagons.

    A $\frac{c}{8}$ **B** $c + 8$ **C** $8c$ **D** $\frac{8}{c}$

12. _____

13. Paula is painting T-shirts for a craft show. She will make a profit of $1.50 for every shirt she sells. She paid $15 to be in the show. What is the formula for the total profit (P), after covering the entrance fee, that Paula will make for any number of T-shirts (s) she sells?

    A $P = 1.5s + 15$ **B** $P = 1.5s - 15$
    C $P = 15s + 1.5$ **D** $P = 15s - 1.5$

13. _____

14. Solve $n - 6 = 11$.

    A $n = 5$ **B** $n = 17$ **C** $n = 66$ **D** Not here

14. _____

15. Solve $21 = x + 30$.

    A $x = -9$ **B** $x = 51$ **C** $x = 9$ **D** Not here

15. _____

16. George spent $28 on food and on a souvenir at a concert. He had $7 left. How much money did he take with him to the concert?

    A $7   **B** $21   **C** $28   **D** $35

16. _____

17. Solve $9g = -72$.

    A $g = 8$ **B** $g = 81$ **C** $x = -63$ **D** Not here

17. _____

Continued

18. Solve $\frac{2}{3}x = 36$.

    A $x = 24$ **B** $x = 54$ **C** $x = 35\frac{1}{3}$ **D** Not here

18. _____

19. Libby bought necklaces for 4 of her friends. She spent a total of $8 for the necklaces. How much did each necklace cost if they all cost the same amount?

    A $2   **B** $4   **C** $8   **D** $32

19. _____

20. Solve $4y - 9 = 27$.

    A $y = 36$ **B** $y = 32$ **C** $y = 9$ **D** Not here

20. _____

21. Solve $6h + 43 = 19$.

    A $h = -4$ **B** $h = -24$ **C** $h = -30$ **D** Not here

21. _____

22. A parking garage charges $2.50 to get in and $1.00 for each hour. If Al paid $8.50, for how long was his car parked in the garage?

    A 4 hours   **B** 6 hours   **C** 8.5 hours   **D** Not here

22. _____

23. Thomas made 72 muffins. He gave 24 to his school's bake sale. He divided the rest equally among 6 of his friends. How many muffins did he give each friend?

    A 6   **B** 8   **C** 12   **D** 24

23. _____

24. Solve $5z - 3 \geq 12$.

    A $z \geq 3$ **B** $z \geq 1.8$ **C** $z < 3$ **D** Not here

24. _____

25. Graph the solution to $3x + 16 < 10$.

25. _____

    A
```
<---+---+---+---+---+---+--o-+---+-->
   -4  -3  -2  -1   0   1   2   3   4
```
    B
```
<---+---+--o-+---+---+---+---+---+-->
   -4  -3  -2  -1   0   1   2   3   4
```
    C
```
<---+---+--o-+---+---+---+---+---+-->
   -4  -3  -2  -1   0   1   2   3   4
```
    D Not here

26. Val makes $7 an hour at his part-time job. He is saving to buy an $899 computer. He already has $121 saved. Assuming that he receives his entire pay (no deductions), how many hours does he need to work in order to buy the computer?

26. _____

    A $7x + 121 \leq 899$ **B** $7x - 121 \leq 899$ **C** $7x + 121 \geq 899$ **D** $7x - 121 \geq 899$

You are helping a friend move. You and your friend want to pack some
boxes today and then move several boxes that are already packed.

Items to Pack	Approx. Wt.	Items to Pack	Approx. Wt.
50 books	$\frac{1}{2}$ lb per book	CDs, 10 cases	6 lb per case
4 book ends	3 lb total	assorted tapes	x
miscellaneous	m	tape cabinet	24 lb

a. Suppose you will pack the book ends and the miscellaneous items (m) in
one box. Write an expression that tells how much the box will weigh.

b. If you decide to pack the book ends with some books, write an expression
that tells how much a box will weigh if you pack the book ends and any
number of books (b).

c. You want any packed box to weigh no more than
30 pounds. Use the expression in part **b** to write an inequality for the
number of books you could pack in a box with the book ends.

d. The box packed with the books and book ends weighs 24 pounds. How
many books are in the box?

e. Now you will carry the CD cases (c) and the tape cabinet to the ground
floor. You and your friend decide to each carry an equal weight. If your
friend carries the cabinet, how many CD cases should you carry? Write and
solve an equation.

f. You want to know if the tapes (x) weigh as much as a case of CDs. You
know you weigh 118 pounds. When you weigh yourself holding the tapes,
you weigh 123 pounds. Do the tapes weigh as much as a case of CDs?
Use an equation to explain your answer.

g. The new apartment is 18 miles from the old one. If your average traveling
speed is 40 mph, how long will it take you to make a one-way trip? Use the
formula $d = rt$.

h. You want to move 48 packed boxes (p) today. You can carry 6 boxes in a
hatchback or 8 boxes in a station wagon. You figure a round trip will take about
1 hour. The hatchback gets 25 mpg and the station wagon gets 15 mpg. Write an
equation for the number of trips required to move the boxes in each car. Think
about the factors involved. Then decide which car to use. Explain your decision.

Teacher Notes

Concepts and Skills This activity requires students to:

- use information from a table to create expressions, equations, and inequalities.
- use a formula and constants for rate and distance to calculate time.
- solve equations.
- use mathematics and weigh different factors to make a decision.

Guiding Questions

- Suppose you wanted to pack a box with several of the same item. How could you use mathematics to figure out how much the packed box weighs?
- Suppose you knew the distance (d) and time (t) it took you to drive from one apartment to another. You want to find out the rate (r) you traveled. By what would you multiply both sides of the equation $d = rt$ to find the rate?

Answers

a. $m + 3$

b. $\dfrac{b}{2} + 3$

c. $30 \geq \dfrac{b}{2} + 3$

d. 42 books

e. $24 = 6c$; 4 cases

f. $118 + x = 123$, $x = 5$; no; the tapes do not weigh as much as a case of CDs.

g. 0.45 hour, or 27 minutes

h. Station wagon: 8 *boxes/trip* $\times$ *n* trips = 48 boxes; Hatchback: 6 *boxes/trip* $\times$ *n* trips = 48 boxes; hatchback needs $\dfrac{1}{3}$ more trips (8 to 6), but gets $\dfrac{2}{3}$ more miles per gallon (25 to 15). A student interested in saving money (cost of gasoline) and who does not care as much about time would choose to use the hatchback. A student interested in saving time and who does not care as much about cost would choose to use the station wagon.

Extension

Have students write about a move they remember or have them interview other students or relatives who have moved. Have them discuss the many ways mathematics could be used to make a move easier and more efficient.

Evaluation

Level	Standard to be achieved for performance of specified level
4	The student demonstrates a clear understanding of the differences among expressions, equations, and inequalities; how to create them; and how to solve equations. All calculations are accurate and complete. The answer to which car to use is supported logically.
3	The student demonstrates an understanding of the differences among expressions, equations, and inequalities and how to create them, although some confusion may occur. The student successfully solves equations. All or most calculations are accurate and complete. The answer to which car to use is supported logically.
2	The student demonstrates some understanding of the differences among expressions, equations, and inequalities, although there is some confusion. The student attempts to solve all equations, but many calculations are inaccurate or incomplete. The answer to which car to use is given but is not supported.
1	The student demonstrates little or no understanding of the differences among expressions, equations, and inequalities. The student makes little or no attempt to solve equations, and calculations are inaccurate or incomplete.

© Scott Foresman Addison Wesley 8

1. Use the formula $A = lw$ to find the area of a
rectangle whose length is 6 and width is 4.5.

1. _____

2. Jessica has 9 stamps to start her collection. Each time
she goes to the stamp store she will buy 5 more. How many
stamps will she have after she goes to the store 3 times?

A 42   **B** 24   **C** 17   **D** Not here

2. _____

3. Solve $x = -2(9 - 4)$.

3. _____

4. Which equation has $x = 8$ as its solution?

A $x + 2 = 6$ **B** $x - 2 = 4$ **C** $4x = 32$ **D** $\frac{x}{4} = 4$

4. _____

5. Which inequality can be graphed by using an open
circle on 3 and shading the number line to the right?

A $x > 3$ **B** $x \geq 3$ **C** $x < 3$ **D** $x \leq 3$

5. _____

In 6–9, write an algebraic expression for each.

6. 2 more than a number n

A $2n$ **B** $n + n$ **C** $n + 2$ **D** $n - 2$

6. _____

7. Selma had 24 apples which she divided among
x friends.

7. _____

8. 1 less than twice a number a

8. _____

9. Richard started with 2 horses and added an additional
y horses at his ranch. Then he doubled his total.

A $2(y^2)$ **B** $2y + 2$ **C** $2y - 2$ **D** $2(y + 2)$

9. _____

In 10–15, solve each and check your solution.

10. Mandy had some marbles (m). She lost 8 of them
through a hole in her pocket. Now she has only 5 in
her pocket. How many did she have at first?

A 3   **B** 5   **C** 8   **D** 13

10. _____

11. $c + 14 = 6$

A $c = -6$ **B** $c = -8$ **C** $c = -14$ **D** $c = -20$

11. _____

12. $6n = -72$ **12.** _____

13. $\dfrac{b}{3} = -6$ **13.** _____

14. Tony had 9 bags of oranges. Each bag contained   **14.** _____
x oranges. He ate 4 oranges. Then he had 23 oranges
left. How many oranges were originally in each bag?

   A 2   **B** 3   **C** $\dfrac{21}{9}$ **D** 9

15. $\dfrac{w}{7} + 2 = 11$ **15.** _____

In 16 and 17, solve each and graph the solution.

16. $4x \geq 8$ **16.** _____

17. $\dfrac{n}{2} + 2 > 1$ **17.** _____

18. A machine can produce electrical connectors at a rate   **18.** _____
of 25 per minute. How many minutes will it take the
machine to produce at least 800 connectors?

19. Use the formula $d = rt$ to find out the   **19.** _____
distance traveled in 2 hours by a car going
45 miles per hour.

20. Performance Task Write an equation that   **20.** _____
can be solved by subtracting and multiplying,
and then solve it. Write an inequality that
can be solved by adding and dividing. Then   _____
solve the inequality and graph the solution.

                                                _____

Date _____ Score _____

— Computation —

1. Evaluate the formula $r = \dfrac{d}{t}$ for $d = 200$
and $t = 4$.

1. _____

   A 12   **B** 25   **C** $5r$ **D** Not here

2. Evaluate the expression $5x - 3y$
for $x = 5$ and $y = 3$.

2. _____

3. Evaluate the expression $3x(5 + y)$
for $x = 7$ and $y = -2$.

3. _____

4. Compute $-8 + 11 - (-4)$.

4. _____

   A -1 **B** -2 **C** 7   **D** Not here

5. Evaluate $|4 - 9|$.

5. _____

6. Evaluate $\dfrac{2 + 3(8 - 2)}{(-2)(-3) - 8}$.

6. _____

In 7–14, solve and check each equation.

7. $x = -6(11 - 4)$

7. _____

8. $y = \dfrac{-35}{(2 - 7)}$

8. _____

9. $n - 15 = 9$

9. _____

10. $16 = z + 20$

10. _____

11. $-10w = 75$

11. _____

12. $\dfrac{k}{6} = -2$

12. _____

13. $\dfrac{a}{3} + 7 = 1$

13. _____

14. $12w - 11 = 25$

14. _____

Name _____

— Concepts —

15. Which equation can be solved by adding 4 to both sides and then dividing both sides by 3?

    A $4x + 3 = 11$ **B** $\frac{x}{3} + 4 = 5$

    C $3x - 4 = 8$ **D** $\frac{x}{4} - 3 = 6$

15. _____

16. Write an expression for 10 less than twice a number n.

16. _____

17. Give a phrase for $4(n + 8)$.

_____

18. Give a phrase for $3x - 7$.

_____

19. Write the number 4.21×10^4 in standard notation.

    A 0.000421   **B** 0.0421   **C** 4,210   **D** 42,100

19. _____

In 20 and 21, solve and graph the solution.

20. $7x + 11 \geq 4$

20. _____

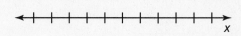

21. $\frac{x}{3} - 5 < 1$

21. _____

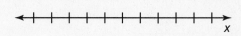

Continued

━ Applications ━

22. Find the mean and the median of the following scores that a student made on seven tests: 75, 81, 80, 90, 84, 78, and 86.

22. _____

23. Charles scored 9 points. This was 3 less than one-fourth the number of points that Michael scored. How many points did Michael score? Write an equation and solve.

_____

24. A parking garage charges $2.50 per hour. What is the longest time Ed can park his car for $16?

A 1 hour   **B** 2 hours   **C** 6 hours   **D** 7 hours

24. _____

25. The formula $P = 2l + 2w$ is used for a rectangle's perimeter. A rectangular Olympic swimming pool has a perimeter of 148 m and length of 50 m. Find its width.

25. _____

26. To go at least 240 miles on 10 gallons of gasoline, how many miles per gallon must a car average?

A 10 mpg   **B** 100 mpg   **C** 24 mpg   **D** 240 mpg

26. _____

27. The distance in miles that a light plane will glide is its altitude in feet divided by 500. What must the plane's altitude be in order to glide at least 10 miles?

27. _____

Give the letter of the correct answer.

In 1–4, use the line plot.

**Ages at Which Students
Began Band**

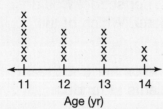

Age (yr)

1. The line plot represents the ages at which students began band instruction. At what age did the most students begin?

    A 11   **B** 12   **C** 13   **D** 14

    1. _____

2. Which figure does *not* represent the range of ages at which the students began band?

    A 3   **B** 11–14   **C** 4   **D** Not here

    2. _____

3. Give the mean of the data.

    A 11   **B** 12.125   **C** 12   **D** 12.9

    3. _____

4. Give the median of the data.

    A 11   **B** 14   **C** 12   **D** 13

    4. _____

5. What is the range of the data in this box-and-whisker plot?

    **Ages of People
    in an Exercise Class**

    47 50 52   57   67

    A 47–50   **B** 50–57   **C** 57–67   **D** 47–67

    5. _____

6. The bar graph shows the number of certain pets owned by students in an eighth-grade class. There are twice as many of one kind of pet as there are fish. Which pet is it?

    A Cats   **B** Dogs
    C Gerbils   **D** Turtles

    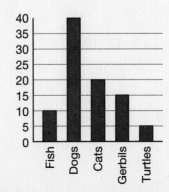

    6. _____

7. A survey company stopped 1000 people in a large U.S. city
to answer a questionnaire. Of these people, 547 refused to
answer. What is the sample size of the survey?

7.

   A 547   **B** 100   **C** 453   **D** Not here

8. Molly wants to find out how the students at her school would
feel about starting the school day an hour later. Which of the
samples is most representative?

8. _____

   A 28 students in her art class   **B** Everyone on her track team
   C 14 students at lunch   **D** 25 students at random

9. Jaleel is surveying a group of about 300 students to find out
how many students surf the Internet more than twice a week.
Which method should he use to organize his data?

9. _____

   A Frequency table   **B** Stem-and-leaf
   C Line plot   **D** Histogram

10. What trend is shown
in the scatterplot?

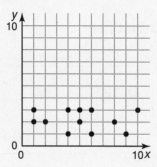

10.

   A No trend   **B** Positive
   C Negative   **D** Not here

11. Which of the following are listed in order from least to greatest?

11.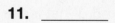

   A 10, 4, 1, −5, −2   **B** −3, 3, 2, 5, 7
   C −4, −1, 1, 0, 2   **D** −11, −1, 0, 11, 21

12. Find $|-9| - 3$.

12. _____

   A −12   **B** 6   **C** −6   **D** −3

13. Add $53 + (-11)$.

13. _____

   A −42   **B** 64   **C** −64   **D** 42

14. Subtract $-58 - (-98)$

14. _____

   A 56   **B** 40   **C** −40   **D** −156

15. Multiply $-15\,(-23)$.   **15.** _____

  A 345   **B** -345 **C** -38 **D** Not here

16. Divide -81 by (-9).   **16.** _____

  A -9 **B** 729   **C** 9   **D** Not here

17. Evaluate $-4(10 - 4)$.   **17.** _____

  A 24   **B** -24 **C** -36 **D** -44

18. Find the coordinates of point *A*.   **18.** _____

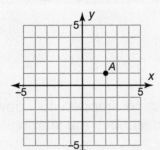

  A $(1, 2)$ **B** $(2, 2)$
  C $(2, 1)$ **D** $(2, 0)$

19. What is the exponential form of $-5 \times -5 \times -5 \times -5$?   **19.** _____

  A -5^4 **B** $(-5)^{-4}$ **C** $(-5)^4$ **D** 5^{-4}

20. Which expression represents 3.725×10^6 in standard notation?   **20.** _____

  A 372,500   **B** 3,725,000   **C** 37,250,000   **D** 37,250

21. The approximate diameter of a mumps virus is 0.0000001 m. How should this number be written in scientific notation?   **21.** _____

  A 1×10^7 **B** 1×10^{-7} **C** 1×10^{-6} **D** 1×10^{-8}

22. Evaluate $A = l \times w$ for $l = 12$ and $w = 5$.   **22.** _____

  A 17   **B** 144   **C** 60   **D** 25

23. Evaluate $V = l \times w \times h$ for $l = 6$, $w = 4$, and $h = 10$.   **23.** _____

  A 24   **B** 40   **C** 240   **D** 60

24. If a Boeing 747 cruises at 600 mi/hr, how far would it fly
in 3.5 hours? Use the formula $d = rt$.

    A 171.4 mi   **B** 2000 mi   **C** 2100 mi   **D** Not here

24. _____

25. Which formula would give $Q = 25$ if 5 is substituted for d?

    A $Q = \dfrac{d}{5}$ **B** $Q = (d - 1)^2$ **C** $d = Q \times 3$ **D** $Q = 3d + 10$

25. _____

26. Write an algebraic expression for $29.99 each, plus $5 handling fee.

    A $5x + 29.99$ **B** $29.99x + 5$ **C** $29.99 + 5$ **D** $5 + 29.99$

26. _____

27. Solve the equation $f + 23 = 32$.

    A $f = 9$ **B** $f = 55$ **C** $f = -9$ **D** Not here

27. _____

28. In one day, the temperature in Chicago dropped 45°, down to
40°F. Which algebraic expression describes the starting
temperature, t?

    A $t = 45° - 40°$ **B** $t = 40° - 45°$
    C $t + 45° = 40°$ **D** $t - 45° = 40°$

28. _____

29. Solve $7x = 56$.

    A $x = 7$ **B** $x = 56$ **C** $x = 8$ **D** $x = 6$

29. _____

30. Solve $25x - 5 = 145$.

    A $x = 5$ **B** $x = 6$ **C** $x = 4$ **D** $x = 7$

30. _____

31. Give the inequality
for the graph.

    4 5 6 7 8 9 10 11 x

    A $x \geq 9$ **B** $x > 9$ **C** $x < 9$ **D** $x \leq 9$

31. _____

32. Solve $3p + 3 \leq 24$.

    A $p = 7$ **B** $p \geq 7$ **C** $p \leq 7$ **D** Not here

32. _____

Name _____

Date _____   Score _____

In 1 and 2, find the value of y for $x = 5$ in each equation.

1. $y = \frac{1}{5}x + 1$

1. _____

2. $y = 3x - 1$

2. _____

3. Make a table of values for the equation $y = 2x + 1$. Use 0, 1, 2, 3, and 4 for x values.

3.

x					
y					

In 4 and 5, determine whether each ordered pair is a solution of the equation $y = 4x - 3$.

4. $(5, 23)$

4. _____

5. $(-1, -7)$

5. _____

6. Find a rule that relates x and y.

6. _____

x	0	1	2	3	4
y	3	5	7	9	11

7. Graph $y = -x + 2$ and $y = x + 2$ on the same grid.

7.

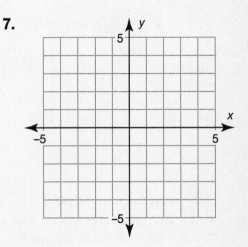

8. **Test Prep** Which of these ordered pairs is *not* a solution of $y = x + 7$?

    A $(1, 8)$ **B** $(4, 11)$ **C** $(2, 10)$ **D** $(7, 14)$

8. _____

1. Find the slope, the *x*-intercept, and the *y*-intercept of the line below.

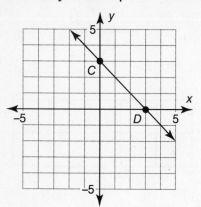

_____

2. Graph the equation $y = -3x$.

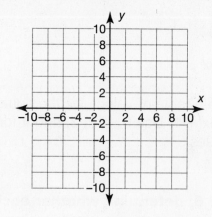

3. Find the slope and the *x*- and *y*-intercepts for the line you graphed in Item 2.

3. _____

4. Solve the following system by graphing $y = 2x - 3$ and $y = x + 1$.

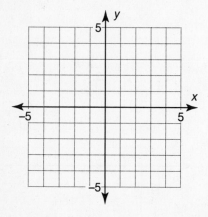

5. Graph the inequality $y > 2x + 1$.

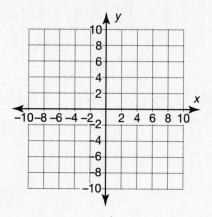

6. John can park a car for either $24 plus $1 per hour or $7 per hour. Use either tables or a graph to find the number of hours for which the cost would be the same.

6. _____

7. Test Prep Which is the slope for a ski run that rises 4 feet for every 40 feet it runs?

A $\frac{1}{10,000}$ **B** $\frac{1}{1,000}$ **C** $\frac{1}{100}$ **D** $\frac{1}{10}$

7. _____

Name _____

Date _____ Score _____

1. Find the value of *y* when *x* = 2 in the equation *y* = 3*x*.

1. _____

2. Find the rule that relates *x* and *y* in the table. Then find *y* when *x* = 12.

x	1	2	3	4	5
y	3	6	9	12	15

2. _____

3. The number of boys (*y*) on the softball team is equal to 4 less than the number of girls (*x*) on the team. Determine whether each is a solution of this situation: (6 girls, 2 boys); (7 girls, 11 boys); (1 girl, 4 boys).

3. _____

4. Give two solutions for the equation 2*x* − 3*y* = 18.

4. _____

5. Graph the ordered pairs in the table. Connect the points to determine if the graph is linear.

x	1	2	3	4	5
y	4	−3	2	−1	0

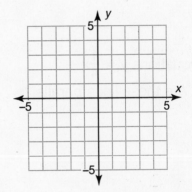

_____

6. Thom has a bucket of moss mixture for planting. The bucket weighs 6 ounces and each scoop of mixture weighs 2 ounces. Graph the weight of the bucket of mixture. Use *x* for the number of scoops of mixture.

6.

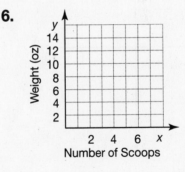

7. For each line, find the slope, the *x*-intercept, and the *y*-intercept.

   a. Line through *A* and *B*

   b. Line through *B* and *C*

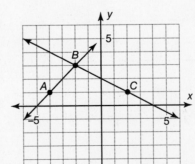

7. **a.** _____

   b. _____

8. Graph the line $y = \frac{1}{2}x - 2$. Find the slope, the x-intercept, and the y-intercept.

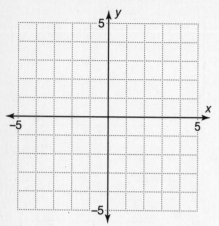

9. Solve the system by graphing $y = x$ and $y = \frac{1}{2}x + 2$.

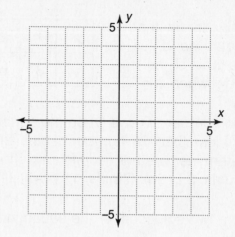

_____

10. Graph the equations $y = \frac{1}{4}x + 2$ and $y = \frac{1}{4}x$. Are these lines parallel? Explain.

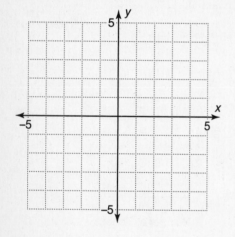

_____

_____

11. Walter has x books. Lynda (y) has more than double this amount, minus 1. Graph the inequality.

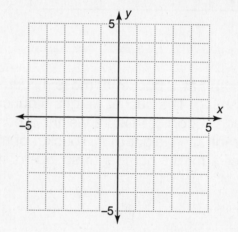

1. Find the value of y when $x = 7$ in the equation $y = 2x + 2$.

1. _____

2. Find the rule that relates x and y in the table. Then find y when $x = 9$.

x	1	2	3	4	5
y	6	7	8	9	10

2. _____

3. The number of red cars (y) in the lot is equal to 3 times the number of blue cars (x) plus 1. Determine whether each is a solution of this situation: (1 blue car, 4 red cars); (6 blue cars, 18 red cars); (10 blue cars, 31 red cars).

3. _____

4. Give two solutions for the equation $3x + 2y = 24$.

4. _____

5. Graph the ordered pairs in the table. Connect the points to determine if the graph is linear.

x	1	2	3	4	5
y	4	5	6	7	8

_____

5.

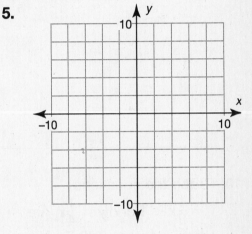

6. Jill has yards of material wrapped around a board. The board weighs 12 ounces and each yard of material weighs 4 ounces. Graph the weight of the material and board. Use x for the number of yards of material.

6.

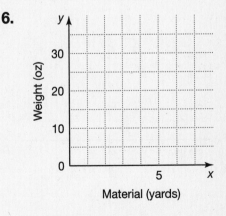

Material (yards)

7. For each line, find the slope, the *x*-intercept, and the *y*-intercept.

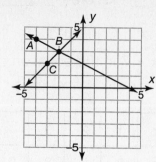

7. a. _____

b. _____

    a. Line through
       A and *B*
    b. Line through
       B and *C*

8. Graph the line $y = \frac{1}{3}x + 1$. Find the slope, the *x*-intercept, and the *y*-intercept.

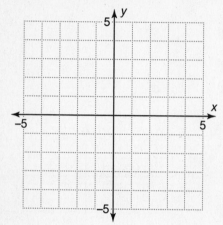

9. Solve the system by graphing $y = x - 1$ and $y = 2x - 3$.

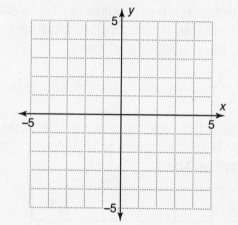

10. Graph the equations $y = \frac{1}{2}x - 1$ and $y = \frac{1}{4}x$. Are these lines parallel? Explain.

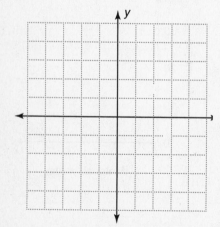

11. Al makes *x* dollars per hour. Hal (*y*) makes *at most* twice that amount plus 3 dollars per hour more.

Graph the inequality.

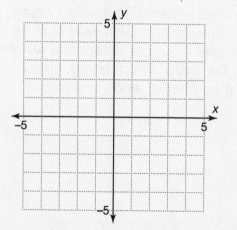

Give the letter of the correct answer.

1. What is the value of y when $x = 6$ in the equation
$y = \frac{1}{2}x + 1$?

   A $y = 2$ **B** $y = 4$ **C** $y = 13$ **D** $y = 11$

   1. _____

2. The table below is represented by which equation?

x	0	1	2	3	4
y	4	7	10	13	16

   A $y = x + 4$ **B** $y = 3x - 4$
   C $y = 3x + 4$ **D** Not here

   2. _____

3. Gretchen boxes widgets for shipment. Each box
   weighs 2 pounds. Each widget weighs 3 pounds.
   Which equation represents the combined weights of
   a box and the widgets?

   A $y = 3x + 2$ **B** $y = 2x + 3$
   C $y = -\frac{1}{2}x + \frac{3}{2}$ **D** $y = -\frac{2}{3}x$

   3. _____

4. Determine which ordered pair is *not* a solution of the
   equation $2x + 4y = 16$.

   A $(4, 2)$ **B** $(2, 3)$ **C** $(6, 1)$ **D** $(3, 2)$

   4. _____

5. Which of the following represents solutions for the
   equation $2x + 5 = y$?

   A $(1, 8)$ and $(4, 16)$ **B** $(0, 5)$ and $(2, 9)$
   C $(-1, 2)$ and $(3, 13)$ **D** $(0, -5)$ and $(4, 16)$

   5. _____

6. A line having which slope would rise upward from left
   to right?

   A $-\frac{1}{4}$ **B** -4 **C** $\frac{3}{7}$ **D** Not here

   6. _____

7. Which is true about parallel lines?

   A Parallel lines intersect.
   B One of the parallel lines has to go through the origin.
   C Parallel lines curve.
   D Parallel lines have the same slope.

   7. _____

Continued **105**

8. Cynthia (*y*) has double the dollars Kay (*x*) has plus 3 more. Which of the following represents this situation?

8. _____

A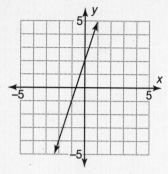

B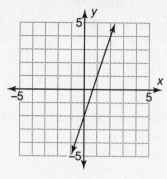

C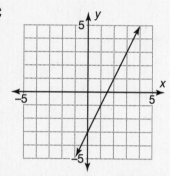

D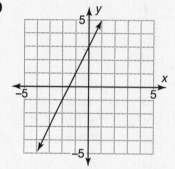

9. Which graph represents a line through the origin with a slope of $-\frac{2}{3}$?

9. _____

A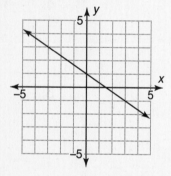

B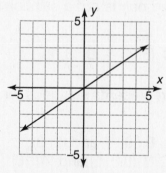

C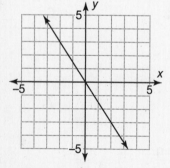

D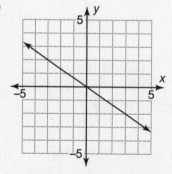

Continued

Name _____

In 10–12, use the graph below.

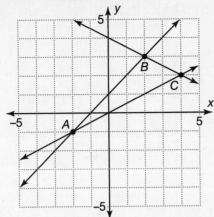

10. Which is the slope of the line through A and C?

    A $-\dfrac{1}{2}$ **B** $\dfrac{1}{2}$ **C** -2 **D** 2

10. _____

11. What is the x-intercept of the line through A and B?

    A -1 **B** 0   **C** 1   **D** 2

11. _____

12. What is the y-intercept of the line through B and C?

    A -2 **B** 0   **C** 2   **D** 4

12. _____

13. The point (2, 3) is a solution of which system of equations?

    A $y = 3x - 3$ and $y = -x + 2$
    B $y = 2x - 1$ and $y = \dfrac{1}{2}x + 2$
    C $y = 2x + 1$ and $y = 3x - 3$
    D $y = -x + 2$ and $y = 2x + 1$

13. _____

14. Which of these points is the solution of this system of equations? $2x + 4y = 4$ and $x - y = 8$

    A (6, 2)   **B** $(-2, 6)$ **C** $(6, -2)$ **D** Not here

14. _____

15. The number of cars parked in Lot Y (y) is more than the total of twice the number of cars parked in Lot X (x) minus 4. Which is a solution of this inequality?

    A 2 cars in X, 0 cars in Y   **B** 3 cars in X, 1 car in Y
    C 5 cars in X, 4 cars in Y   **D** Not here

15. _____

16. Jody's test score (*y*) is *at most* equal to Jane's test score (*x*) plus 2 points. Which of these represents this situation?

16. _____

A
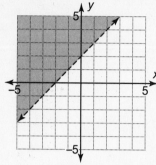

B
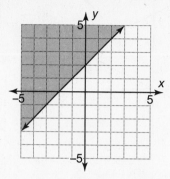

C
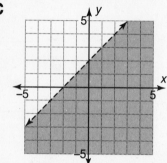

D
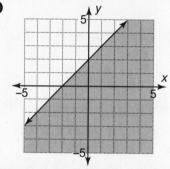

17. The cost (*y*) of a pound of cashews is more than $3 over the cost (*x*) of a pound of peanuts. Which of these represents this situation?

17. _____

A
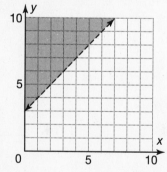

B
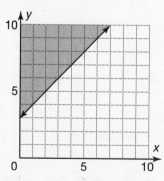

C
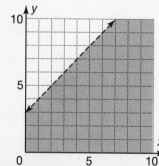

D
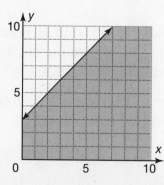

Continued

Name _____

18. There are two times as many red roses as white roses in Ellen's garden. Which is a solution of this situation?

18. _____

    A (4 white roses, 6 red roses)   **B** (2 white roses, 1 red rose)
    C (8 white roses, 8 red roses)   **D** Not here

19. Which is the slope of the line on the graph at the right?

    A 3   **B** −3   **C** $\frac{1}{3}$ **D** $-\frac{1}{3}$

19. _____

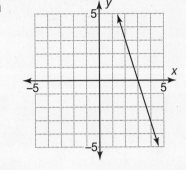

20. Which of the following is the solution to $y = -\frac{1}{2}x + 1$ and $y = x - 2$?

    A (0, 1)   **B** (2, 0)   **C** (0, −2)   **D** Not here

20. _____

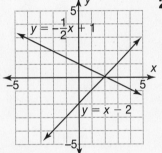

21. The number of "yes" votes and the number of "no" votes is the same. Which graph shows this relationship?

21. _____

A

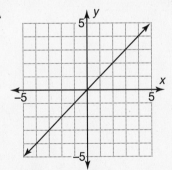

B

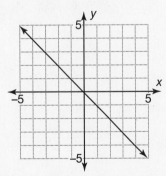

C

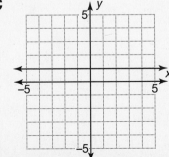

D

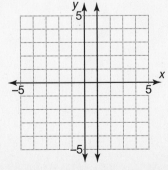

You will need graph paper and a ruler.

You want to start up a small business selling birdhouses that you build and then paint. Materials for the birdhouses cost $4 each. You are thinking about selling them for $8 each. You want to rent a booth at the mall. Rent for a booth at the Millhouse Mall, a very busy shopping center, is $100 per month. Rent for a booth at Mini Marketplace, a shopping center that is not as busy, is $30 per month plus 0.25 times the ticketed price of each item you sell.

a. Write an equation for each mall that represents your monthly expenses if you build x birdhouses during the month.

b. Write an equation for each mall to represent your monthly income if you sell x birdhouses during the month.

c. Solve the system of equations for each mall that represent your monthly expenses and your monthly income. Graph the equations for each mall using the grids below. How many birdhouses must you sell to break even for the month if you rent at Millhouse Mall? At Mini Marketplace?

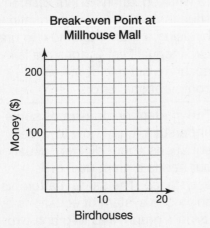

Break-even Point at
Millhouse Mall

Break-even Point at
Mini Marketplace

Regardless of which mall you choose, you would like to know how much money you would take in if you sold your birdhouses for at least $8 but less than $10.

d. On a sheet of graph paper, graph the two inequalities that represent the lower and upper range of your income before expenses. Shade the region that represents your possible earnings before expenses.

Teacher Notes

Concepts and Skills This activity requires students to:

- write equations for monthly expenses and income.
- solve systems of equations.
- graph inequalities.

Guiding Questions

- Does the monthly rent at either shopping center change based on the number of birdhouses you make or sell?
- Are you operating at a profit or a loss if you sell fewer birdhouses than it takes to cover your expenses?
- What would be the advantages to renting an expensive booth at a busy mall and renting a moderately-priced booth at a less busy mall?

Answers

a. $y = 4x + 100$; $y = 6x + 30$

b. $y = 8x$; $y = 8x$

c.

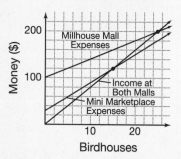

Break-even Points at the Two Malls

Note: Students will make separate graphs for the two malls, but here they are combined into one. The income line will be the same on both graphs.

25 birdhouses; 15 birdhouses

d.

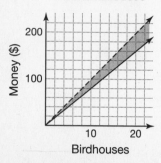

Possible Income from Birdhouses

Extension

You want to ask your parents for start-up costs for your business. Write a proposal to convince them that the business will be profitable enough to enable you to pay back the loan and make a profit. Include where you will rent a booth, how many birdhouses you plan to make and sell, and how much you will charge for each birdhouse. Also include graphs and computations showing income, expenses, and profits.

Evaluation

Level	Standard to be achieved for performance of specified level
4	The student demonstrates a clear understanding of how to write equations about different situations, how to solve two systems of equations by using a graph, and how to graph two inequalities.
3	The student demonstrates a fundamental understanding of how to write equations about different situations, how to solve equations by using a graph, and how to graph two inequalities. Graphs are fairly accurate but reflect minor computational errors.
2	The student demonstrates some understanding of how to write equations about different situations but needs a great deal of assistance. The student attempts to solve one system of equations by using a graph, and to graph two inequalities, although the graphs contain many innacuracies.
1	The student demonstrates little if any understanding of how to write equations about different situations. The student may attempt to solve equations without a graph but is completely unsuccessful. There is no meaningful effort to solve equations by using a graph or to graph inequalities.

Name _____

Date _____ Score _____

1. What is the value of y when $x = 3$ in the equation $y = 2x - 4$?

1. _____

2. Which of the following is the rule that relates x and y in the table?

x	1	2	3	4	5
y	5	9	13	17	21

2. _____

A $y = 4x + 1$ **B** $y = 4x - 1$
C $y = x + 4$ **D** $y = 4x$

3. Give two solutions for the equation $2x - 3y = 24$.

3. _____

4. Make a table of values for the equation $y = 2x + 6$. Use 0, 1, 2, 3, 4, and 5 for x.

4.

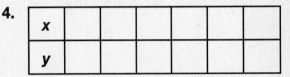

x						
y						

5. Which of the following ordered pairs is *not* a solution for the equation $y = -3x + 6$?

5. _____

A $(0, 6)$ **B** $(3, -3)$ **C** $(5, -1)$ **D** $(2, 0)$

6. Graph the equation $y = 3x$.

6.

7. Find the slope, the x-intercept, and the y-intercept.

A $\frac{4}{3}$; -3; 4 **B** $\frac{3}{4}$; -4; 3

C $\frac{4}{3}$; 4; -3 **D** $\frac{3}{4}$; -3; 4

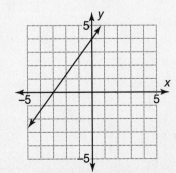

7. _____

Name _____

8. Audrey has a pot of soup. The pot weighs 10 ounces. Each ladle of soup weighs 12 ounces. Graph the weight of the pot and the soup, if x represents the number of ladles of soup in the pot.

8.

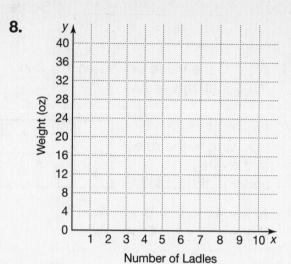

9. Which graph represents the equation $y = \frac{2}{3}x + 1$?

9. _____

A

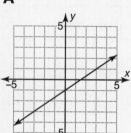

B

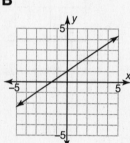

C

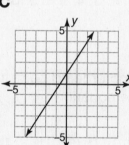

D

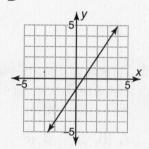

10. Graph a line through the origin with a slope of $-\frac{5}{3}$.

10.

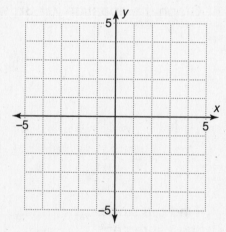

Continued

© Scott Foresman Addison Wesley 8

Name _____

11. Graph the line $y = -\frac{1}{4}x + 1$.
Find the slope, the x-intercept,
and the y-intercept.

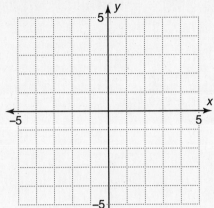

_____

12. Solve the system by graphing
$y = 3x + 1$ and $y = -x - 3$.

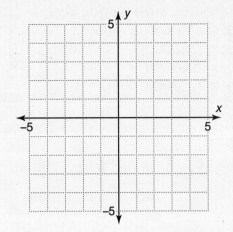

_____

13. Graph the equations $y = 2x + 2$ and $y = 2x - 2$.
Are the lines parallel? Explain.

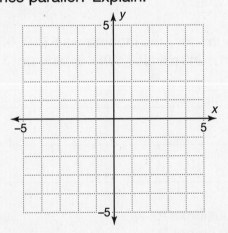

13. _____

_____

_____

_____

_____

14. Lester (y) has less than one more than $\frac{2}{3}$ the number
of silver dollars that Greg (x) has. Graph this situation.

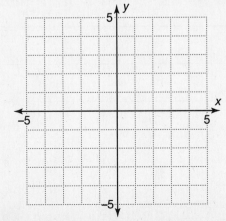

Name _____

15. Performance Task You are
plotting the success of
your family's new business
for the first three weeks. You
plot the following data:
Week 1: $3000;
Week 2: $5000;
Week 3: $7000.

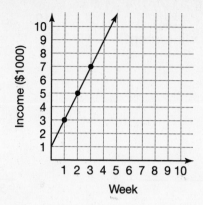

Give two points that fall on this line.

_____

Find the slope of the income line. Then write an
equation for the income line.   _____

In which week did the business break even if the
cost to run the business is $5000 per week?   _____

Is the statement "Before the start of business, the income was $1000" true
according to the graph? Would it be true in real life? Why or why not?

_____

_____

_____

Would you expect the income of the business to
follow this line for a full year? Why or why not?

_____

_____

_____

_____

— Computation —

1. Find the value of y when $x = 3$ in the equation $y = -2x + 6$.

1. _____

2. Give two solutions for the equation $-2x + 3y = 12$.

2. _____

3. Graph the line $y = -2x + 4$. Find the slope, the x-intercept, and the y-intercept.

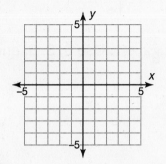

3. _____

4. Which ordered pair is *not* a solution of the equation $-2x + 5y = 20$?

A $(0, 4)$ **B** $(5, 4)$ **C** $(-10, 0)$ **D** $(5, 6)$

4. _____

5. Which of the following is *not* equal to 25?

A $6 \times 5 - 5$ **B** $20 + 10 \div 2$
C $15 - (-10)$ **D** $1 + 4 \times 5$

5. _____

6. Solve $t - 19 = 17$.

6. _____

7. Solve $y = 4x - 9$ for $x = 3$.

7. _____

— Concepts —

8. Find the rule that relates x and y in the table.

8. _____

x	1	2	3	4	5
y	1	4	7	10	13

9. Which of the following shows the graph of $y = x + 3$?

9. _____

A
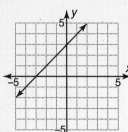

B
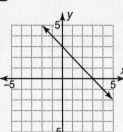

C
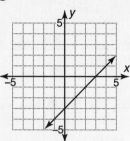

D
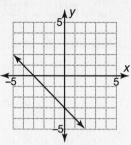

10. Graph the equation $y = \frac{1}{3}x - 1$. Use 0, 3, 6, and 9 as x values.

10.
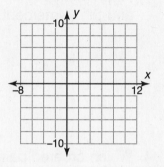

11. Solve the system of equations by graphing $y = -4x + 6$ and $y = 2x$.

11. _____

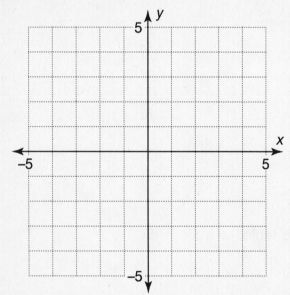

Continued

Name _____

12. Graph the equations $y = \frac{1}{2}x + 1$ and $y = 2x + 1$.
Are the lines parallel? Explain.

12. _____

_____

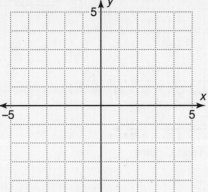

13. Graph the inequality $y > 2x - 3$.

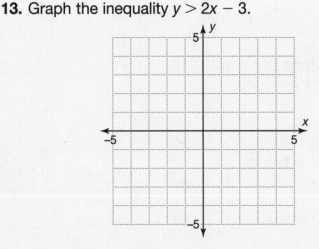

14. Consider this data: 4, 7, 8, 9, 3, 14, 6. Which of the
following is equal to 7?

14. _____

    A Mean   **B** Median   **C** Mode   **D** Range

15. Write an expression to represent four more than
twice a number.

15. _____

16. It costs $12 plus the cost of fish for Jo to set up
a fish tank. She wants to add fish costing $4 each.
Make a graph showing her costs for a fish tank
and x fish. How much money will she spend for
the tank and 7 fish?

16.

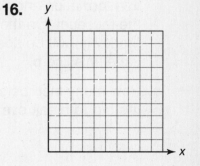

_____

Name _____

— Applications —

17. The amount of string (*y*) needed to go around a box shaped like a cube depends on the length of a side (*x*) of the box. Write and graph the equation for how much string (*y*) you would need to go once around a box with sides of length *x*.

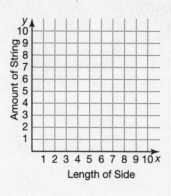

17. _____

18. A scoop of ice cream is $1.50. Each topping costs $0.15. Write an equation representing the cost of a scoop of ice cream with *x* toppings.

18. _____

19. Find the slope of a ramp if the ramp starts at ground level and rises to a height of 2 feet. The horizontal distance of the ramp is 20 feet.

19. _____

20. Which costs less if you need 15 tickets? You can pay a group rate of $5 plus $2 per ticket, or spend $2.50 per ticket.

20. _____

_____

21. Earth is 93,000,000 miles from the sun. Write 93,000,000 in scientific notation.

21. _____

22. Each member contributes $8 a month to a fund of a student club for activities. The fund has $15.

   a. Graph how much money (*y*) will be in the fund after *x* members contribute. Label this line **a.**

   b. The group wants to go on a trip to a museum in another town. It will cost $40 total for the group's transportation and $3 per member for admission to the museum. On the grid above, graph how much money (*y*) will be spent if *x* members make the trip. Label this line **b.**

   c. How many members must contribute and make the trip to break even?

22.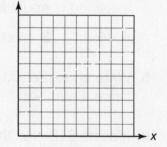

c. _____

In 1 and 2, use the picture to estimate the following ratios.

1. The shaded area to the unshaded area

1. _____

2. The unshaded area to the total area

2. _____

3. What unit rate is equal to $63 for 3 hours?

3. _____

4. What ratio equal to $\frac{2}{5}$ is found when you multiply by $\frac{4}{4}$?

4. _____

5. Complete the table to create ratios equal to $\frac{7}{8}$.

6. Are $\frac{20}{48}$ and $\frac{25}{60}$ proportional? Find the cross products and give your answer.

5.

7			28
	16	24	

In 7 and 8, use the graphed data of Leon's highway gas mileage.

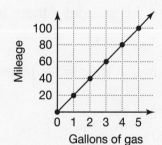

7. Find the slope of the line.

7. _____

8. Is the graphed relationship proportional? How do you know?

_____

_____

9. **Test Prep** Which rate is equal to 32 words in 1 minute?

9. _____

A 66 words in 2 minutes   **B** 320 words in 5 minutes
C 160 words in 4 minutes   **D** 96 words in 3 minutes

**Quiz
5B**

In 1 and 2, solve each proportion.

1. $\dfrac{12}{30} = \dfrac{18}{m}$

2. $\dfrac{14}{96} = \dfrac{p}{24}$

3. Monica is putting together demonstration packs for a large business convention. She can put together 8 packs in 3 minutes. How many packs can she put together in 60 minutes?

4. What is the unit rate equal to the rate 1008 words typed in 24 minutes?

5. Judy pays $9 for 2.5 pounds of dried fruit that is on sale for $0.35 off per pound. What is the *nonsale* price of the fruit?

6. Pam asked 20 students in her class if they will vote for her for class president. Of these 20 students, 16 will vote for her. If her sample is representative of her entire class, how many votes will she get if there are 265 students voting?

7. Find the two missing measures in the similar figures.

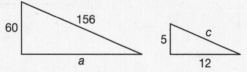

In 8 and 9, use a scale of 1 inch = 350 miles.

8. What is the actual distance between two cities that are 6.25 inches apart on the map?

9. How many inches apart on the map are two cities if the actual distance between them is 1225 miles?

10. **Test Prep** Kenneth pays between $30 and $40 each month for telephone calls. Which should he use as the best estimate for his yearly telephone budget?

   A Less than $150   **B** Between $150 and $350
   C Between $350 and $500   **D** Between $500 and $750

1. _____

2. _____

3. _____

4. _____

5. _____

6. _____

7. _____

8. _____

9. _____

10. _____

1. Tammy was covering her bulletin board with pictures when a friend called to see how she was doing on the project. Estimate the ratio of the amount of bulletin board she covered to the amount of bulletin board she has left to do.

   1. _____

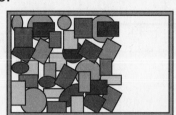

2. Write the ratio 77 students to 6 teachers as a fraction.

   2. _____

3. Draw a picture to show a ratio 5:4 of plus signs to minus signs.

   3.

4. Doug typed 105 words in 3 minutes. Kenny typed 70 words in 2 minutes. State if the typing rates are equal or not equal. If the rates are not equal, state who types faster.

   4. _____

5. Jack can ride his bicycle 6 miles in 40 minutes. Complete the table to create ratios equal to 6:40.

   5.

Miles		6		12		18
Minutes	20	40	60		100	

6. Are $\frac{8}{17}$ and $\frac{16}{34}$ proportional? Find the cross products and give your answer.

_____

In 7 and 8, solve each proportion.

7. $\frac{2}{14} = \frac{m}{84}$

   7. _____

8. $\frac{18}{q} = \frac{30}{65}$

   8. _____

9. The constant of proportionality of a graphed relationship is 0.25. What is the slope of the line?

   9. _____

10. Rachel made 12 sandwiches in 15 minutes. At that rate, how long would it take her to make 20 sandwiches?

   10. _____

Name _____

11. The graph at the right shows
a bowler's total score after
several games. What is the
bowler's total score after
playing $2\frac{1}{2}$ games?

11. _____

Bowler's Total
Score

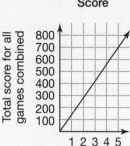

Number of games

12. Choose two pairs of ratios shown by the
graph at the right. Use them to decide if
the graph shows a proportional relationship.

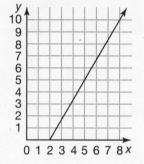

_____

_____

13. Find the unit rate and create a rate formula for a rate
of $26.50 of pay for 5 hours of work.

_____

14. Carol found she had a science fiction to comedy
videotape ratio of 8 to 3. If she has 36 comedy tapes
in her collection, find the number of science fiction
tapes she has and the total number of tapes she has.

14. _____

15. Andrew is helping to build a theatrical set from a scale
drawing. If the set needs to be enlarged 18 times from
the scale drawing, how large will a platform be if it is
1.5 inches by 6 inches on the drawing?

15. _____

_____

16. A flower shop sells 12 roses for $18.00. How much
do they charge for 18 roses?

16. _____

17. A map of the United States uses the scale
1 inch = 120 miles. On the map, Boston and
Washington, D.C. are about 3.6 inches apart. What is
the actual distance between these cities?

17. _____

_____

Name _____

Date _____   Score _____

1. Students at Carver Middle School voted for new band   1. _____
   uniforms. Estimate the ratio of students choosing
   Uniform B to students choosing Uniform A.

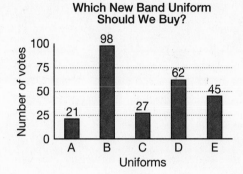

2. Write the rate of 12 pages per minute as a fraction.   2. _____

3. Draw a picture to show a ratio 5:6 of dots to dashes.   3.

4. Kathy ate 32 grapes and had 16 grapes left. Saundra   4. _____
   ate 30 grapes and had 15 grapes left. Are the ratios of
   eaten grapes to uneaten grapes equal? If not, state
   who ate a higher ratio of available grapes.

5. Pat paid 35¢ for 5 sticks   5.
   of gum. Complete the
   table to create ratios
   equal to 35:5.

Cost (cents)	7			28	
Sticks of Gum		2	3		5

6. Are $\frac{7}{26}$ and $\frac{4}{17}$ proportional? Find the cross
   products and give your answer.

_____

In 7 and 8, solve each proportion.

7. $\frac{b}{92} = \frac{55}{115}$ 7. _____

8. $\frac{5}{12} = \frac{60}{x}$ 8. _____

9. The constant of proportionality of a graphed   9. _____
   relationship is 4.5. What is the slope of the line?

10. Ed put together 10 display cases in 3 hours. About   10. _____
    how many display cases can he put together in
    40 hours?

11. The graph at the right shows the cost for various amounts (by weight) of bananas. How many pounds of bananas could you buy for $1.75?

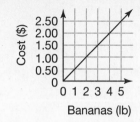

Bananas (lb)

11. _____

12. Choose two pairs of ratios shown by the graph at the right. Use them to decide if the graph shows a proportional relationship.

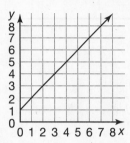

_____

13. Find the unit rate and create a rate formula for a rate of 123 words typed in 3 minutes.

_____

14. Nina attends a school with a male to female ratio of 4 to 5 among students. If 192 students at this school are male, find the number of female students and the total number of students.

14. _____

15. Tony built a scale model of a house he designed. The model is $\frac{1}{60}$ the size of the actual house. If he designs a 30 ft by 45 ft deck for the house, how large will it be on the scale model?

15. _____

_____

16. At a fruit and vegetable stand, 5 pounds of peaches cost $7.80. How much will 3 pounds of peaches cost?

16. _____

17. A map uses the scale 1 inch = 75 miles. On the map, two cities are $3\frac{1}{2}$ inches apart. What is the actual distance between the cities?

17. _____

Give the letter of the correct answer. In 1–3, use the graph below, which shows the Brandt family's long-distance telephone call costs.

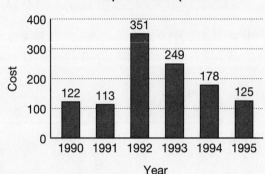

Amount Paid for Long-Distance
Telephone Calls per Year

1. Estimate the ratio of the cost in 1993 to the cost in 1995.

   A 1:1   **B** 1:2   **C** 2:1   **D** 3:1

   1. _____

2. Estimate the ratio of the cost in 1990 to the cost in 1995.

   A 1:1   **B** 1:2   **C** 2:1   **D** 3:1

   2. _____

3. Estimate the ratio of the cost in 1992 to the cost in 1993.

   A 2:3   **B** 3:3   **C** 4:7   **D** 7:5

   3. _____

4. Jeff is preparing for a party. He has 16 walnuts and 20 pecans in a dish. He would like to have a ratio of 2 walnuts to every 3 pecans. What does he need to add?

   A 4 walnuts   **B** 4 pecans
   C 4 walnuts and 4 pecans   **D** Not here

   4. _____

5. Ellen wants to dilute a detergent so the solution is 1 part of detergent to 3 parts of water. How much water should she add to 1 cup of detergent?

   A 1 cup   **B** 2 cups   **C** 3 cups   **D** 4 cups

   5. _____

6. Which of these rates is the same as 3 cans for $0.99?

   A 1 can for $0.30   **B** 4 cans for $1.25
   C 8 cans for $3.99   **D** Not here

   6. _____

7. Kay would like to serve her guests cheese and meat in a 2 to 1 ratio. Which should she buy?

7. _____

   A 1 lb Swiss, 1 lb cheddar, 1 lb roast beef

   B $\frac{1}{2}$ lb American, $\frac{1}{2}$ lb Swiss, 1 lb ham

   C 1 lb cheddar, 1 lb roast beef, 1 lb turkey

   D $\frac{1}{2}$ lb cheddar, $\frac{1}{2}$ lb ham, 1 lb turkey

8. What are the missing numbers in this table of equal rates?

8. _____

x	3	6	9	?	15	18
y	4	8	?	16	20	24

   A 8, 10   **B** 10, 16   **C** 12, 12   **D** 12, 16

9. What would be the next column in the table?

9. _____

   A 18, 20   **B** 20, 26   **C** 21, 28   **D** 24, 32

10. Which of the following is true about $\frac{23}{41}$ and $\frac{133}{246}$?

10. _____

   A $23 \cdot 246 \neq 41 \cdot 133$

   B $\frac{23}{41} \cdot \frac{6}{6} = \frac{133}{246}$

   C $\frac{23}{41} = \frac{133}{246}$

   D $23 \cdot 133 = 41 \cdot 246$

11. Laura can type 210 words in 5 minutes. David can type 126 words in 3 minutes. Which of the following is true?

11. _____

   A The two ratios of words typed to number of minutes are equal.

   B Laura and David do not type at the same speed.

   C $210 \cdot 5 = 126 \cdot 3$

   D You cannot compare the ratios without additional information.

12. Which of the following is true about a graph that shows a proportional relationship?

12. _____

   A The line passes through the origin.

   B The constant of proportionality is the value $\frac{x}{y}$.

   C Most likely, the coordinates of two random points on the line will have unequal cross products.

   D The line connecting the points may be either straight or curved.

Continued

13. Which does this graph show?

13. _____

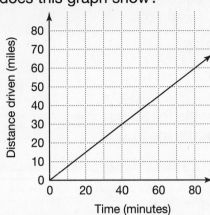

A 15 mi in 15 min is the same rate as 30 mi in 40 min.
B 15 mi in 10 min is the same rate as 45 mi in 60 min.
C 25 mi in 20 min is the same rate as 50 mi in 40 min.
D 30 mi in 40 min is the same rate as 45 mi in 60 min.

14. Use the slope of the line to determine the constant of proportionality for the graph below.

14. _____

A $\frac{0}{4}$ **B** $\frac{1}{4}$ **C** $\frac{4}{4}$ **D** $\frac{16}{4}$

15. If the constant of proportionality of a graph is 1.5, which point must the line pass through?

15. _____

A (0, 1.5) **B** (1, 5) **C** (3, 2) **D** (4, 6)

16. Solve the proportion $\frac{3}{9} = \frac{p}{45}$.

16. _____

A $p = 9$ **B** $p = 15$ **C** $p = 30$ **D** $p = 135$

17. Marla helped her mother and father fold invitations and put them into envelopes. If Marla can fill 36 envelopes in 30 minutes, how many envelopes can she fill in 40 minutes?

17. _____

A 38 **B** 40 **C** 48 **D** 72

Name _____

18. Barbara bought 3.5 lb of mixed nuts for $22.75. How much
    was the cost per pound (unit price) of the mixed nuts?

    A $3.50   **B** $6.50   **C** $19.25   **D** $22.75

18. _____

19. Which is the best buy for orange juice?

    A An 8-oz bottle for $0.55   **B** A 12-oz bottle for $0.80
    C A 16-oz bottle for $1.00   **D** A 20-oz bottle for $1.30

19. _____

20. Which rate formula describes driving 220 miles in 4 hours?

    A $d = 4t$ **B** $d = 44t$ **C** $d = 55t$ **D** $d = 220t$

20. _____

21. A special lens makes an object that is 1.5 inches long appear
    as if it is 2 inches long. If an object under the lens appears as
    if it is 3 inches long, how long is the original object?

    A 1.5 inches   **B** 2 inches   **C** 2.25 inches   **D** 6 inches

21. _____

22. At Cook Middle School, each grade is represented in the
    student council. Each grade elects a number of students that
    is proportional to the number of students in that grade. There
    are 30 council members and there are 603 students in the school.
    If there are 182 eighth-grade students, how many representatives
    will they have in the council?

    A 9   **B** 11   **C** 18   **D** 20

22. _____

23. Kayla is making a model of a car where 1 in. is equal to 2.5 ft.
    If the finished model is 7.5 in. long, how long is the original car?

    A 7.5 ft   **B** 16.25 ft   **C** 18.75 ft   **D** 22.5 ft

23. _____

24. On the map below, which city is 153 miles from Central City?

24. _____

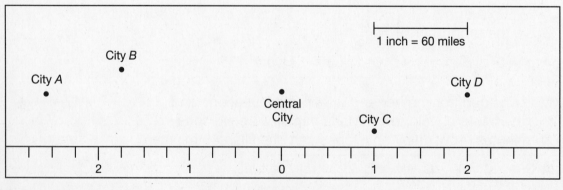

    A City A   **B** City B   **C** City C   **D** City D

You will need a ruler.

You have entered a contest to design a new park in the center of town.
Create your design in the scale drawing of the park area below.

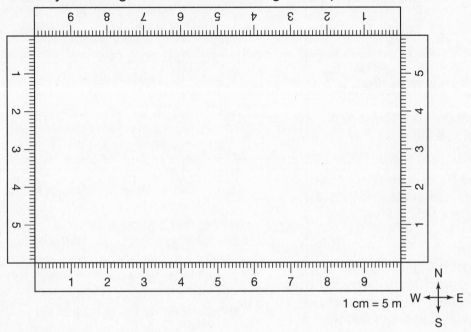

1 cm = 5 m

N
W ←┼→ E
S

a. You decide to put a 10 m by 25 m garden at the east end of the park
so that the long side of the garden runs north and south. Draw the
garden in the park area.

b. The park committee wants the ratio of grass area to garden area to
be at least 3:1. Estimate the ratio of grass area to garden area in your
design. Does your design meet the requirement?

c. You decide to add a circular fountain 5 m in diameter and 4 m in
height. Draw the top view of the fountain on your design.

d. Add 12 benches to your design. Each real bench will be 2 meters long.

e. The committee also wants to consider maintenance costs. You
estimate it will cost $22 each time a crew cuts the grass. Complete
the table showing how much the committee will spend throughout
the summer if they get the grass cut 10 times.

Number of times grass is cut	1	2	3	4	5	6	7	8	9	10
Total grass-cutting cost to date ($)										

Teacher Notes

Concepts and Skills This activity requires students to:
- estimate using a picture.
- compare a scale drawing and actual measurements.
- express equal rates in a table.
- use proportions.

Guiding Questions
- When would you want a scale drawing or a model?
- How can you apply the information in a scale drawing to a real-life situation?

Answers
a. See student drawings. Garden should be on east end and run lengthwise north and south. Dimensions should be 2 cm by 5 cm.
b. Yes
c. See student drawings. Circular fountain may be placed anywhere in the park. Dimensions should be 1 cm in diameter.
d. See student drawings. Length of each bench should be 4 mm.
e. 22; 44; 66; 88; 110; 132; 154; 176; 198; 220

Extension
Give students additional real-life (or approximate) information, such as cost per square foot of different types of decorative brick, cost and dimensions of a roll of sod, costs and growing room for plants, and so forth. Then give them a budget for their park. Have them complete their designs of the park within the restraint of the budget.

Evaluation

Level	Standard to be achieved for performance of specified level
4	The student demonstrates a clear understanding of using proportions by making an accurate estimation and by accurately completing calculations. The table containing equal rates is accurate and completely filled out. The student also correctly converts measurements between a scale drawing and actual measurements.
3	The student demonstrates a fundamental understanding of using proportions by making an accurate estimation and by accurately completing most calculations. The table containing equal rates may contain one or two errors. The student also correctly converts measurements between a scale drawing and actual measurements, although the student may commit some minor errors.
2	The student demonstrates some understanding of using proportions by making a reasonable estimation and by completing some calculations. The table containing equal rates is incomplete or contains significant errors. The student attempts to convert measurements between a scale drawing and actual measurements, although there are several errors.
1	The student demonstrates little if any understanding of using proportions, even with assistance. The estimation is unreasonable and many calculations are incorrect. The table containing equal rates is incomplete. The student makes little or no attempt to convert measurements between a scale drawing and actual measurements.

In 1 and 2, use the graph.

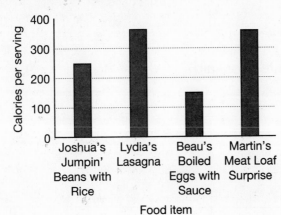

1. Estimate the ratio of calories from Joshua's Jumpin'
   Beans with Rice to calories from Beau's Boiled Eggs
   with Sauce.

   1. _____

2. When comparing calories, which two ratios are almost
   the same?

   2. _____

   A Lasagna to Boiled Eggs; Meat Loaf to Boiled Eggs
   B Beans with Rice to Meat Loaf; Lasagna to Meat Loaf
   C Meat Loaf to Beans with Rice; Boiled Eggs to
   Beans with Rice
   D Beans with Rice to Boiled Eggs; Lasagna to
   Boiled Eggs

3. Pete can jog 2 miles in 14 minutes. Neil can jog 3 miles
   in 18 minutes. Cale can jog 5 miles in 40 minutes.
   Who jogs the fastest?

   3. _____

4. Which rate is equal to sewing 3 seams in 2 minutes?

   4. _____

   A 6 seams in 9 minutes   **B** 12 seams in 8 minutes
   C 9 seams in 4 minutes   **D** 15 seams in 12 minutes

5. Complete the table to create
   ratios equal to 4 to 5.

   5.

4	8	12			24
5			20	25	

6. Lea can fit 42 photographs onto 7 pages in her
   photograph album. How many photographs can
   she fit onto 13 pages?

   6. _____

7. A 3-lb bag of nuts costs $12.45. A 5-lb bag of nuts costs $20.50. Are the prices proportional to the weights? Give the cross products to support your answer.

_____

8. Which graph shows a proportional relationship?

8. _____

A

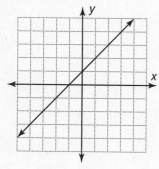

B

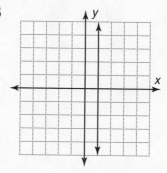

C

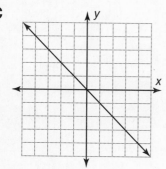

D

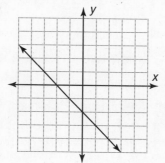

9. Complete the table of equal rates for 2 miles (*y*) to 1 hour (*x*). Then graph the values. What is the slope of the line?

_____

9.

x	0			3	4	
y	0	2	4			10

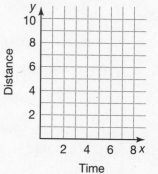

Continued

10. Cassie pays $52.75 per month on an equal-payment budget plan for her electric bill. What would be a good estimate for her yearly electrical costs?

10. _____

    A Between $450 and $500
    B Between $500 and $550
    C Between $550 and $600
    D Between $600 and $650

11. At a garage sale, a box of 78 cookie cutters costs $19.50. What was the cost per cookie cutter?

11. _____

12. Mae can make 2 reception favors in 5 minutes. How many minutes will it take her to make favors for a reception of 141 people?

12. _____

13. You need to make a model of a playground for a contest. The *minimum* size model you can make based on the scale is 1 inch:10 feet. You want to make your model as small as possible but still meet the contest requirements. Which scale might you use?

13. _____

    A 2 inches:19 feet   **B** 3 inches:5 feet
    C 1 inch:12 feet   **D** 4 inches:44 feet

14. Write a proportion for this situation, but do not solve it: Carlos read 150 pages in 5 hours. How long would it take him to read 400 pages?

_____

15. Which of these rates is the same as 6 ears of corn for $2.10?

15. _____

    A 4 ears of corn for $1.40   **B** 8 ears of corn for $2.40
    C 3 ears of corn for $1.10   **D** Not here

16. Mia drove 80 miles in 2 hours. How far could she drive in 3 hours?

16. _____

17. Angela made a model of a car using the scale 2 in. = 10 ft. If the model is 2.9 in. long, how long is the actual car?

17. _____

Name _____

18. Performance Task You and your friends are building
a ramp to a front door. You know a short ramp would
be easier to store but a long ramp would be easier
to use. You decide to build a scale model.

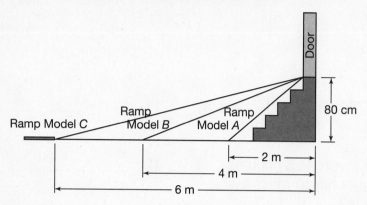

If you build a model where the ratio of the model to
real life is 1:2, how tall will the model's steps be?

_____

You find you have only 1.5 meters of space in which to
build your model. You decide to use the entire space.
How tall will the model's steps be?

_____

The lengths of the 3 ramps you will need to make are
A: 2.154 m, B: 4.079 m, and C: 6.053 m. Are the lengths
of the ramps proportional to the horizontal distance
from the door? How do you know?

_____

The materials to build your ramp cost about $2.50 per
0.5 m of ramp. Complete the table of equal ratios for
ramps from 3.0 m long to 6.5 m long. Choose which
ramp you will make. *Estimate* how much money it will
cost to build that ramp.

Ramp (m)	3.0	3.5	4.0	4.5	5.0	5.5	6.0	6.5
Cost ($)								

Estimate: _____

— Computation —

1. What is the unit rate equal to a rate of 165 miles in 3 hours?

1. _____

2. A ratio is equal to $\frac{2}{3}$. The numerator is 50. Which of these numbers is the denominator?

A 25   **B** 50   **C** 75   **D** 100

2. _____

3. Complete the table to find rates equal to $1.40:3 minutes.

Cost ($)	0	$1.40			$5.60	
Minutes	0		6	9		15

4. Are $\frac{5}{35}$ and $\frac{7}{49}$ proportional? Find the cross products and give your answer.

_____

5. What is the constant of proportionality for the table below?

x	0	5	10	15	20	25
y	0	2	4	6	8	10

5. _____

6. Solve $\frac{1}{3} = \frac{x}{66}$.

6. _____

7. Use the scale 3 cm = 10 m. If the scale dimension is 12 cm, how long will the actual dimension be?

A 30 cm   **B** 40 m   **C** 36 cm   **D** 120 m

7. _____

8. Find the value of y if $x = 2$ and $y = -4x$.

8. _____

9. Solve the equation $\frac{1}{5}x + 1 = 13$.

9. _____

10. Draw a line through the origin with a slope of $\frac{1}{2}$.

10.

━ Concepts ━

11. What would you multiply $\frac{4}{3}$ by to find the equal ratio of $\frac{40}{30}$?

11. _____

12. Which is true about the cross products of two ratios that form a proportion?

    A They always equal zero.
    B They always equal one.
    C They always equal the same number.
    D They always equal a positive number.

12. _____

13. A straight line passing through the point (0, 0) _____ a proportional relationship.

    A Always shows   **B** Often shows
    C Sometimes shows   **D** Never shows

13. _____

14. Which points might be on a graph showing a nonproportional relationship but never on a graph showing a proportional relationship?

    A (0, 2), (2, 4), (4, 6)   **B** (−1, 1), (2, −2), (3, −3)
    C (1, 3), (2, 6), (3, 9)   **D** (−5, −4), (−2.5, −2), (5, 4)

14. _____

15. On a graph, the constant of proportionality is the same as the _____.

    A Origin   **B** Slope   **C** x-intercept   **D** y-intercept

15. _____

16. Write, but do not solve, the following proportion: How much should 20 cans of peas cost if 4 cans cost $0.99?

Continued

17. Which shows a unit rate?

    A Buy 3 cans of corn for 2 dollars.
    B The speed limit is 10 miles per hour.
    C Today, 99 out of 100 people prefer our jeans.
    D Not here

17. _____

18. Which must be identical in both a scale drawing and the actual object it represents: shape, area, length, or width?

18. _____

19. Which would you do first to solve for x? $\frac{x}{3} + 5 = -7$

    A Divide both sides by x.
    B Divide both sides by 3.
    C Subtract 5 from both sides.
    D Subtract 7 from both sides.

19. _____

20. When 24,638,000 is written in scientific notation, how many digits are to the *left* of the decimal point?

20. _____

— Applications —

In 21 and 22, use the bar graph.

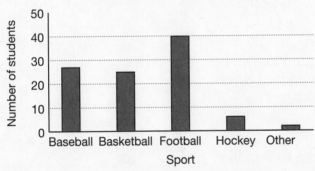

Students' Favorite Sport to Watch

21. Estimate the ratio of students who watch football to students who watch basketball.

    A 3:2   **B** 5:1   **C** 8:5   **D** 10:1

21. _____

22. For which two sport-watching groups is the ratio approximately 1:1?

_____

23. There are 10 dogs and cats at the Carrick Kennel.
The ratio of dogs to cats is 7:3. How many
dogs and cats would have to be added to change
the ratio to 3:2?

_____

24. Ted can make 3 book bags out of 2 feet of cloth.   **24.** _____
Complete the table of equal ratios to show how many
feet of cloth he would need to make 24 book bags.

Book bags	0	3	6	9	12	15	18	21	24
Cloth (ft)	0								

25. Gwen is buying nuts for a party. She can buy   **25.** _____
2 pounds of cashews for $13.90, 3 pounds of
pecans for $19.05, or 4 pounds of smoked almonds
for $25.80. Which is the best buy per pound?

26. Mandy can type a 500-word article in 9 minutes.   **26. a.** _____

   a. If she types at the same speed, how long
      will it take her to type a 750-word article?   **b.** _____
   b. If she types at the same speed, how many
      words will an article have that takes her
      22.5 minutes to type?

27. The number (y) of runs Claire batted in (RBIs) is   **27.** _____
4 more than 3 times the number (x) that Brett
batted in. How many RBIs does Claire have if Brett
has 6 RBIs?

28. Members of Mac's biking club like to ride their bikes   **28.** _____
on a bike path at an average speed of 7 miles per
hour. Use $d = rt$ to find out how far Mac would ride
during a 6-hour biking trip.

**Quiz
6A**

1. Write the fraction, decimal, and percent that describe how much of the figure is shaded.

1. _____

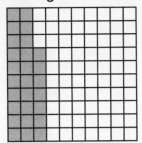

2. Write $1\frac{4}{5}$ as a percent.

2. _____

3. Write 20% as a decimal and as a fraction in lowest terms.

3. _____

4. What number is 62% of 400?

4. _____

5. What percent of 88 is 22?

5. _____

6. 18 is 60% of what number?

6. _____

7. Estimate, to the nearest 5%, the percent of the figure that is shaded.

7. _____

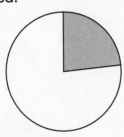

8. Estimate 19% of 204.

8. _____

9. Jamie treated her guests to dinner, leaving a 15% tip. If the tip was $16.50, what was the cost of the dinner without the tip?

9. _____

10. Test Prep On a carnival ride, 29 out of 90 people were riding the Ferris wheel for the second time. Which is the best estimate of the percent of second-time riders?

10. _____

    A 22%   **B** $33\frac{1}{3}$%   **C** $66\frac{2}{3}$%   **D** 25%

1. Find the percent increase. Old $50.50; new $75.75

   1. _____

2. Jesse made ceramic figurines for a fair. The materials for each figurine cost $10.35. He sold them for $14.50. What was the percent increase?

   2. _____

3. What is the wholesale price of a CD player if the percent increase is 75% and the amount of increase is $30?

   3. _____

4. The cost of a pair of jeans is $27.56. The cost before taxes is $26.00. What is the tax rate?

   4. _____

5. Find the percent decrease. Old 35; new 14

   5. _____

6. The original price of a suit is $250. Find the sale price after it is marked down 20%.

   6. _____

7. Sherry was marking down merchandise 33% in a store. She marked down a blouse to $10.40. To the nearest 5 cents, what was the original cost of the blouse?

   7. _____

8. Start with 100. Find the result of a 50% increase followed by a 30% decrease.

   8. _____

9. An album that costs $8 is on sale for 25% off. The sales tax is 5%. What is the total cost?

   9. _____

10. Find the simple interest paid on a loan of $500 at 12% for 3 years.

    10. _____

11. Cody's family borrowed $4000 for 2 years at 15% interest compounded annually. How much will they owe?

    11. _____

12. **Test Prep** The price of a camera has dropped from $75 to $60. Which of the following is the percent decrease?

    12. _____

    A 25%   **B** 75%   **C** 20%   **D** 80%

© Scott Foresman Addison Wesley 8

1. Write the fraction, decimal, and percent that describe how much of the figure is shaded.

   1. _____

2. Write $\frac{3}{8}$ as a decimal and as a percent.

   2. _____

3. Write 46% as a fraction in lowest terms and as a decimal.

   3. _____

4. What number is 30% of 180?

   4. _____

5. 50 is what percent of 25?

   5. _____

6. Thirty percent (84 students) of the eighth graders at Washington School ride a bus to school. How many eighth graders are in the school?

   6. _____
      _____

7. Estimate the percent 27 is of 55.

   7. _____

8. Estimate 41% of 151.

   8. _____

9. Estimate, to the nearest 10%, the percent that the shaded region represents.

   9. _____

In 10–13, find the percent increase or decrease for each and specify whether it is an increase or a decrease.

10. Old $30; new $40

    10. _____

11. Old $250; new $200

    11. _____

12. Old $75; new $45

    12. _____

13. Old $55; new $110

    13. _____

14. William bought roses at a wholesale store for $17.25 per dozen. He sold them in a booth for $25.00 per dozen. What was the percent increase?

14. _____

15. Find the retail cost of a coat if the wholesale cost is $90 and the price increase is 58%.

15. _____

16. What is the wholesale price if the percent increase is 25% and the amount of increase is $15.65?

16. _____

17. The selling price for a bottle of cologne was $14.95. With her employee discount, Antonia was charged only $12.70 (before tax). What percent is her employee discount?

17. _____

18. How much less will you pay for a CD priced at $12.99 if it is on sale for 15% off?

18. _____

19. What is the original price of a pair of boots if the percent discount is 20% and the sale price is $85?

19. _____

20. A shirt's selling price is marked up 50% and then decreased by 20%. If the shirt was originally $15, what is the new selling price?

20. _____

21. Perry made $20,000 per year. He took a 10% cut in wages for a new job. He soon received a promotion with a 20% increase in pay. What is his new salary?

21. _____

22. Joshua deposited $250 into a savings account that pays 6% simple interest per year. How much interest will Joshua have earned after 3 years?

22. _____

23. To open her restaurant, Ruth borrowed $40,000 for 3 years at 8% interest compounded annually. How much will she owe?

23. _____

1. Write the fraction, decimal, and percent that describe how much of the figure is shaded.

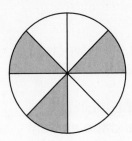

1. _____

2. Write $\frac{7}{50}$ as a decimal and as a percent.

2. _____

3. Write 45% as a fraction in lowest terms and as a percent.

3. _____

4. What number is 40% of 260?

4. _____

5. 75 is what percent of 25?

5. _____

6. Twenty percent (15 books) of Kayla's books are historical novels. How many books does Kayla have?

6. _____

7. Estimate 32% of 271.

7. _____

8. Estimate 40% of 59.

8. _____

9. Estimate, to the nearest 5%, the percent that the shaded region represents.

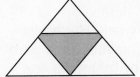

9. _____

In 10–13, find the percent increase or decrease for each and specify whether it is an increase or a decrease.

10. Old 20; new 30

10. _____

11. Old 300; new 250

11. _____

12. Old $200; new $100

12. _____

13. Old $350; new $385

13. _____

14. Mona bought shorts that cost $18. With sales tax, she paid $19.44. What percent was charged for sales tax?

14. _____

15. Find the retail cost of a jacket if the wholesale cost is $50 and the price increase is 75%.

15. _____

16. What is the wholesale price of a bicycle if the percent increase is 40% and the amount of increase is $50?

16. _____

17. Brad won a toaster worth $20. He preferred the one he had, so he sold the toaster at a garage sale for $8. What percent discount did the buyer receive?

17. _____

18. How much weight will you lose altogether if you have already lost 2 pounds, and this is 20% of your goal?

18. _____

19. How much less will you pay for a videotape priced at $19.99 if it is on sale at 20% off?

19. _____

20. A pair of jeans priced at $25 is first marked down 20% when they go on sale and then marked up 20% after the sale. What is the final selling price of the jeans?

20. _____

21. Marlie worked 40 hours per week. Her hours got cut by 20%. Three months later, they were increased by 25%. How many hours did she work after the increase?

21. _____

22. Jenna took out a loan of $500 for 5 years. If she pays 8% simple interest, what is the interest she must pay?

22. _____

23. The Hayes family borrowed $7000 for 2 years at 12% interest compounded annually. How much will they owe?

23. _____

Give the letter of the correct answer.

1. Which shows $\frac{3}{1000}$ as a percent?

   A 0.003%   **B** 0.03%   **C** 0.3%   **D** 3%

   1. _____

2. Which shows 12.6% as a decimal?

   A 0.126   **B** 12.6   **C** 0.012   **D** 1.26

   2. _____

3. Which shows 65% as a fraction in lowest terms?

   A $\frac{3}{4}$ **B** $\frac{65}{100}$ **C** $\frac{13}{25}$ **D** $\frac{13}{20}$

   3. _____

4. What number is 30% of 660?

   A 188   **B** 1980   **C** 198   **D** Not here

   4. _____

5. 150 out of 450 is what percent?

   A 30%   **B** $33\frac{1}{3}$%   **C** $\frac{1}{3}$%   **D** 300%

   5. _____

6. Ninety percent (270 students) of the eighth-grade class voted for Nikki as class president. How many eighth graders are there at the school?

   A 3000   **B** 243   **C** 2700   **D** 300

   6. _____

7. Fifty percent of what number is 12?

   A 6   **B** 60   **C** 24   **D** 600

   7. _____

8. Estimate the percent 27 is of 542.

   A 5%   **B** 50%   **C** 20%   **D** Not here

   8. _____

9. Estimate 19% of 59.

   A 1.2   **B** 12   **C** 120   **D** 300

   9. _____

Name _____

10. Which percent best estimates the percent represented
by the shaded region?

10. _____

A 20%   **B** 33%   **C** 40%   **D** 67%

**In 11–16, find the percent of change and indicate if
it is an increase or a decrease.**

11. Old 250; new 275

11. _____

A 10% decrease   **B** 10% increase
C 9% decrease   **D** 9% increase

12. Old 178; new 89

12. _____

A 50% decrease   **B** 50% increase
C 100% increase   **D** 100% decrease

13. Old 350; new 70

13. _____

A 80% increase   **B** 80% decrease
C 20% increase   **D** 20% decrease

14. Old 80; new 120

14. _____

A $33\frac{1}{3}$% increase   **B** $33\frac{1}{3}$% decrease
C 50% increase   **D** 50% decrease

15. Old 60; new 45

15. _____

A $33\frac{1}{3}$% increase   **B** $33\frac{1}{3}$% decrease
C 25% increase   **D** 25% decrease

16. Old 120; new 150

16. _____

A 25% decrease   **B** 20% increase
C 25% increase   **D** 20% decrease

17. Which of these is the total price of a $149 microwave
oven with a price increase of 12%?

17. _____

A $166.88   **B** $181.78   **C** $131.12   **D** Not here

Continued

18. Which is the result if a $90.90 radio goes through a price increase of 10%?

    A $97.90   **B** $98.90   **C** $98.99   **D** $99.99

18. _____

19. After a price increase of 8%, the new cost of a book is $27. What was the original price?

    A $23   **B** $25   **C** $24.84   **D** $29.16

19. _____

20. What is the original price of a shirt if the percent discount is 25% and the sale price is $6?

    A $4.50   **B** $24   **C** $8   **D** Not here

20. _____

21. The price of a certain VCR has dropped 40% over the last three years. If the VCR sold for $425 three years ago, what would it sell for now?

    A $170   **B** $255   **C** $595   **D** Not here

21. _____

22. A manufacturer offers a 15% rebate on all models. If the original price of Model 1960 is $2400, what will be the "rebated" price (the price after the rebate is received)?

    A $360   **B** $2760   **C** $1666   **D** $2040

22. _____

23. Start with 100. Find the result of a 30% increase followed by a 20% decrease.

    A 104   **B** 56   **C** 84   **D** 110

23. _____

24. Sales for January were $100,000. In February, sales increased 42% from January. Sales in March dropped 28% from February. What were the March sales?

    A $114,000   **B** $102,240   **C** $74,240   **D** $110,760

24. _____

25. Arlene invested $2500 in the stock market. She lost 38% of her investment through bad choices. After making changes, she reinvested what was left of her investment and saw a gain of 48%. How much money did she have in the stock market at this point?

    A $2294   **B** $1550   **C** $2750   **D** $3700

25. _____

26. Find the simple interest if Kyle deposited $750 in a savings account at a rate of 5% interest for 4 years.

    A $37.50   **B** $150   **C** $900   **D** Not here

26. _____

27. Find the total amount to be repaid if Mari takes out a loan of $1000 at 12% simple interest for 5 years.

    A $1120   **B** $5000   **C** $1600   **D** $400

27. _____

28. Meldi borrowed $4000 for 2 years at 10% interest compounded annually. How much will she owe?

    A $8000   **B** $4840   **C** $3240   **D** $4400

28. _____

29. Cindy's math score was 80% on a 50-item test. How many items did she get wrong?

    A 40   **B** 80   **C** 10   **D** Not here

29. _____

30. Tony got 48 items correct for a grade of 75%. How many items were on the test?

    A 75   **B** 64   **C** 36   **D** Not here

30. _____

31. After a 3% raise, Cathy's salary was $25,750. What was her previous salary?

    A $25,000   **B** $25,500   **C** $24,000   **D** Not here

31. _____

32. Michael received a raise of $1,050 on his salary of $21,000. What was the percent of Michael's raise?

    A 10%   **B** 4%   **C** 3.5%   **D** Not here

32. _____

You work in a clothing store owned by Leah. You are helping Leah decide how much to charge for a new shirt the store will carry. The shirt sells for $20 wholesale. Leah has done much research on the most common percent increases she charges.

Wholesale Price	Percent Increase	Increased Price	Amount of Increase (AI)	With 8% Tax	Sales/100 Cust. (S)	Profit (AI × S)
$20	45				61	
$20	48				57	
$20	50				55	
$20	52				53	
$20	55				50	

a. Complete the table for increased price and amount of increase. Round all figures up to the nearest cent.

b. Leah would like to know how much each retail price is with tax. Fill in the cost of the shirt with tax.

c. Complete the table for profit, the amount of increase times the number of possible sales per 100 customers.

Leah occasionally has multiple-item sales. Although she makes less profit on the sale items, the increased business at her store often results in more sales for *all* store items. She found out that the percent increase of the number of people who purchase the new shirt at her store is about the same as the percent decrease in the shirts' price.

d. Consider the case where Leah charges $30 for the shirt. Complete the table. The amount over wholesale will be computed from $20, *the wholesale price.* The expected sales per 100 customers will be 55 for a $30 price. Complete the table.

Retail Price	Percent Decrease	Discounted Price	Amount over Wholesale	Sales Increase/ 100 Cust.	Sales/ 100 Cust.(s)	Profit (AI × S)
$30	5			5		
$30	10			10		
$30	15			15		

e. Suggest a retail price to Leah along with a suggestion for a future sale. Explain why you chose these figures.

Teacher Notes

Concepts and Skills This activity requires students to:
- find a result given the percent of increase.
- find the amount of increase.
- compute sales tax.
- find a result given the percent of decrease.

Guiding Questions
- When a store has a sale, do you think the discounted price is less than the wholesale price?
- Have you ever used a sales tax chart? How do you think a sales tax chart is made?

Answers
a. Increased Price: $29, $29.60, $30, $30.40, $31; Amount of Increase: $9, $9.60, $10, $10.40, $11
b. $31.32, $31.97, $32.40, $32.84, $33.48
c. $549, $547.20, $550, $551.20, $550
d. Discounted Price: $28.50, $27, $25.50; Amount over Wholesale: $8.50, $7, $5.50; Sales/100 Cust: 60, 65, 70; Profit: $510, $455, $385
e. Answers will vary. Any answer is acceptable as long as it is supported logically. Sample answer: $30, since it is a round number in price and the price after sales tax is also a nice amount to work with. A 5%-off sale would be good, because the least amount of profit is lost on the sale items.

Extension
List factors that influence how much markup is given to a wholesale item and when sales are held. Assume this shirt proves to be very popular with consumers. According to the chart, now what percent increase would you give the shirt? What percent decrease would you give the shirt if you were to put it on sale? Assume some slacks you have in the store are not very desirable to consumers. What percent decrease would you give the slacks if you were to put them on sale? Explain your decisions in a brief note to Leah.

Evaluation

Level	Standard to be achieved for performance of specified level
4	The student demonstrates a clear understanding of percents and is able to compute percent increases and decreases. All calculations are accurate and complete. The decided-upon retail price and sale percent are well supported.
3	The student demonstrates a fundamental understanding of percents and is able to compute percent increases and decreases. All calculations are accurate and complete, although some errors occur. The decided-upon retail price and sale percent are reasonably well supported.
2	The student demonstrates some understanding of percents and is able to compute some percent increases and/or decreases. Calculations are attempted, but several are incorrect and there are some blanks left in the table. The decided-upon retail price and sale percent are supported, but not in a thorough manner.
1	The student demonstrates little if any understanding of percents and may attempt, but not complete, percent increases and/or decreases, even with assistance. Some calculations may be attempted but are incorrect. The table is incomplete. Support for the decided-upon retail price is missing or is vague and illogical. No attempt is made to choose a good sales percent.

Date _____ Score _____

1. Which three expressions are *not* equivalent?

   A $\frac{4}{5}$, 0.8, 80%   **B** $\frac{3}{50}$, 0.03, 3%

   C $\frac{6}{5}$, 1.2, 120%   **D** $\frac{1}{3}$, 0.333..., $33\frac{1}{3}$%

   1. _____

2. Express 87.5% as a fraction in lowest terms and as a decimal.

   2. _____

3. 28 is 25% of what number?

   3. _____

4. Forty percent (356 students) of the eighth graders at Franklin School wear glasses or contacts. How many eighth graders are there at Franklin School?

   4. _____

5. Which is the best estimate for the percent 24 out of 201?

   A $12\frac{1}{2}$%   **B** 25%   **C** 75%   **D** $87\frac{1}{2}$%

   5. _____

6. Estimate the percent represented by the shaded region.

   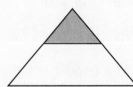

   6. _____

In 7–9, find the percent increase or decrease.

7. Old 280; new 322

   7. _____

8. Old 70; new 56

   8. _____

9. Old 500; new 480

   9. _____

10. What is the original price if the percent increase is 40% and the amount of increase is $16?

    10. _____

11. What is the final price of a sweatshirt that sells for $15.99, if the tax is 7.25%?

    11. _____

12. Which of these is the percent decrease on a cap that normally sells for $7.99 but is now on sale for $4.69?

    A 59%   **B** 41%   **C** 70%   **D** Not here

    12. _____

13. What is the original price of a pair of shoes if the discount is 30% off and the sale price is $28.50?

13. _____

14. What is the sale price of a $24.99 book marked 10% off?

14. _____

15. Which of these represents the final selling price of a $25 jacket that is first marked up 25% and then goes on sale for 20% off?

15. _____

    A $25   **B** $6.25   **C** $31.25   **D** $40.00

16. Start with 20. Apply a decrease of 80% followed by an increase of 50%. Which is the result?

16. _____

    A 24   **B** 6   **C** 8   **D** Not here

17. A savings account of $500 is left in the bank for 4 years at 3% simple interest per year. How much money is in the account at the end of this time?

17. _____

18. Which of these is the interest on a loan of $1500 for 2 years at 5% compound interest per year?

18. _____

    A $1653.75   **B** $1575   **C** $153.75   **D** $75

19. Performance Task Howie went to a used-car lot to buy a car. He found a car he likes for $800.

    a. The sales tax on this car is 8%. How much money will Howie need to buy this car?

19. **a.** _____

    b. You are told by a friend who works at the lot that tomorrow, prices will be increased by 23%. The day after that, prices will be marked down 20% for a sale. Should Howie buy the car now or wait 2 days? Explain your answer.

_____

_____

    c. Howie's first loan option is to borrow $800 for 2 years at 10% simple interest per year. His second option is to borrow $800 for 2 years at 8% compound interest per year. Find the total amount Howie would owe for each loan.

_____

— Computation —

1. 85 is 40% of what number?

   1. _____

2. Give 55% as a fraction in lowest terms and as a decimal.

   2. _____

3. Estimate 61% of 4192.

   A 3600   **B** 2400   **C** 3000   **D** Not here

   3. _____

4. Which of the following is equal to 20?

   A $40 \div (-2)$ **B** $18 + (-2)$
   C $(10 - 2) \times 3$ **D** $1 + 3 \times 3 + 10$

   4. _____

5. Solve $7x - 4 = 31$.

   5. _____

6. 63 is what percent of 90?

   6. _____

7. What is the percent increase? Old 400; new 450

   7. _____

8. What is the percent decrease? Old 800; new 500

   8. _____

— Concepts —

9. Find the slope of the line through $(4, -1)$ and $(6, 3)$.

   9. _____

10. Which is a percent increase?

    A Rebate   **B** Sales tax
    C Discounted price **D** Pay cut

    10. _____

11. Which is a percent decrease?

    A Markup   **B** Tip   **C** Sale price   **D** Retail price

    11. _____

12. A jacket costs $100. Which results in a higher final selling price: a 20% increase followed by a 10% decrease, or a 10% decrease followed by a 20% increase? Explain.

13. Express 52,000,000 in scientific notation.   **13.** _____

    A 5.2×10^8 **B** 5.2×10^7
    C 52×10^6 **D** 0.52×10^8

━ Applications ━

14. The sale price of a pair of slacks marked 25% off is   **14.** _____
$30. What was the original price?

15. Connie paid $6 for lunch. He left a 20% tip. How   **15.** _____
much money did he leave for the tip?

16. The price of a meal, including the sales tax, was   **16.** _____
$12.19. If the tax is 6%, what was the price of
the meal without tax?

17. What amount must be repaid on a loan if the loan was   **17.** _____
$1000 for 5 years? Simple interest was charged at 8%
per year.

    A $600   **B** $1000   **C** $1080   **D** $1400

18. How much less will you pay if you buy a boat   **18.** _____
for $2500 at 15% off?

19. You can join Body Works health club for $300 per   **19.** _____
year, plus $5 per session. You can join Healthy Hearts
health club for $500 per year, plus $2 per session.
If you think you will use the club 100 times per year,
which health club is a better value?

20. A retailer bought a blouse and marked it up 50%.   **20.** _____
If the blouse is sold to a customer for $30, what was
the wholesale price?

21. A loan for $6000 was given for 3 years at 10% interest   **21.** _____
compounded annually. What will be the total owed
by the borrower?

    A $5400   **B** $6600   **C** $7986   **D** Not here

Give the letter of the correct answer.

In 1 and 2, use the stem-and-leaf diagram below, which displays the ages of the teachers at Robert Frost Middle School.

Stem	Leaf
5	0 3 4 5 6 7
4	1 2 2 3 4 7 8
3	1 2 8 8 9

1. Which age is not represented in the data?

   A 39   **B** 44   **C** 55   **D** 45

1. _____

2. Give the mode of the data.

   A 42   **B** 38   **C** 38 and 42   **D** Not here

2. _____

3. What is the lower quartile of the data in the box-and-whisker plot?

3. _____

**Ages of
Hospital Volunteers**

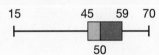

   A 15   **B** 45   **C** 50   **D** 45–50

4. Emmie made a line graph to show the amount of time she spent practicing softball pitching for a week. On which day did she practice the longest?

   A Monday   **B** Tuesday
   C Saturday   **D** Sunday

4. _____

Pitching Practice Time

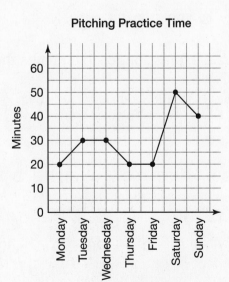

Name _____

5. 1500 people were mailed a questionnaire. Only 473 people answered and mailed back the questionnaire. What is the sample size of the survey?

    A 473   **B** 1500   **C** 1027   **D** Not here

5. _____

6. Which of the following is *not* correct?

    A $-5 < 0$ **B** $-12 = -|12|$ **C** $-1 > -10$ **D** $-|-1| > 0$

6. _____

7. A submarine first went down 725 feet below sea level. It then went up 150 feet. What was the final depth of the submarine?

    A -875 feet   **B** -575 feet   **C** -725 feet   **D** $+575$ feet

7. _____

8. Paul withdrew $25 a week for 12 weeks from his bank account. Which of the following shows how to calculate the change in his account balance?

    A $12 \times (-25)$ **B** $-25 + 12$ **C** $-25 \div 12$ **D** $-25 - 12$

8. _____

9. Evaluate $-3 + (7 + 5) \div (-3)$.

    A 7   **B** 1   **C** -7 **D** -3

9. _____

10. The approximate diameter of a cowpox virus is written as 2.5×10^{-7} m in scientific notation. How should this number be written in standard notation?

    A 0.000025   **B** 0.0000025   **C** 0.000000025   **D** 0.00000025

10. _____

11. Evaluate $P = 2l + 2w$ for $l = 6$ and $w = 8$.

    A 48   **B** 14   **C** 192   **D** 28

11. _____

12. Write an algebraic expression for three times the sum of a number and 7.

    A $3n + 7$ **B** $3(n + 7)$ **C** $3n + (7)$ **D** Not here

12. _____

13. Solve $\frac{n}{2} = -60$.

    A $n = 120$ **B** $n = -30$ **C** $n = -120$ **D** $n = 30$

13. _____

14. Solve $\frac{p}{3} - 5 = 15$.

    A $p = 20$ **B** $p = 15$ **C** $p = 80$ **D** $p = 60$

14. _____

Continued

Name _____

15. Which rule relates x and y in this table?   15. _____

x	1	2	3	4
y	-2	-8	-18	-32

   A $y = x^2 - 2$ **B** $y = -2(x^2)$ **C** $y - 2 = x^2$ **D** $-2y = x^2$

16. Which of the following is *not* a solution of $y = x + 5$?   16. _____

   A $(3, 8)$ **B** $(5, 12)$ **C** $(0, 5)$ **D** $(1, 6)$

17. Which point is *not* on the graph of the equation $y = -3x + 1$?   17. _____

   A $(1, 0)$ **B** $(3, -8)$ **C** $(0, 1)$ **D** $(2, -5)$

In 18 and 19, use the graph of $y = 2x - 3$.

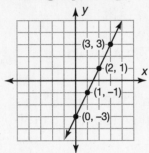

18. Give the slope of the line.   18. _____

   A $\dfrac{1}{2}$ **B** 4   **C** 2   **D** 0

19. Give the y-intercept of the line.   19. _____

   A -3 **B** 0   **C** $1\dfrac{1}{2}$ **D** Not here

20. Kate plans to go to a water park to go tubing. She can go to   20. _____
Tube Town for $15 a day plus $1 per tube ride or to Tubaruba
for $5 a day plus $3 a ride. For what number of rides would the
cost be the same?

   A 8   **B** 11   **C** 10   **D** 5

21. Choose the inequality
that describes the graph.   21. _____

   A $y \geq 3x$ **B** $y \geq 3x - 1$
   C $y \leq 3x$ **D** $y \leq 3x - 1$

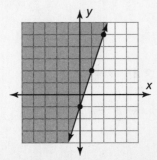

22. The ratios in which pair do *not* form a proportion?

   A $\dfrac{9}{24} = \dfrac{27}{72}$ **B** $\dfrac{30}{70} = \dfrac{4}{10}$ **C** $\dfrac{24}{72} = \dfrac{8}{24}$ **D** $\dfrac{30}{50} = \dfrac{12}{20}$

22. _____

23. Is the table below an equal-ratio table? If so, find the value of *k*.

23. _____

x	1	2	3	4
y	10	20	30	40

   A $k = \dfrac{1}{10}$ **B** $k = \dfrac{2}{20}$

   C $k = 10$ **D** Not an equal-ratio table

24. Solve the proportion $\dfrac{10}{25} = \dfrac{16}{q}$.

24. _____

   A $q = 40$ **B** $q = 400$ **C** $q = 160$ **D** $q = 25$

25. Carlan's car payment is $88.76 per month. What would be a good estimate for her yearly payment?

25. _____

   A Less than $1000   **B** Between $1000 and $1050
   C Between $1050 and $1100   **D** Between $1100 and $1150

26. If a 24-inch-tall model were built to the scale $\dfrac{3}{4}$ in. = 1 ft, how tall would the actual figure be?

26. _____

   A 18 ft   **B** 32 in.   **C** 24 ft   **D** 32 ft

27. Which shows 5.35 expressed as a percent?

27. _____

   A 535%   **B** 5.35%   **C** 53.5%   **D** 5350%

28. 200 is 5% of what number?

28. _____

   A 40   **B** 400   **C** 4000   **D** 1000

29. Computer Depot buys a certain computer for $2000 and sells it for $2750. What is the percent increase?

29. _____

   A 37.5%   **B** 137.5%   **C** 1.375%   **D** 750%

30. Find 15% of 230.

30. _____

   A 3450   **B** 34.5   **C** 3.45   **D** 345

31. A blouse normally sells for $25. Find its price during a 15%-off sale.

31. _____

In 1–3, use divisibility rules. State whether the given number is divisible by 2, 3, 4, 5, 6, 9, or 10. Indicate when the number is prime.

1. 390

2. 127

3. 474

1. _____

2. _____

3. _____

In 4–6, find the prime factorization of each number.

4. 520

5. 284

6. 80

4. _____

5. _____

6. _____

In 7–9, find the GCF of each pair of numbers.

7. 3, 15

8. 18, 24

9. 125, 75

7. _____

8. _____

9. _____

In 10–12, find the LCM of each pair of numbers.

10. 7, 21

11. 18, 24

12. 4, 25

10. _____

11. _____

12. _____

13. **Test Prep** Several students belong to different car pools. Jonah drives every other week, Sarah drives every third week, and Chris drives every fourth week. If all three drove the first week of school, how often do all three drive again on the same week?

13. _____

A Every 6 weeks   **B** Every 12 weeks
C Every 24 weeks   **D** Every 9 weeks

Order the numbers from least to greatest.

1. -2.1, 1.6, -0.5

1. _____

2. $\frac{3}{4}$, $\frac{5}{6}$, $\frac{13}{16}$

2. _____

3. $1\frac{3}{4}$, $2\frac{1}{3}$, 1.7

3. _____

Write each decimal as a fraction in lowest terms and tell whether it is terminating or repeating.

4. 0.64

4. _____

5. $0.\overline{35}$

5. _____

Calculate.

6. $3\frac{1}{4} + 2\frac{2}{3}$

6. _____

7. $3\frac{1}{2} \times 2\frac{1}{3}$

7. _____

8. $4\frac{1}{5} - 2\frac{5}{6}$

8. _____

9. $2\frac{1}{2} \div 2\frac{1}{4}$

9. _____

10. $3\frac{1}{4} - 2\frac{7}{8}$

10. _____

11. $5\frac{5}{6} \div 1\frac{3}{4}$

11. _____

12. **Test Prep** Brent has a board $2\frac{11}{12}$ feet long. He needs a board $3\frac{1}{6}$ feet long. How much longer does Brent's board need to be?

12. _____

A $\frac{1}{3}$ ft   **B** $\frac{1}{4}$ ft   **C** $\frac{11}{12}$ ft   **D** Not here

1. Is 121 a perfect square?

1. _____

2. $\sqrt{84}$ is between which two consecutive integers?

2. _____

3. Determine $-\sqrt{\dfrac{121}{225}}$.

3. _____

4. Identify $\sqrt{48}$ as rational or irrational.

4. _____

5. Find $\sqrt{821}$ and round to the nearest thousandth.

5. _____

6. Find the side length of a square with an area of 82 in.^{2}.

6. _____

**In 7–9, find the missing side length of each
right triangle.**

7.

7. _____

8.

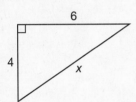

8. _____

9.

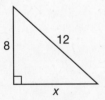

9. _____

10. Test Prep Which of the following measures could be
sides of a right triangle?

A 3, 4, 6   **B** 5, 8, 12   **C** 8, 15, 17   **D** 5, 12, 15

10. _____

1. Determine whether 360 is divisible by
   2, 3, 4, 5, 6, 8, 9, or 10.

1. _____

   _____

In 2 and 3, determine the prime factorization.

2. 425

2. _____

3. 890

3. _____

4. Find the GCF of 40 and 64.

4. _____

5. Find the GCF of 24 and 120.

5. _____

In 6–8, write each fraction in lowest terms.

6. $\frac{56}{120}$

6. _____

7. $\frac{840}{1260}$

7. _____

8. $\frac{88}{132}$

8. _____

9. Find the LCM of 18 and 24.

9. _____

10. Find the LCM of 30 and 96.

10. _____

11. Myra works every third day. Cassie works every
    fourth day, and Joel every sixth day. If all three work
    on the first of April, when will all three work together
    again?

11. _____

12. Determine whether $\frac{5}{32}$ is a repeating or
    terminating decimal.

12. _____

In 13 and 14, write >, =, or < to compare.

13. $\frac{3}{16}$ ☐ 0.2

13. _____

14. $\frac{9}{17}$ ☐ $\frac{12}{25}$

14. _____

15. Write $0.\overline{45}$ as a fraction in lowest terms.

15. _____

16. Subtract 12.7429 − 4.86.

16. _____

© Scott Foresman Addison Wesley 8

Continued

In 17–20, express the answer as a mixed number in lowest terms.

17. $3\frac{7}{8} + 4\frac{5}{6}$ 17. _____

18. $4\frac{1}{2} \times 1\frac{1}{3}$ 18. _____

19. $3\frac{3}{4} \div 1\frac{1}{2}$ 19. _____

20. $8 - 4\frac{3}{4}$ 20. _____

21. State whether 246 is a perfect square.   21. _____

22. Find the two closest perfect squares to 140.   22. _____

23. Estimate the square root of 250.   23. _____

24. Find $\sqrt{\dfrac{50}{2}}$.   24. _____

25. Find $\sqrt{3} \times \sqrt{27}$.   25. _____

26. Use a calculator to find $\sqrt{88}$ and round to the nearest thousandth.   26. _____

27. Determine whether the lengths 5, 12, and 13 could form a right triangle.   27. _____

In 28 and 29, find the length of the missing side.

28. 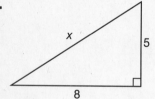   28. _____

29. 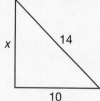   29. _____

30. A football field is 53 yards wide and 100 yards long. What is the distance from one corner to the opposite corner?   30. _____

1. Determine whether 350 is divisible by
   2, 3, 4, 5, 6, 8, 9, or 10.

1. _____

In 2 and 3, determine the prime factorization.

2. 560

2. _____

3. 3000

3. _____

4. Find the GCF of 24 and 56.

4. _____

5. Find the GCF of 35 and 90.

5. _____

In 6–8, write each fraction in lowest terms.

6. $\dfrac{80}{124}$

6. _____

7. $\dfrac{15}{90}$

7. _____

8. $\dfrac{240}{720}$

8. _____

9. Find the LCM of 24 and 40.

9. _____

10. Find the LCM of 30 and 36.

10. _____

11. Hot dogs come in packages of eight. Hot-dog buns
    come in packages of 12. Find the minimum number
    of each you need to buy to have the same number of
    hot dogs and hot-dog buns.

11. _____

    _____

12. Determine whether $\dfrac{5}{45}$ is a repeating or
    terminating decimal.

12. _____

In 13 and 14, write >, =, or < to compare.

13. $\dfrac{9}{24}$ ☐ $\dfrac{6}{16}$

13. _____

14. $\dfrac{7}{12}$ ☐ $\dfrac{5}{9}$

14. _____

15. Write 0.71 as a fraction in lowest terms.

15. _____

16. Add 15.42 + 9.7426.

16. _____

Name _____

In 17–20, express the answer as a mixed number in lowest terms.

17. $8\frac{7}{16} - 2\frac{1}{3}$

17. _____

18. $5\frac{1}{2} \times 3\frac{1}{3}$

18. _____

19. $4\frac{2}{3} \div 2\frac{1}{2}$

19. _____

20. $5\frac{7}{8} + 3\frac{5}{12}$

20. _____

21. State whether 324 is a perfect square.

21. _____

22. Find the two closest perfect squares to 250.

22. _____

23. Estimate the square root of 380.

23. _____

24. Find $\sqrt{\frac{75}{3}}$.

24. _____

25. Find $\sqrt{2} \times \sqrt{8}$.

25. _____

26. Use a calculator to find $\sqrt{74}$ and round to the nearest thousandth.

26. _____

27. Determine whether 5, 13, and 17 would make a right triangle.

27. _____

In 28 and 29, find the length of the missing side.

28.

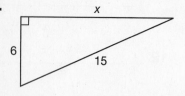

29.

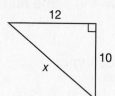

28. _____

29. _____

30. A park is a square 200 meters on each side. How long is a sidewalk from one corner of the park to the opposite corner?

30. _____

Give the letter of the correct answer.

1. Which of the following represents the greatest set of divisors of 276?

   A 2   **B** 2 and 3   **C** 2, 3, and 4   **D** Not here

   1. _____

2. Which is the prime factorization of 200?

   A $2^3 \times 5^2$ **B** 2×5 **C** $2^2 \times 5^2$ **D** $2^4 \times 5^2$

   2. _____

3. Which of the following is *not* a divisor of 420?

   A 6   **B** 5   **C** 9   **D** 10

   3. _____

4. What is the GCF of 60 and 90?

   A 10   **B** 30   **C** 15   **D** 360

   4. _____

5. Which of the following is $\frac{270}{900}$ in lowest terms?

   A $\frac{90}{300}$ **B** $\frac{3}{10}$ **C** $\frac{9}{30}$ **D** $\frac{27}{90}$

   5. _____

6. What is the GCF of 7 and 27?

   A 3   **B** 7   **C** 189   **D** Not here

   6. _____

7. Find the LCM of 24 and 36.

   A 4   **B** 12   **C** 72   **D** 864

   7. _____

8. Find the LCM of 8 and 9.

   A 1   **B** 6   **C** 72   **D** Not here

   8. _____

9. A red number cube is weighted so that it lands on 6 every fourth toss. A green number cube is weighted so that it lands on 6 every third toss. How many times will you have to toss the number cubes before you get two 6s?

   A 1   **B** 6   **C** 7   **D** 12

   9. _____

10. Which of the following fractions represents a repeating decimal?

    A $\frac{1}{32}$ **B** $\frac{4}{35}$ **C** $\frac{7}{10}$ **D** $\frac{9}{16}$

    10. _____

11. Which statement is true?

    A $\frac{3}{4} > \frac{5}{6}$ **B** $\frac{10}{15} = \frac{14}{21}$ **C** $\frac{7}{8} < \frac{87}{100}$ **D** $\frac{2}{3} > 0.67$

11. _____

12. Which of the following represents $0.\overline{24}$ as a fraction in lowest terms?

    A $\frac{24}{99}$ **B** $\frac{8}{33}$ **C** $\frac{24}{100}$ **D** $\frac{6}{25}$

12. _____

13. Subtract $17.42 - 8.9621$.

    A 8.4579   **B** 9.4579   **C** 26.3821   **D** 8.4621

13. _____

In 14–21, express each answer as a whole number or as a fraction or mixed number in lowest terms.

14. $3\frac{5}{6} + 2\frac{2}{3}$

    A $5\frac{9}{6}$ **B** $6\frac{3}{6}$ **C** $5\frac{1}{2}$ **D** $6\frac{1}{2}$

14. _____

15. $6\frac{3}{8} - 2\frac{1}{6}$

    A $4\frac{2}{24}$ **B** $4\frac{13}{24}$ **C** $4\frac{5}{24}$ **D** $3\frac{5}{24}$

15. _____

16. $8\frac{2}{5} - 7\frac{3}{4}$

    A $1\frac{13}{20}$ **B** $1\frac{1}{20}$ **C** $\frac{13}{20}$ **D** Not here

16. _____

17. $5\frac{5}{8} + 6\frac{7}{8}$

    A $11\frac{1}{2}$ **B** $12\frac{1}{2}$ **C** $11\frac{12}{8}$ **D** $11\frac{1}{4}$

17. _____

18. $3\frac{1}{5} \times 2\frac{3}{4}$

    A $8\frac{4}{5}$ **B** $6\frac{3}{20}$ **C** $\frac{44}{5}$ **D** Not here

18. _____

19. $2\frac{1}{2} \times 1\frac{1}{3}$

    A $\frac{20}{6}$ **B** $\frac{10}{3}$ **C** $3\frac{1}{3}$ **D** $3\frac{2}{3}$

19. _____

20. $4\frac{1}{2} \div 1\frac{3}{4}$

    A $\frac{36}{14}$ **B** $2\frac{4}{7}$ **C** $\frac{18}{7}$ **D** $\frac{7}{18}$

20. _____

Continued

Name _____

21. $12 \div 2\frac{1}{2}$

    A $4\frac{4}{5}$ **B** $\frac{24}{5}$ **C** $\frac{5}{24}$ **D** $\frac{1}{30}$

21. _____

22. Which of the following is *not* a perfect square?

    A 121   **B** 325   **C** 196   **D** 324

22. _____

23. Between which two consecutive integers does $\sqrt{426}$ lie?

    A 20 and 21   **B** 19 and 20
    C 21 and 22   **D** Not here

23. _____

24. Find $\sqrt{\frac{169}{225}}$ in lowest terms.

    A $\frac{13}{25}$ **B** $\frac{13}{5}$ **C** $\frac{13}{15}$ **D** Not here

24. _____

25. Which of the following numbers is irrational?

    A $\sqrt{100}$ **B** $\sqrt{121}$ **C** $\sqrt{169}$ **D** $\sqrt{18}$

25. _____

26. Find $\sqrt{319}$ to the nearest thousandth.

    A 17.9   **B** 17.861   **C** 17.86   **D** 101,761

26. _____

27. Which of the following numbers is rational?

    A $\sqrt{200}$ **B** $\sqrt{125}$ **C** $\sqrt{196}$ **D** $\sqrt{99}$

27. _____

28. Find the length of the missing side of the triangle.

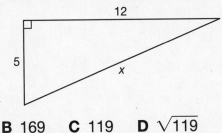

    A 5   **B** $\sqrt{97}$ **C** 65   **D** $\sqrt{65}$

28. _____

29. Find the length of the missing side of the triangle.

    A 13   **B** 169   **C** 119   **D** $\sqrt{119}$

29. _____

30. Determine which set of lengths can be sides of a right triangle.

    A 6, 8, 12   **B** 15, 36, 40   **C** 8, 15, 17   **D** 9, 12, 16

30. _____

31. A fence is to be constructed around a park shaped like a right triangle with short sides measuring 120 feet and 100 feet. How many feet of fencing will be needed?

    A $\approx$ 376 ft   **B** $\approx$ 360 ft   **C** $\approx$ 286 ft   **D** Not here

31. _____

32. The size of a TV screen is denoted by its diagonal, the distance from one corner to the opposite corner. Which dimensions below could be the sides of a 25-inch TV screen? Dimensions are approximate.

    A 12.5 in., 12.5 in.   **B** 14 in., 21 in.
    C 16 in., 18 in.   **D** Not here

32. _____

33. Paving stones that are $1\frac{1}{4}$ ft long are being used to edge a garden that is $18\frac{3}{4}$ ft long. How many paving stones are needed?

    A 14   **B** $14\frac{1}{2}$ **C** 15   **D** 20

33. _____

34. A pattern for drapes requires $4\frac{1}{4}$ yd of fabric. A pattern for a matching bedspread requires $3\frac{1}{2}$ yd of fabric. How much fabric is needed to make both of these items?

    A $7\frac{3}{4}$ yd   **B** $14\frac{7}{8}$ yd   **C** $\frac{3}{4}$ yd   **D** Not here

34. _____

35. A bottle contained $3\frac{1}{4}$ oz of balsamic vinegar. Then $1\frac{3}{4}$ oz of the vinegar was poured into a measuring cup. How much was left in the bottle?

    A 5 oz   **B** $5\frac{11}{16}$ oz   **C** $2\frac{1}{2}$ oz   **D** Not here

35. _____

You are making a secret code based on GCFs and LCMs. You plan to start by assigning a number to each letter of the alphabet as follows: A = 1, B = 2, C = 3, D = 4, and so forth. Then you will use GCFs and LCMs to code each letter with a number.

a. You begin making a secret code. You decide to code each letter using the LCM of the letter's assigned number and the number 2. For example, A is originally assigned the number 1. The LCM of 1 and the number 2 is 2. Therefore, the code number for A would be 2. Complete the code for each of the letters of the alphabet up through J.

Letter	Assigned Number	Code Number	Letter	Assigned Number	Code Number
A	1	2	F	6	
B	2		G	7	
C	3		H	8	
D	4		I	9	
E	5		J	10	

b. When does the code number for a letter equal its originally assigned number (the number corresponding to its position in the alphabet)? Why does this happen?

c. Using this rule, is it possible for any letter to have an odd number as its code number? Explain.

d. To have a usable code, it is necessary that a code number represent one and only one letter. From this point of view, what are the problems in the code described in part **a**? How might you use the GCF to solve this problem?

e. Your code does not have to be limited to whole numbers—you may choose to use fractions or decimals in your code. How might you use the GFC and LCM when working with fractions?

f. Keeping what you have learned in mind, create a code using both GCFs and LCMs to "convert" all 26 letters of the alphabet. You may use fractions or decimals in your code. Be sure your code has specific rules for converting each letter to a code number. State your rules and give the code number for each letter.

Teacher Notes

Concepts and Skills This activity requires students to:
- use the LCM to create a numerical code.
- use the GCF to create a numerical code.

Guiding Questions
- What do the initials GCF and LCM stand for?
- How can you use the GCF and LCM when adding or subtracting fractions?

Answers
a. A—2; B—2; C—6; D—4; E—10; F—6; G—14; H—8; I—18; J—10
b. The code number for a letter equals its originally assigned number whenever the letter has an even-numbered position in the alphabet. This happens because 2, the number with which the LCM code is made, is a factor of every even (assigned) number.
c. No, it is not possible. By definition, the code is the LCM of an assigned number and the number 2, and therefore always has a factor of 2.
d. Answers may vary, but should indicate an understanding that the letters A and B, and the letters E and J, have the same code number after applying the rule. Students may decide to use the GCF in cases where the same duplicated code number occurs. Students may decide to take the GCF of each of these numbers and a large number, such as 100, to come up with a unique number.
e. The GCF can be used to simplify fractions, especially after addition or subtraction. The LCM can be the denominator when adding or subtracting fractions.
f. Student codes will vary but should include a rule or set of rules, and result in a unique code number for each letter of the alphabet.

Extension
Have students encode a message using their secret code. Then have them exchange code rules with a partner. Can the partner decipher the message knowing the rules?

Evaluation

Level	Standard to be achieved for performance of specified level
4	The student demonstrates a clear understanding of greatest common factors and least common multiples and relates this understanding when making a secret code. All calculations are accurate and complete. Encoding rules are thorough, logical, and well-organized.
3	The student demonstrates a fundamental understanding of greatest common factors and least common multiples, and reasonably relates this understanding when making a secret code. The student does all necessary calculations, but may make some minor errors. Encoding rules are fairly well-organized and easy to follow, but the resulting code reflects minor computational errors.
2	The student has some understanding of greatest common factors and least common multiples, and applies this understanding, with assistance, when making a secret code. The student attempts to write encoding rules, but the resulting code is illogical and incomplete.
1	The student demonstrates little if any understanding of greatest common factors and least common multiples, even when prompted. The student attempts some calculations, but they are superfluous or irrelevant. The student makes little attempt, or no attempt, at creating encoding rules or a code using the GCF and LCM.

1. Which of the following represents the greatest set of divisors of 900?

    A 9, 10   **B** 2, 3, 4, 5, 6, 9, 10
    C 2, 3, 4, 5, 9, 10   **D** 2, 3, 4, 5, 6, 10

1. _____

2. Determine the prime factorization of 850.

2. _____

3. Which of the following is the GCF of 225 and 60?

    A 15   **B** 5   **C** 3   **D** 180

3. _____

4. Write $\frac{250}{300}$ in lowest terms.

4. _____

5. Find the LCM of 72 and 90.

    A 9   **B** 18   **C** 6   **D** 360

5. _____

6. Ariel visits her grandfather every three days. She visits her aunt every four days. She also visits her cousin every six days. How often does she visit all three family members?

6. _____

7. Write $0.3\overline{24}$ as a fraction in lowest terms.

7. _____

8. Which of the following statements is true?

    A $\frac{7}{8} > \frac{15}{16}$ **B** $\frac{8}{3} = \frac{15}{6}$ **C** $\frac{4}{5} > 0.7999$ **D** $\frac{5}{6} < 0.83$

8. _____

In 9–12, express each answer as a mixed number or fraction in lowest terms.

9. $4\frac{2}{3} + 2\frac{4}{5}$

9. _____

10. $8\frac{1}{8} - 2\frac{5}{6}$

    A $5\frac{7}{24}$ **B** $6\frac{7}{24}$ **C** $6\frac{17}{24}$ **D** $10\frac{23}{24}$

10. _____

11. $4\frac{2}{3} \times 2\frac{1}{4}$

11. _____

12. $8 \div 4\frac{1}{2}$

    A $\frac{1}{4}$ **B** $32\frac{1}{2}$ **C** $1\frac{7}{9}$ **D** $\frac{19}{9}$

12. _____

Name _____

13. Which of the following is *not* a perfect square?

    A 289   **B** 441   **C** 625   **D** 675

13. _____

14. Find the two closest perfect squares to 127.

14. _____

15. Determine whether $\sqrt{90}$ is rational or irrational.

15. _____

16. Find $\sqrt{246}$ to the nearest thousandth.

    A 15.68   **B** 15.684   **C** 15.6844   **D** 60,516

16. _____

17. Decide whether 15, 20, and 24 can be the sides of a right triangle.

17. _____

In 18 and 19, find the length of the missing side.

18.

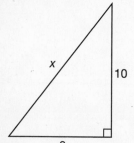

19.

18. _____

19. _____

20. Performance Task Find the prime factorization of each number. Use the prime factorization of each number to find its square root. Explain your method.

    a. 15,876

_____

_____

    b. 2500

_____

    c. 8100

_____

Date _____ Score _____

— Computation —

1. Which of the following represents the greatest set of divisors of 720?

   A 2, 5, 10   **B** 2, 3, 4, 5, 6, 8, 9, 10
   C 2, 3, 5   **D** 2, 3, 4, 5, 6, 9, 10

   1. _____

2. Add $2\frac{3}{8} + 2\frac{2}{3}$.

   2. _____

3. Subtract $5\frac{1}{6} - 2\frac{7}{8}$.

   3. _____

4. Multiply $2\frac{2}{3} \times 1\frac{1}{2}$.

   4. _____

5. Divide $1\frac{3}{4} \div 2\frac{1}{3}$.

   5. _____

6. Find $\sqrt{441}$.

   A −21   **B** $\pm\sqrt{21}$ **C** 21   **D** 221

   6. _____

7. Solve $-2x + 4 = 6$.

   7. _____

8. Find 18% of 20.

   A 111.11   **B** 27.78   **C** 36   **D** 3.6

   8. _____

— Concepts —

9. Find the slope of the line through $A(-1, 4)$ and $B(8, -2)$.

   9. _____

10. Find the GCF of 24 and 40.

    A 4   **B** 8   **C** 24   **D** 120

    10. _____

11. Find the GCF of 8 and 15.

    11. _____

12. Find the LCM of 8 and 15.

    12. _____

13. Find the LCM of 12, 18, and 30.

    A 6   **B** 90   **C** 12   **D** 180

    13. _____

14. Order the numbers from least to greatest:

$-\dfrac{3}{4}, -1.2, \dfrac{5}{6}, \dfrac{2}{3}$

14. _____

15. Order the numbers from greatest to least:

$5.16, 5\dfrac{1}{6}, 5.2, 5\dfrac{1}{8}$

15. _____

16. Which of the following is *not* a perfect square?

A 196   **B** 729   **C** 325   **D** 169

16. _____

17. Find the square root of 372 to the nearest tenth.

17. _____

18. Which of the following is an irrational number?

A $\sqrt{20}$ **B** $\sqrt{225}$ **C** $\sqrt{1}$ **D** $\sqrt{64}$

18. _____

19. Write the equation of the line parallel to $y = 2x + 1$ that has a *y*-intercept of -3.

19. _____

━━ Applications ━━

In 20 and 21, find the length of the missing side.

20.

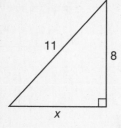

21.

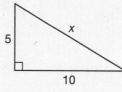

20. _____

21. _____

22. Determine the measurements of a rectangle such that the width and length are divisible by 3 and have an LCM of 36.

22. _____

23. There were 8 members in the pep band. Now there are 12. What is the percent of increase?

23. _____

24. Nell has collected $23\dfrac{3}{4}$ pounds of pop cans. Joel has collected $18\dfrac{7}{8}$ pounds. How many more pounds must they collect if their goal is to collect 50 pounds?

24. _____

25. Suppose you run $3\dfrac{1}{8}$ miles each day. How far do you run in a 5-day week?

25. _____

1. What customary U.S. unit would you use to measure the distance traveled in 1 hour by an airplane?

1. _____

2. What metric unit would you use to measure the area of a book cover?

2. _____

3. Convert 250 mm to m.

3. _____

4. Convert 36 oz to lb. Write as a decimal.

4. _____

In 5 and 6, determine which measurement is more precise.

5. 8.55 m or 0.8 cm

5. _____

6. 15 in. or 5.5 in.

6. _____

In 7 and 8, calculate and give each answer with the correct number of significant digits.

7. 9.6 g + 6.25 g

7. _____

8. 4.25 ft × 6.5 ft

8. _____

In 9 and 10, use the map of Nevada.

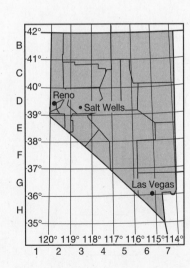

9. How many degrees of longitude are between Las Vegas and Reno?

9. _____

10. Give the map coordinates of Salt Wells.

10. _____

11. **Test Prep** Which measurement has 4 significant digits?

11. _____

A 1.070 m   **B** 0.0750 m
C 12.660 m   **D** 10.000 m

You will need a ruler and a protractor.

1. Classify a 103° angle as right, straight, obtuse, or acute.

1. _____

2. Find the measure of the supplement of a 92.5° angle.

2. _____

In 3 and 4, use the figure at the right.

3. Use a protractor to measure ∠TWU.

3. _____

4. Draw two lines that are perpendicular to $\overleftrightarrow{VWT}$.

4.

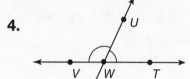

In 5 and 6, use the figure at the right, in which $\overleftrightarrow{XZ}$ ‖ $\overleftrightarrow{PQ}$.

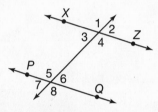

5. Name all alternate interior angles.

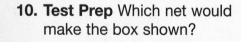

6. If m∠7 = 62°, find m∠6.

6. _____

7. Is every parallelogram a quadrilateral?

7. _____

8. Can a trapezoid have four congruent angles?

8. _____

9. Draw a base plan for the cube tower shown at the right.

9.

10. **Test Prep** Which net would make the box shown?

10. _____

A

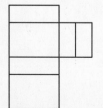

B

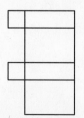

C

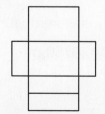

D

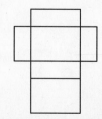

Date _____ Score _____

You will need a ruler and a protractor.

1. What metric unit would you use for the distance to the moon?

1. _____

2. Convert 19 ft 7 in. to inches.

2. _____

3. Katie measured a distance as 0.25 mi. Elizabeth measured a distance to be 1319.5 ft. Whose measurement was more precise?

3. _____

4. Calculate 34.09 mL − 27.2 mL. Express the answer with the correct number of significant digits.

4. _____

In 5–7, use the map of Montana.

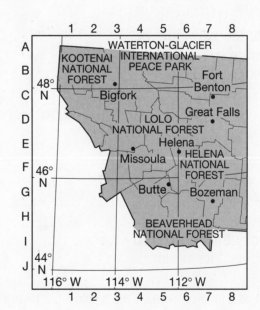

5. You are traveling from Missoula to Helena. Through how many degrees of longitude are you going?

_____

6. What are the latitude and longitude lines closest to Bigfork?

_____

7. You are in H-4. Which national forest is closest?

_____

8. Use a protractor to draw an angle of 45°.

8.

9. Measure ∠BAC.
   Measure ∠CAD.

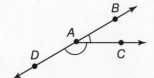

9. _____

Name _____

10. Classify a 120° angle as right, straight, obtuse, or acute.   **10.** _____

11. Find the complementary and supplementary angles of 35°.   **11.** _____

12. Draw a square with horizontal sides $\overline{AB}$ and $\overline{DC}$ (both read from left to right). Name two other parallel sides in the square.   **12.** _____

13. Using the square in Item 12, which sides are perpendicular to $\overline{AD}$?   **13.** _____

14. Name the two pairs of alternate exterior angles in the figure.   **14.** _____

15. Determine which of the following polygons are regular.   **15.** _____

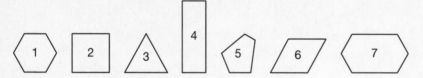

16. Classify this polygon by the number of its sides.   **16.** _____

17. What is the measure of an angle of a regular hexagon?   **17.** _____

18. Draw a base plan of the 3-D object shown.   **18.**

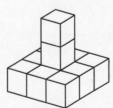

19. Draw the net of the object shown.   **19.**

You will need a ruler and a protractor.

1. What metric unit would you use for distance in track and field competitions?

1. _____

2. Convert 4560 cm to km.

2. _____

3. Ralph measured a distance as 21.34 m. Bobby measured a distance to be 0.125 km. Whose measurement was more precise?

3. _____

4. Calculate 56.9 km × 37.25 km. Express the answer with the correct number of significant digits.

4. _____

In 5–7, use the map of Montana.

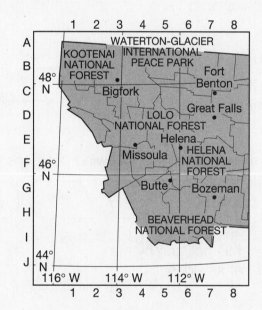

5. You are traveling from Butte to Fort Benton. Through how many degrees of latitude are you going?

_____

6. What are the latitude and longitude lines closest to Helena?

_____

7. You are in F-8. Which national forest is closest?

_____

8. Use a protractor to draw an angle of 60°.

8.

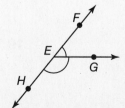

9. Measure ∠FEG. Measure ∠GEH.

9. _____

Name _____

10. Classify 85° as a right, straight, obtuse, or acute angle. **10.** _____

11. Find the complementary and supplementary angles of 49°. **11.** _____

12. Draw a rectangle with horizontal sides $\overline{EF}$ and $\overline{HG}$ (both read from left to right). Name two other parallel sides in the rectangle. **12.** _____

13. Using the rectangle in Item 12, which sides are perpendicular to $\overline{EH}$? **13.** _____

14. In the figure, name the four pairs of corresponding angles. 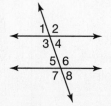 **14.** _____

15. Determine which of the following polygons are quadrilaterals.   **15.** _____

16. Classify this polygon by the number of its sides.  **16.** _____

17. What is the measure of an angle of a regular pentagon? **17.** _____

18. Draw a base plan of the 3-D object shown. 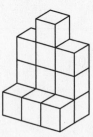 **18.**

19. Draw a net for the 3-D object shown.   **19.**

Date _____ Score _____

You will need a ruler and a protractor.
Give the letter of the correct answer.

1. Which of these would be an appropriate unit to measure the distance from Earth to the sun?

   A Meter   **B** Kilometer   **C** Centimeter   **D** Millimeter

   1. _____

2. Which of these would be an appropriate unit to measure the weight of the newest truck at Matt's Trucking Service?

   A Ounce   **B** Pound   **C** Ton   **D** Not here

   2. _____

3. Which of these would be an appropriate unit to measure the area of this page?

   A Square foot   **B** Square meter
   C Cubic inch   **D** Square centimeter

   3. _____

4. Convert 45 km to m.

   A 45,000 m   **B** 0.045 m   **C** 4500 m   **D** 0.45 m

   4. _____

5. Michelle needs 68 in. of rope. How many feet of rope does she need?

   A 1 ft 1 in.   **B** 5 ft 8 in.   **C** 101 in.   **D** 480 in.

   5. _____

6. Choose the most precise measurement.

   A 2 yd   **B** 5.5 ft   **C** 6 ft   **D** 67 in.

   6. _____

7. Which measurement has 3 significant digits?

   A 0.0520 m   **B** 3.012 m   **C** 12.060 m   **D** 500 m

   7. _____

8. Calculate 13.6 g + 3.75 g, giving the answer with the correct number of significant digits.

   A 17.35 g   **B** 17 g   **C** 17.4 g   **D** 173.5 g

   8. _____

9. Calculate 5.01 mi $\times$ 1.9 mi, giving the answer with the correct number of significant digits.

   A 9.519 mi^2 **B** 9.52 mi^2 **C** 9.5 mi^2 **D** 10 mi^2

   9. _____

Name _____

In 10–13, use the map of Texas.

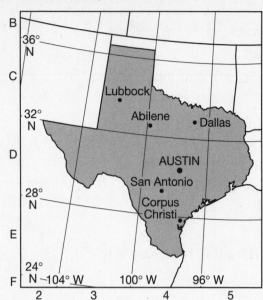

10. About how many degrees of longitude are there from Dallas to Abilene?

    A 1°   **B** 3°   **C** 5°   **D** 10°

10. _____

11. About how many degrees of latitude are there from Corpus Christi to Austin?

    A 2°   **B** 5°   **C** 7°   **D** 10°

11. _____

12. What are the approximate latitude and longitude of San Antonio?

    A 29° S, 99° W   **B** 25° N, 101° W
    C 29° N, 99° W   **D** 25° S, 101° W

12. _____

13. What are the map coordinates of Lubbock?

    A C-3   **B** C-2   **C** B-3   **D** B-4

13. _____

14. What is the measure of ∠ABC?

    A 125°   **B** 35°
    C 55°   **D** 145°

14. _____

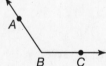

15. How would you classify an angle with a measure of 65°?

    A Right   **B** Straight   **C** Obtuse   **D** Acute

15. _____

© Scott Foresman Addison Wesley 8

186 Chapter 8 Test Form C   *Continued*

16. What is the measure of the supplement of an angle with a measure of 41°?

    A 49°   **B** 139°   **C** 39°   **D** 149°

16. _____

17. What is the measure of the complement of an angle with a measure of 16°?

    A 174°   **B** 64°   **C** 74°   **D** 164°

17. _____

18. A figure is named using the symbol $\overline{AB}$. What is the figure?

    A Line segment   **B** Line   **C** Ray   **D** Angle

18. _____

In 19–21, use this diagram, in which $\overleftrightarrow{AB} \parallel \overleftrightarrow{CD}$.

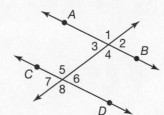

19. Which pair of angles are alternate interior angles?

    A ∠1 and ∠8   **B** ∠2 and ∠6
    C ∠3 and ∠5   **D** ∠4 and ∠5

19. _____

20. If m∠2 = 62°, what is the measure of ∠7?

    A 18°   **B** 28°   **C** 62°   **D** 118°

20. _____

21. What kind of angles are ∠1 and ∠5?

    A Alternate interior angles   **B** Corresponding angles
    C Alternate exterior angles   **D** Vertical angles

21. _____

22. Which statement describes perpendicular lines?

    A They intersect at a 90° angle.   **B** They never intersect.
    C They intersect at a 60° angle.   **D** They bisect each other.

22. _____

23. Which statement is true about an isosceles triangle?

    A It must have three congruent sides.
    B It has at least two congruent sides.
    C It has no congruent sides.
    D It must have three congruent angles.

23. _____

24. Which statement most accurately describe the figure shown?

A It is a regular hexagon.
B It is an irregular pentagon.
C It is an irregular hexagon.
D It is a regular pentagon.

24. _____

25. Which figure must have four right angles?

A Trapezoid   B Rhombus
C Parallelogram   D Rectangle

25. _____

26. What is the sum of the measures of all angles in a hexagon?

A 720°   B 360°   C 180°   D 1080°

26. _____

27. Which is *not* a way to show a 3-D object built from cubes?

A Draw right, front, and side views.
B Draw a base plan.
C Draw a number-line graph.
D Not here

27. _____

28. Which net would make the solid shown?

28. _____

A

B

C

D

29. What is shown by the base plan of a 3-D object built from cubes?

29. _____

A The right, front, and top views of the object
B A net for the object
C A front view of the object
D The height and position of the stacks of cubes that form the object

You will need a ruler and a protractor.

The historic district of an old town has been neglected for a very long time. Four historic sites are on a large plot of land at the edge of town, but no one has ever laid out streets to connect them. The street plan below consists of a map proposed several years ago.

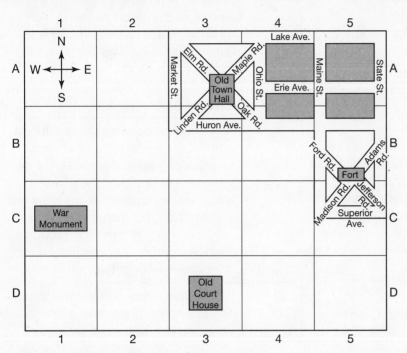

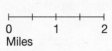

a. Name all the streets that appear to be parallel. Name all the streets that appear to be perpendicular. If streets end at a building, treat them as if they run to the center of the building.

b. Use a protractor to measure the angle formed by Maple Road and Lake Avenue. Explain how to find the measure of the angle formed by Linden Road and Huron Avenue without using a protractor.

c. What are the map coordinates of Old Town Hall? Of the Fort?

d. There is a contest to design a street plan for the historic district. Each of the four historic sites must be surrounded by streets that form a rectangle and then be accessible by at least four different streets. Draw a map that you can enter in this contest. Either complete the map above or design a new map. Make your map as neat and as accurate as possible.

Teacher Notes

Concepts and Skills This activity requires students to:
- analyze a map involving angles and grid lines.
- determine measures of angles formed by parallel lines and perpendicular lines.
- find the measurement of angles.
- locate the position on a map using map coordinates.
- plan and make a precise drawing involving parallel lines and perpendicular lines.

Guiding Questions
- What assumptions do you think can be made about the geometric figures formed by intersecting lines in the map?
- What additional lines might you draw to help you answer the questions and draw your map?

Answers
a. Parallel: Lake, Erie, Huron, Superior; Market, Ohio, Maine, State; Perpendicular: Lake and Market, Lake and Ohio, Lake and Maine, Lake and State, Ohio and Erie, Maine and Erie, State and Erie, Huron and Market, Huron and Ohio, Huron and Maine, Huron and State, Maine and Superior, State and Superior, Elm and Linden, Elm and Maple, Maple and Oak, Linden and Oak, Ford and Madison, Ford and Adams, Adams and Jefferson, Jefferson and Madison
b. 45°; The angles are alternate internal angles so the angle measures will be the same.
c. A-3; B-5
d. Answers may vary. Check students' drawings.

Extension
Have students bring in maps of the city or town in which your school is located or of some cities or towns they have visited, such as Washington, D.C. Have them list ways in which the layout of the streets on the map relates to the concepts they have studied in this chapter.

Evaluation

Level	Standard to be achieved for performance of specified level
4	The student demonstrates a clear understanding of angles, lines, and map coordinates, as well as a keen sense of the given situation. All questions are answered correctly and completely. The proposed map reflects careful thought, and the map is drawn neatly and accurately and is easy to read.
3	The student demonstrates a fundamental understanding of angles, lines, and map coordinates, as well as a sound grasp of the given situation. All questions are answered thoughtfully, but some answers may contain minor errors. The proposed map is appropriate, but the drawing may lack some detail.
2	The student has some understanding of angles, lines, and map coordinates, but can only apply them to the given situation with a great deal of assistance. There are several major errors in the student's calculations. The student attempts to draw a map, but some aspects of the map may be inappropriate, and the student may make one or more errors or omit critical steps in drawing the map.
1	The student demonstrates little if any understanding of angles, lines, and map coordinates, and, even when prompted, cannot apply them to the given situation. The student attempts to answer the questions, but the answers are superfluous or irrelevant. The student may prepare a map simply by copying the one given, and there is no meaningful effort to draw a map.

You will need a ruler and a protractor.

1. What customary unit would you use to measure the weight of a quarter?

1. _____

2. Convert 8.6 cm to m.

   A 0.86 m   **B** 86 m   **C** 0.086 m   **D** 860 m

2. _____

3. Choose the most precise measurement.
   A 5,282 ft   **B** 1 mi   **C** 63,386 in.   **D** 1,761 yd

3. _____

4. Calculate 62 mi + 8.3 mi, giving the answer with the correct number of significant digits.

4. _____

In 5–7, use the map of Texas.

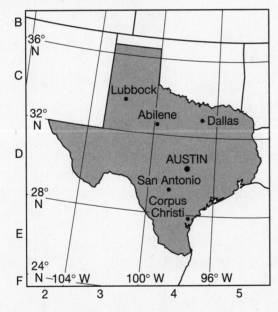

5. What are the approximate latitude and longitude of Dallas?

5. _____

6. What are the map coordinates of Austin?

   A C-3   **B** C-4   **C** D-3   **D** D-4

6. _____

7. On the map, how many degrees of longitude are between Dallas and Lubbock?

7. _____

Name _____

8. Use a protractor to draw an angle of 60°.

8.

In 9 and 10, use the figure at the right.

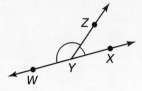

9. Measure ∠XYZ.

9. _____

10. Measure ∠ZYW.

10. _____

11. How would you classify an angle with a measure of 180°?

A Right   **B** Acute   **C** Obtuse   **D** Not here

11. _____

12. Find the complementary and supplementary angles of 25°.

12. _____

13. In the figure, name the two pairs of alternate exterior angles.

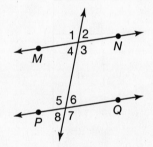

13. _____

_____

14. In the figure above, if m∠3 = 110°, what is m∠4?

A 20°   **B** 55°   **C** 70°   **D** 110°

14. _____

15. Complete the statement to make it true: Perpendicular lines intersect at a _____ angle.

15. _____

16. Which of the following polygons is *not* regular?

16. _____

Continued

Name _____

In 17 and 18, use the polygon below.

17. Classify this polygon by
the number of sides.

17. _____

18. Find the sum of the
angles in this polygon.

18. _____

19. Draw a base plan of the 3-D object shown.

19.

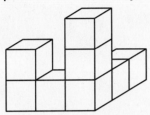

20. Which net would make the solid shown below?

20. _____

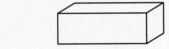

A

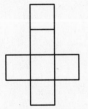

B

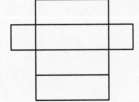

C

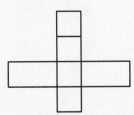

D

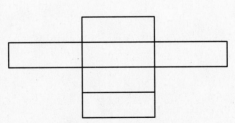

21. Performance Task Draw an obtuse angle without using
a protractor. Label your angle *MNP*. Explain how you
know that ∠*MNP* is obtuse. Then use your protractor
to find m∠*MNP*.

Name _____

Date _____ Score _____

━ Computation ━

In 1 and 2, simplify.

1. $(3 + 7)^2 - 5$

1. _____

2. $\dfrac{3}{10} + \dfrac{1}{15}$

2. _____

3. Solve $6x - 4 = 20$.

   A $x = 4$ **B** $x = -4$ **C** $x = 10$ **D** $x = -10$

3. _____

4. Find the solution of the system $y = 2x - 5$ and $y = -x + 1$.

   A $(2, 3)$ **B** $(-2, -9)$ **C** $(2, -1)$ **D** $(-2, 1)$

4. _____

5. Find 45% of 180.

5. _____

6. Which number is divisible by 6?

   A 114   **B** 136   **C** 189   **D** 215

6. _____

7. Find the missing side length of a right triangle with legs 5 and 6.

   A 61   **B** $\sqrt{61}$ **C** 11   **D** $\sqrt{11}$

7. _____

8. Convert 16 ft 2 in. to inches.

8. _____

━ Concepts ━

9. In the product of 14.25 cm × 6.5 cm, how many significant digits should there be?

9. _____

10. Which of the following is a rational number?

   A $\sqrt{12}$ **B** $\sqrt{20}$ **C** π **D** $\sqrt{4}$

10. _____

11. What metric unit would you use to measure the height of a room?

11. _____

12. Which is more precise, 0.685 ft or 8 in.?

12. _____

13. Use a protractor to draw an angle of 125°.
Classify your angle as acute or obtuse.

13. _____

14. Measure ∠JKL. Find the
measure of an angle that
is supplementary to ∠JKL.

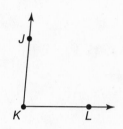

14. _____

15. If $\overleftrightarrow{AB}$ and $\overleftrightarrow{CD}$ are parallel,
which of the following best
describes the pair
∠1 and ∠2?

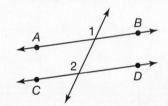

15. _____

A Congruent   **B** Supplementary
C Vertical   **D** Complementary

16. Which side in triangle ABC
is parallel to $\overline{EF}$?

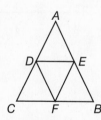

16. _____

17. Which figure *must* be a rectangle?

17. _____

A Rhombus   **B** Trapezoid
C Square   **D** Parallelogram

18. Which statement is true of an equilateral triangle?

18. _____

A It has no more than two congruent sides.
B It has three congruent angles.
C It has three angles with different measures.
D It has no congruent sides.

Continued

19. What is the most specific name for a regular convex quadrilateral?

19. _____

20. Draw a base plan of the 3-D object shown.

20.

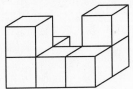

— Applications —

In 21–23, use the map of California.

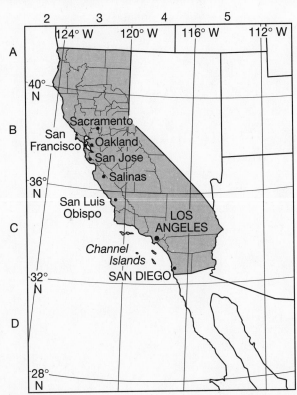

21. What are the approximate latitude and longitude of Los Angeles?

21. _____

22. How many degrees of latitude are there between Salinas and Sacramento?

22. _____

23. On the map, what city is located in C-3?

23. _____

In this quiz, use 3.14 for π.

1. Find the perimeter
and area of the triangle.

2. Find the perimeter and
area of the polygon
after the given dilation.

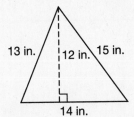

13 in. 12 in. 15 in.

14 in.

Scale factor = 3

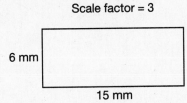

6 mm

15 mm

1. _____

_____

2. _____

_____

3. Find the circumference
and area of the circle.

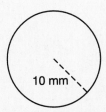

10 mm

3. _____

_____

In 4–7, find the surface area of the figure. Round to the nearest tenth.

4.

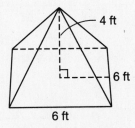

3 ft

7.5 ft   1.5 ft

5. 2 cm

11 cm

6.

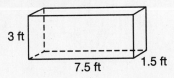
4 ft

6 ft

6 ft

7.

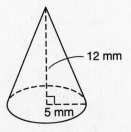
12 mm

5 mm

4. _____

5. _____

6. _____

7. _____

8. Test Prep Find the
area of the figure.

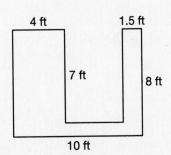

4 ft   1.5 ft

7 ft   8 ft

10 ft

8. _____

A 36 ft² **B** 50 ft² **C** 80 ft² **D** Not here

© Scott Foresman Addison Wesley 8

In this quiz, use 3.14 for π.

In 1 and 2, find the volume of the prism.

1.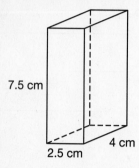

   7.5 cm

   4 cm
   2.5 cm

2.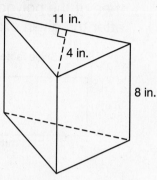

   11 in.
   4 in.
   8 in.

1. _____

2. _____

3. Find the volume of the rectangular prism after the dilation by a scale factor of 4.

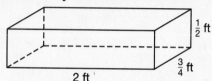

$\frac{1}{2}$ ft

$\frac{3}{4}$ ft

2 ft

3. _____

4. A cylindrical can has a base 4 cm in diameter and is 17 cm tall. Find the volume of the can.

4. _____

In 5 and 6, find the volume of the figure.

5.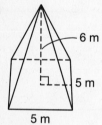

   6 m
   5 m
   5 m

6.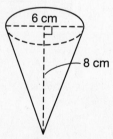

   6 cm
   8 cm

5. _____

6. _____

7. **Test Prep** After a dilation according to a scale factor of 10, the volume of a rectangular prism is increased by what factor?

   A 10   **B** 30   **C** 100   **D** 1000

7. _____

In this test, use 3.14 for π. In 1 and 2, find the perimeter and area of the figure.

1.

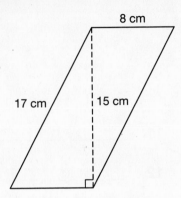

8 cm

17 cm   15 cm

2.

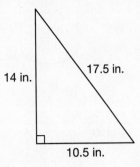

14 in.   17.5 in.

10.5 in.

1. _____

_____

2. _____

_____

3. Find the perimeter and area of the polygon after the dilation by a scale factor of 3.5.

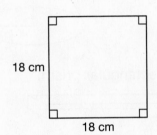

18 cm

18 cm

3. _____

_____

On a scale drawing, a rectangular room measures 3 cm by 4 cm. The scale factor is 90.

4. Find the perimeter of the room.

5. Find the area of the room.

4. _____

5. _____

In 6 and 7, find the circumference and area of the circle.

6.

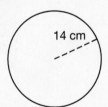

14 cm

7.

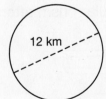

12 km

6. _____

_____

7. _____

_____

8. A lawn sprinkler head rotates in a circular motion. It can propel the water a distance of 20 feet. What is the area of the lawn that the sprinkler can water?

8. _____

In 9–12, find the surface area of each figure.

9.

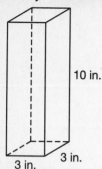

10 in.

3 in.   3 in.
3 in.

10.

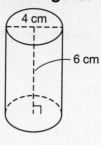

4 cm

6 cm

9. _____

10. _____

11.

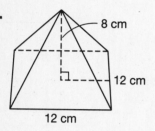

8 cm

12 cm

12 cm

12.

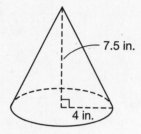

7.5 in.

4 in.

11. _____

12. _____

13. Find the volume of the rectangular prism.

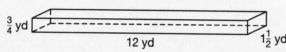

$\frac{3}{4}$ yd

12 yd $1\frac{1}{2}$ yd

13. _____

14. A swimming pool is 60 feet long, 25 feet wide, and 4 feet deep. What is the volume of the pool?

14. _____

15. Find the volume of the rectangular prism after scaling one dimension by a scale factor of $\frac{3}{4}$.

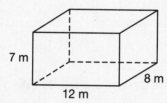

7 m

12 m   8 m

15. _____

16. Find the volume of the rectangular prism after the dilation by a scale factor of 2.

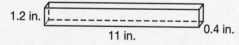

1.2 in.

11 in.   0.4 in.

16. _____

In 17–19, find the volume of the figure.

17.

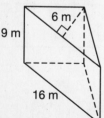

6 m

9 m

16 m

18.

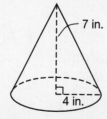

7 in.

4 in.

19.

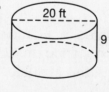

20 ft

9 ft

17. _____

18. _____

19. _____

Date _____   Score _____

In this test, use 3.14 for π. In 1 and 2, find the perimeter and area of the figure.

1.
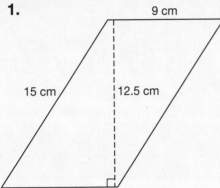

2.
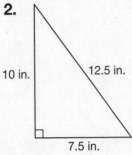

1. _____

_____

2. _____

_____

3. Find the perimeter and area of the polygon after the dilation by a scale factor of 4.5.

Scale factor = 4.5

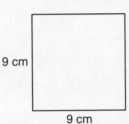

3. _____

_____

On a scale drawing, a rectangular room measures 7 cm by 9 cm. The scale factor is 40.

4. Find the perimeter of the room.

4. _____

5. Find the area of the room.

5. _____

In 6 and 7, find the circumference and area of the circle.

6.
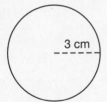

7.
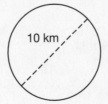

6. _____

_____

7. _____

_____

8. A dog is tied to a stake by a rope that is 18 ft long. What is the area of the ground available for it to play on?

8. _____

Name _____

In 9–12, find the surface area of the figure.

9.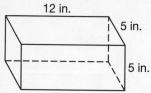

10.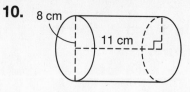

9. _____

10. _____

11.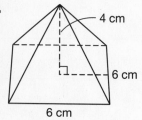

12.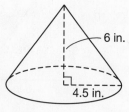

11. _____

12. _____

13. Find the volume of the rectangular prism.

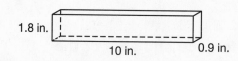

13. _____

14. The foundation for a new home is 40 feet long, 16 feet wide, and 3 feet deep. What is the volume of the foundation?

14. _____

15. Find the volume of the rectangular prism after scaling one dimension by the scale factor of $\frac{2}{5}$.

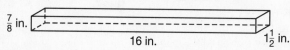

15. _____

16. Find the volume of the rectangular prism after the dilation by a scale factor of 3.

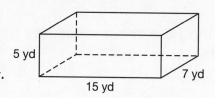

16. _____

In 17–19, find the volume of the solid.

17.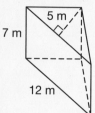

18.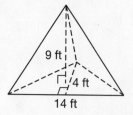

19.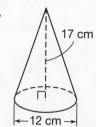

17. _____

18. _____

19. _____

In this test, use 3.14 for π.

1. Find the perimeter of the figure.

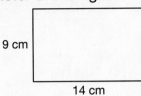

9 cm

14 cm

A 23 cm   **B** 46 cm   **C** 126 cm   **D** Not here

1. _____

2. Find the area of the figure.

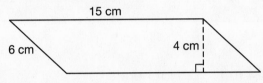

15 cm

6 cm

4 cm

A 60 cm²   **B** 90 cm²   **C** 42 cm²   **D** Not here

2. _____

3. A square has a perimeter of 20 in. Find its area.

A 16 in²   **B** 20 in²   **C** 25 in²   **D** Not here

3. _____

4. Find the perimeter of the figure after a dilation according to a scale factor of 3.2.

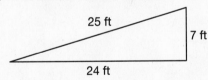

25 ft

7 ft

24 ft

A 56 ft   **B** 59.2 ft   **C** 179.2 ft   **D** Not here

4. _____

5. Find the area of the figure to be used as a storage area after a dilation according to a scale factor of $\frac{3}{4}$.

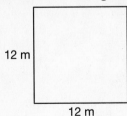

12 m

12 m

A 144 m²   **B** 108 m²   **C** 81 m²   **D** Not here

5. _____

Name _____

6. Find the circumference of the circle.

6. _____

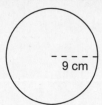

9 cm

A 28.26 cm **B** 56.52 cm **C** 254.34 cm **D** Not here

7. Find the area of the circle.

7. _____

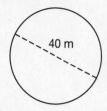

40 m

A 125.6 m² **B** 251.2 m² **C** 5024 m² **D** Not here

8. Find the surface area of the prism.

8. _____

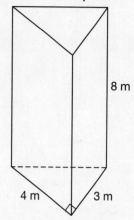

8 m

4 m   3 m

A 96 m² **B** 108 m² **C** 120 m² **D** Not here

9. Find the surface area of the cylinder.

9. _____

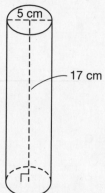

5 cm

17 cm

A 306.15 cm² **B** 463.15 cm² **C** 372.875 cm² **D** Not here

Continued

10. Find the surface area of the cone.

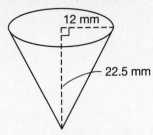

12 mm

22.5 mm

10. _____

A 1413 mm^2 **B** 3391.2 mm^2
C 10173.6 mm^3 **D** Not here

11. A square pyramid is to be 12 ft tall and the base is to be 18 ft on each side. What is its total surface area?

11. _____

A 540 ft^2 **B** 1296 ft^2 **C** 864 ft^2 **D** 3888 ft^2

12. A cereal box is 8 cm wide, 25 cm long, and 40 cm tall. What is the volume of the cereal box?

12. _____

A 2640 cm^3 **B** 8000 cm^3 **C** 3040 cm^3 **D** Not here

13. Find the volume of the prism.

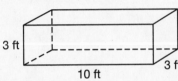

3 ft

10 ft

3 ft

13. _____

A 90 ft^3 **B** 90 ft^2 **C** 16 ft^3 **D** Not here

14. Find the volume of a rectangular prism 5 m wide, 8 m long, and 6 m tall after one dimension is dilated according to a scale factor of $\frac{2}{3}$.

14. _____

A 240 m^3 **B** 160 m^3 **C** 71$\frac{1}{9}$ m^3 **D** Not here

15. Find the volume of a rectangular prism 4.2 ft wide, 11 ft long, and 1.3 ft tall after it is dilated according to a scale factor of 3.

15. _____

A 1621.62 ft^3 **B** 180.18 ft^3 **C** 3561.84 ft^3 **D** Not here

16. Find the volume of the prism.

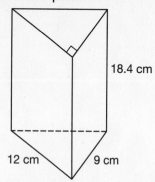

18.4 cm

12 cm   9 cm

16. _____

A 770.4 cm³   **B** 662.4 cm³   **C** 993.6 cm³   **D** Not here

17. Find the volume of the cylindrical water bottle.

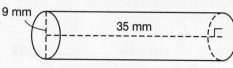

9 mm   35 mm

17. _____

A 989.1 mm³   **B** 2225.475 mm³
C 8901.9 mm³   **D** Not here

18. Find the volume of the pyramid.

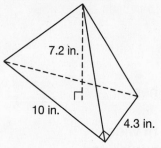

7.2 in.

10 in.   4.3 in.

18. _____

A 51.6 in³   **B** 154.8 in³   **C** 103.2 in³   **D** Not here

19. Find the volume of the cone.

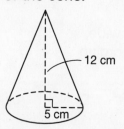

12 cm

5 cm

19. _____

A 942 cm³   **B** 340.17 cm³   **C** 314 cm³   **D** Not here

Continued

20. A rectangle has sides of 8 m and 9 m. After a dilation by a factor of 1.5, what is its perimeter?

20. _____

    A 25.5 m   **B** 34 m   **C** 51 m   **D** Not here

21. Find the area of the rectangle in the previous problem.

21. _____

    A 72 m^2 **B** 108 m^2 **C** 144 m^2 **D** 162 m^2

22. Find the volume of a square pyramid whose sides are 15 feet long and whose height is 18 feet.

22. _____

    A 1350 ft^2 **B** 1650 ft^2 **C** 4050 ft^2 **D** 4860 ft^2

23. A cone-shaped filter rests in a cylindrical beaker. The filter and beaker each have a radius of 5 cm. The beaker is 8 cm high, and the filter reaches to a depth of 3 cm in the beaker. Approximately how many times can the filter be filled before the liquid that seeps through it fills the beaker?

23. _____

    A 1.6   **B** 2.67   **C** 5   **D** 8

You are starting your own part-time business, Geometric Gifts. You plan to buy transparent, geometrically shaped hollow containers. You will fill these shapes with interesting materials and sell them. Each finished container must be filled completely.

Shape	Dimensions	Surface Area	Volume
Sphere	diameter: 3 in.	28.26 in^2	14.13 in^3
Rectangular Prism	width: 2 in. length: 1.5 in. height: 4 in.		
Cylinder	diameter: 4 in. height: 3 in.		
Square Pyramid	base (side): 3 in. height: 2 in. slant height: 2.5 in.		
Cone	base (diameter): 3 in. height: 2 in. slant height: 2.5 in.		

a. Complete the table by finding the surface area and volume for the containers. Use 3.14 for π.

The list below shows materials you have to line or fill the containers.

To line containers (middle is hollow)
- holographic-image pictures . . . . (five 3 in. $\times$ 5 in. each)
- postcard-weight art prints . . . . (five 3 in. $\times$ 5 in. each)
- postcard-weight nature photos . . . . (six 4 in. $\times$ 6 in. each)

To fill containers
- layers of dried seeds . . . . (three 20 in^3 bags)
- colored sand . . . . (six 24 in^3 bags)
- potpourri mix . . . . (one 150 in^3 bag)
- spherical-shaped pine cones* . . . . . . (12, 1 in.-diameter each)
- transparent colored marbles* . . . . . (200, $\frac{1}{2}$ in.-diameter each)
- small colored beads* . . . . (50, $\frac{1}{2}$ in.-diameter each)

   *When working with spherical filling materials, treat them as if they were shaped like cubes.

b. You have many containers in each shape. Plan how you will use your materials. Try to use as much of the materials as you can. Tell which material you would put into which shape. Indicate how much material you will have left.

Teacher Notes

Concepts and Skills This activity requires students to:
- find the area and circumference of circles.
- find the surface area of a rectangular prism and a cylinder.
- find the surface area of a pyramid and a cone.
- find the volume of a rectangular prism.
- find the volume of a cylinder.
- find the volume of a pyramid and a cone.

Guiding Questions
- In what situations might you want to know how to find the surface area of geometric shapes?
- In what situations might you want to know how to find the volume of geometric shapes?

Answers

a.

Shape	Surface Area	Volume
Rectangular Prism	34 in^2	12 in^3
Cylinder	62.8 in^2	37.68 in^3
Square Pyramid	24 in^2	6 in^3
Cone	18.84 in^2	4.71 in^3

b. Answers will vary. In each case, no more than 4.71 in^3 of material should be left over.

Extension
Make an elaborate design for one of your Geometric Gifts. Sketch the shape, using a net if it helps you, and show exactly how you will line or fill the shape. For example, you may list what scenes are on the nature photos or indicate what layers of seeds or colored marbles you will use where. Your shape could be decorated by gluing a ribbon or other type of stringlike decoration around the circumference of the shape or along the edges of the shape. Tell how much of this material you will need.

Evaluation

Level	Standard to be achieved for performance of specified level
4	The student demonstrates a clear understanding of and proficiency in finding surface area and volume. All calculations, including those for the plan, are accurate and complete. The plan uses the maximum amount of materials.
3	The student demonstrates a fundamental understanding of and proficiency in finding surface area and volume. Most calculations, including those for the plan, are correct. The plan uses the maximum amount of materials for at least seven of the items.
2	The student demonstrates some understanding of and proficiency in finding surface area and volume, but may need substantial assistance or may often confuse the two. Most calculations, including those for the plan, are attempted, but several are incorrect and some may be missing. The plan uses the maximum amount of materials for about half of the items.
1	The student demonstrates little if any understanding of and proficiency in finding area and volume, even with substantial assistance. Some calculations, including those for the plan, may be attempted but are not completed, even with assistance. The plan uses the maximum amount of materials for less than half of the items.

In this test, use 3.14 for π.

1. Find the perimeter and area of the polygon.

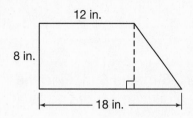

12 in.

8 in.

18 in.

1. _____

2. Find the circumference and area of a circle whose diameter is 48 mm.

2. _____

_____

3. Find the surface area of the cylinder.

12 cm

19 cm

3. _____

In 4 and 5, you are given a package shaped like the square pyramid below. You need to fill it and then wrap it.

4. Find the surface area.

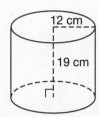

15 m

16 m

16 m

4. _____

5. Find the volume.

5. _____

In 6 and 7, find the surface area and the volume of the figure.

6.

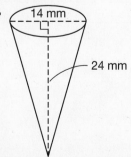

14 mm

24 mm

7.

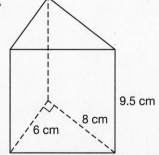

9.5 cm

8 cm

6 cm

6. _____

_____

7. _____

_____

8. You have an empty
cylindrical oatmeal box
that you will fill and use
in a science project. Find
the volume and the surface
area of the cylinder.

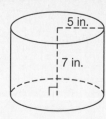
5 in.

7 in.

8. _____

_____

9. A rectangle has dimensions 3.5 m and 6 m. Find the
perimeter of the figure after a dilation according to a
scale factor of 1.5.

A 19 m   **B** 16.625 m   **C** 28.5 m   **D** 31.5 m

9. _____

10. A rectangle has dimensions 4 in. and 9.3 in. Find the
area of the figure after a dilation according to a scale
factor of 5.

A 930 in^2 **B** 665 in^2 **C** 186 in^2 **D** 133 in^2

10. _____

**A rectangular prism is $1\frac{1}{2}$ ft wide, $8\frac{1}{2}$ ft long, and
3 ft tall. Find its surface area (11) and its volume (12).**

11. A 42.75 ft^2 **B** 85.5 ft^2 **C** 38.25 ft^2 **D** 76.5 ft^2

11. _____

12. A 42.75 ft^3 **B** 85.5 ft^3 **C** 38.25 ft^3 **D** 76.5 ft^3

12. _____

13. After a dilation by a scale factor of 3, the volume
of a rectangular prism is increased by what factor?

A 3   **B** 6   **C** 9   **D** 27

13. _____

14. Performance Task Describe a situation in which you would
need to calculate the surface area of a rectangular prism and
a situation in which you would need to calculate the volume of
a rectangular prism. Then sketch and label the dimensions of a suitable
rectangular prism, and calculate the surface area and the volume.

_____

_____

In this test, use 3.14 for π.

— Computation —

1. Find the perimeter and area of the square.

5 in.

1. _____

2. A parallelogram has a perimeter of 20 m. After a dilation according to a scale factor of 2.7, what will be the perimeter of the new parallelogram?

A 22.7 m   **B** 25.4 m   **C** 54 m   **D** 145.8 m

2. _____

3. A square has a side of 6 cm. After a dilation according to a scale factor of 1.5, what will be the area of the new square?

A 39 cm^2 **B** 54 cm^2 **C** 56.25 cm^2 **D** 81 cm^2

3. _____

4. Write $\frac{3}{20}$ as a percent.

4. _____

5. Consider the equations $y = 3x - 4$ and $y = -x$. Which point is a solution of both equations?

A (2, 2)   **B** (1, −1)   **C** (0, 0)   **D** (−3, 3)

5. _____

6. A rectangular prism is 2 in. wide, 5 in. long, and 3 in. tall. Find the surface area and the volume of the prism.

6. _____

7. A rectangular prism has a volume of 100 ft^3. After a dilation according to a scale factor of 2, what will be the volume of the new rectangular prism?

A 106 ft^3 **B** 200 ft^3 **C** 600 ft^3 **D** 800 ft^3

7. _____

Name _____

— Concepts —

8. Find the perimeter.

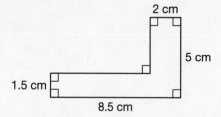

8. _____

    A 17 cm   **B** 19.75 cm   **C** 27 cm   **D** Not here

9. Find the volume of liquid a cone would contain with measurements of 6 in. diameter and a 6 in. height.

9. _____

    A 226.08 in^3 **B** 56.52 in^3 **C** 678.24 in^3 **D** Not here

Find the surface area of the cylinder and the cone and the volume of the cone.

10.
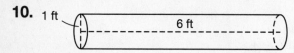

10. _____

11.
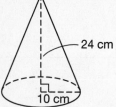

11. _____

    _____

12. Identify the slope, x-intercept, and y-intercept of the graph of the equation $y = 2x + 4$.

12. _____

13. Find the volume of the pyramid.

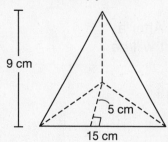

13. _____

    Continued

14. Find the surface area and volume of the cylinder.

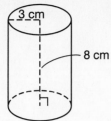

3 cm

8 cm

14. _____

_____

— Applications —

15. A model of a swimming pool was built for a new-home display. The model was $\frac{1}{4}$ ft wide, $\frac{3}{4}$ ft long, and $\frac{1}{6}$ ft deep. The actual swimming pool is to be built according to a scale factor of 64. What will be the volume of the actual pool?

15. _____

16. An item in a store was marked $5.00. Two weeks later, the same item was marked $6.25. By what percent was the price of the item increased?

16. _____

17. A family has a circular swimming pool in their backyard. The pool is 30 feet in diameter. The family wants to fence in the pool, leaving 4 feet of space between the pool and the fence. How many feet of fencing will be required?

17. _____

18. Kinshasa bought a fish tank that measures 18 in. tall, 30 in. long, and 1 ft wide. Find the volume of the fish tank.

18. _____

_____

19. To order a certain item by mail costs $5 per item, plus $3 shipping for the entire order. The cost can be determined by the equation $y = 5x + 3$, where y is the cost of the order and x is the number of items ordered. Complete the table for the cost of ordering x items.

19.

Number of items (x)	1	3	8	15
Cost in dollars (y)				

20. A student scored 85% on a test. The student answered 68 questions correctly. How many questions were on the test?

20. _____

Give the letter of the correct answer.

1. Consider the data in this line plot. Which of the following quantities is equal to 7?

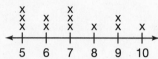

A Mean   **B** Mode   **C** Median   **D** Mean and median

1. _____

2. What is the upper quartile of the data in this box-and-whisker plot?

**Scores on a
Social Studies Test**

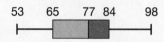

A 65   **B** 84   **C** 77   **D** 53–98

2. _____

3. A survey company mailed 3000 questionnaires to college students. Of all the letters, 567 completed surveys were returned to the survey company. What is the sample size of the survey?

A 3000   **B** 2433   **C** 567   **D** Not here

3. _____

4. Which integer is described by the following? The absolute value is 3 and the number is to the left of 0 on the number line.

A −3   **B** 3   **C** −1   **D** −2

4. _____

5. A hiker first hiked down into a canyon 345 feet below sea level. She then hiked 950 feet up the side of a mountain. What was the final altitude of the hiker?

A −605 feet   **B** −1295 feet   **C** 605 feet   **D** 1295 feet

5. _____

6. Evaluate −9 (7 − 2).

A 45   **B** −61   **C** −81   **D** −45

6. _____

7. Which expression represents 5.784×10^5 in standard notation?

A 578,400   **B** 57,840,000   **C** 57,840   **D** 5,784,000

7. _____

8. Evaluate the formula $F = 1.8C + 32$ for $C = 40$.   **8.** _____

    A 33.8   **B** 104   **C** 102   **D** 72

9. Write an algebraic expression for the quotient of a number and 4.   **9.** _____

    A $n + 4$ **B** $n \times 4$ **C** $\frac{n}{4}$ **D** $n - 4$

10. Solve $6x + 4 = 124$.   **10.** _____

    A $x = 120$ **B** $x = 124$ **C** $x = 20$ **D** $x = 6$

11. $x \geq 10$ is a solution of which inequality?   **11.** _____

    A $x - 7 \geq 3$ **B** $x - 7 > 3$ **C** $x - 7 < 3$ **D** $x - 7 \leq 3$

In 12 and 13, use the graph of $y = 3x + 1$.

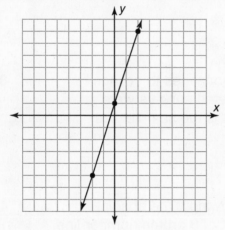

12. Give the slope of the line.   **12.** _____

    A $\frac{1}{3}$ **B** 3   **C** 2   **D** 6

13. Give the *y*-intercept of the line.   **13.** _____

    A -1 **B** $-\frac{1}{2}$ **C** 1   **D** Not here

14. Find the solution of the system $y = 4x - 6$ and $y = 3x - 3$.   **14.** _____

    A (3, 6)   **B** (6, 3)   **C** (4, 2)   **D** (2, 4)

15. The ratios in which pair do *not* form a proportion?   **15.** _____

    A $\frac{20}{35} \stackrel{?}{=} \frac{16}{28}$ **B** $\frac{60}{100} \stackrel{?}{=} \frac{24}{40}$ **C** $\frac{35}{60} \stackrel{?}{=} \frac{30}{80}$ **D** $\frac{3}{8} \stackrel{?}{=} \frac{9}{24}$

   Continued

16. Is the table below an equal-ratio table? If so, find the value of *k*.   **16.** _____

x	20	25	30	35
y	16	20	24	28

A $k = \dfrac{5}{4}$ **B** $k = \dfrac{4}{5}$ **C** $k = \dfrac{5}{5}$ **D** Not an equal-ratio table

17. Which of the following is *not* a unit rate?   **17.** _____

A $\dfrac{3 \text{ ft}}{\text{sec}}$ **B** $\dfrac{50 \text{ words}}{\text{min}}$ **C** $25 for 1 hour   **D** 1 card for $2

18. 162.75 is 35% of what number?   **18.** _____

A 465   **B** 4.65   **C** 46.5   **D** 0.465

19. Mrs. Kosko left $19.47 on the table in a restaurant after receiving a bill for $16.50. If there was no tax, what percent did she tip?   **19.** _____

A 15%   **B** 13%   **C** 17%   **D** 18%

20. A catalog is discounting all sweaters 25%. How much will you pay for a sweater that is regularly $49.99?   **20.** _____

A $24.99   **B** $37.49   **C** $124.98   **D** $49.74

21. Which number is divisible by 3?   **21.** _____

A 198,343   **B** 247,881   **C** 583,624   **D** 752,242

22. Which number is an irrational number?   **22.** _____

A $\sqrt{167}$ **B** $\sqrt{529}$ **C** $\sqrt{361}$ **D** $\sqrt{100}$

23. Find the length of the missing side for the right triangle.   **23.** _____

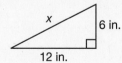

A 180 in.   **B** 13 in.   **C** $\sqrt{180}$ in.   **D** 14 in.

24. Which metric unit is best for measuring the length of a driveway?   **24.** _____

A Foot   **B** Millimeter   **C** Kilometer   **D** Meter

Name _____

25. Which is the most precise measurement?

    A 23.555 m   **B** 23.5 m   **C** 24 m   **D** 23 m

25. _____

26. Angles 3, 4, 5, and 6 are all _____ angles.

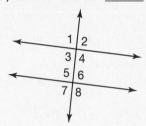

    A Corresponding   **B** Exterior   **C** Interior   **D** Transversal

26. _____

27. Identify the polygon.

    A Hexagon   **B** Heptagon   **C** Octagon   **D** Pentagon

27. _____

28. This triangle will be dilated by a factor of $\frac{1}{3}$. What will be the perimeter of the triangle after dilation?

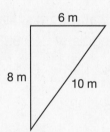

    A 72 m   **B** 24 m
    C 8 m   **D** Not here

28. _____

29. A clock on a building has an hour hand that extends to the outer edge of the clock and measures 9 ft. Which is the best approximation for the area of the clock?

    A 254.34 ft^2 **B** $\sqrt{254.34}$ ft^2 **C** 81 ft^2 **D** $\sqrt{81}$ ft^2

29. _____

30. Find the surface area of the square pyramid.

    A 732 m^2 **B** 624 m^2
    C 1200 m^2 **D** 816 m^2

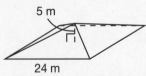

30. _____

31. The dimensions of a box that a radio came in are 12 in. by 8 in. by 5 in. What is the volume of the box?

    A 96 in^3 **B** 480 in^3 **C** 40 in^3 **D** 60 in^3

31. _____

1. In a function, how many output values result from each input value?

1. _____

In 2 and 3, use the function machine shown to find each missing value.

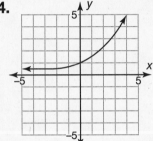

Input 〉 Multiply by 3 〉 Output

2. Input −2   Output _____

2. _____

3. Input _____   Output 15

3. _____

In 4 and 5, tell whether each graph is *linear*, *quadratic*, *exponential*, or *step*.

4.

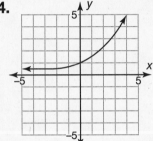

5.

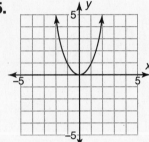

4. _____

5. _____

In 6 and 7, complete the table of input and output values for each function.

6.

Input	Function Rule	Output
x	$5x - 2$	y
−1		
0		
1		

7.

Input	Function Rule	Output
x	$2x^2 - 1$	y
−1		
0		
1		

8. With tax, a watch costs $20. How many watches can Alicia buy if she wants to spend $100 on watches for people in her company?

8. _____

9. **Test Prep** Which is the output value for $y = 2x - 3$ if the input value is 4?

9. _____

A 1 **B** 5 **C** 7 **D** 11

1. Classify $2x^2 + 1$ as a monomial, a binomial, or a trinomial.

1. _____

2. Find the degree of the polynomial $x^3 - 2x^4 + 7x - 1$.

2. _____

3. The volume of a cube can be represented by the function $V = s^3$, where V = volume and s = length of a side. What is the volume of a cube with a side length of 4 cm?

3. _____

In 4–9, simplify.

4. $(8m^2 + 2m - 3) + (m^2 + 4m + 2)$

4. _____

5. $(3u^2 - 8u + 9) + (2u^2 + 4u - 1)$

5. _____

6. $(9c^3 - 7c + 6) - (c^2 + 2c - 9)$

_____

7. $(4v + v^2 - 2) - (2v + 4)$

7. _____

8. $9y^2 \cdot -2y^3$

8. _____

9. $4x(2x^2 + 3x - 1)$

9. _____

10. Bob built a doghouse with an exercise area. Find an expression for the area of the total region. What is the area when $x = 3$ feet?

10. _____

_____

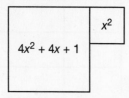

x^2

$4x^2 + 4x + 1$

11. **Test Prep** Which is the product of 4.2×10^4 and 5.3×10^8?

11. _____

    A 9.5×10^{12} **B** 9.5×10^{32}
    C 2.226×10^{13} **D** 22.26×10^{13}

Name _____

Date _____ Score _____

Chapter 10 Test
Form
A

In 1 and 2, use the function machine.

| Input | Add 6 | Output |

1. Find the output for an input of 6.

1. _____

2. Find the input for an output of 60.

2. _____

3. Complete the table of input and output values for $y = 2x + 3$. Then graph the equation. Does the equation describe a function?

3. _____

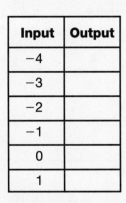

Input	Output
−4	
−3	
−2	
−1	
0	
1	

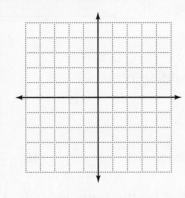

4. Larry (y) walked 1 mile less than 2 times the number of miles Janice (x) walked. Graph this equation.

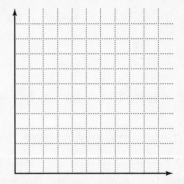

5. Graph the set of functions. Then describe the similarities and differences within the set of graphs. $y = x^2$, $y = x^2 + 1$, $y = x^2 − 1$

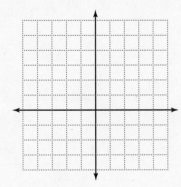

6. A ball is dropped from a height of 200 feet. Ignoring air resistance, the function $h = −16t^2 + 200$, where t is the time in seconds and h is the height in feet, will model the situation. Graph this function. Estimate when the ball will hit the ground.

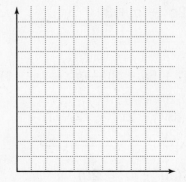

_____

_____

_____

_____   _____

Chapter 10 Test Form A

Continued **225**

7. Graph $y = 2.5^x$.

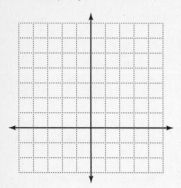

8. Arthur's telephone company rounds each long-distance call to the next whole minute. The rate is 15 cents per minute. Graph how much it will cost (y) if Arthur makes a long-distance telephone call for x minutes.

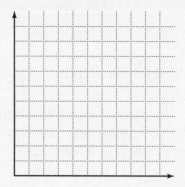

9. Write the polynomial expression
$-2x + 3x^4 + 6 + 4x^2 - 2x^3$ in descending order.

_____

10. Evaluate $3x^4 - 2x^3 + 7x^2 - 5x + 1$ for $x = 3$.

10. _____

11. The volume of a sphere is represented by the formula $V = \frac{4}{3}\pi r^3$, where V = volume and r = radius. Find the volume of air (to the nearest tenth) inside a soap bubble that is 4 inches in *diameter.* Use 3.14 for π.

11. _____

In 12–16, simplify the polynomial expression. Write each answer in descending order.

12. $(3b^2 + 7b - 1) + (b^2 - 4b + 6)$

12. _____

13. $2q^3 - q + 3$
$+ \qquad 7q + 9$

13. _____

14. $(2a^2 + 5a + 3) - (a^2 + 4a + 1)$

14. _____

15. $(3v^3 + 2v^2 - v + 1)$
$- (2v^3 + 2v^2 - 3v - 8)$

15. _____

16. $3u^2(2u^4 + u^3 - 2u)$

16. _____

17. Multiply $(2.3 \times 10^3) \bullet (4.1 \times 10^2)$. Write your answer in scientific notation.

17. _____

In 1 and 2, use the function machine.

| Input | Subtract 1 | Output |

1. Find the output for an input of 20.

   1. _____

2. Find the input for an output of 5.

   2. _____

3. Complete the table of input and output values for $y = -x + 5$. Then graph the equation. Does the equation describe a function?

   3. _____

Input	Output
5	
4	
3	
2	
1	
0	

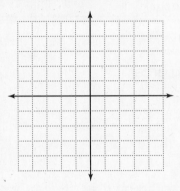

4. Regina (y) read 4 less than 3 times the number of books Tony (x) read. Graph this equation.

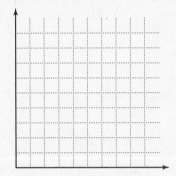

5. Graph the set of functions. Then describe the similarities and differences within the set of graphs.
$y = -x^2$, $y = -2x^2$, $y = -3x^2$

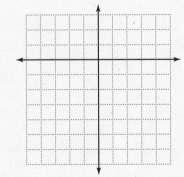

6. A ball is dropped from a height of 450 feet. Ignoring air resistance, the function $h = -16t^2 + 450$, where t is the time in seconds and h is the height in feet, will model the situation. Graph this function. Estimate when the ball will hit the ground.

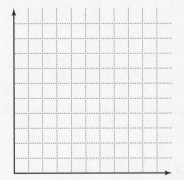

_____

_____

_____

_____

Name _____

7. Graph $y = 2^x$.

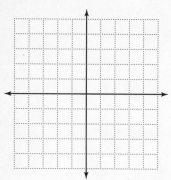

8. Al charges to the next higher half hour for baby-sitting. He charges $3.00 per half hour for baby-sitting the Miller children. Graph how much Al will charge (y) for baby-sitting the Miller children for x half hours.

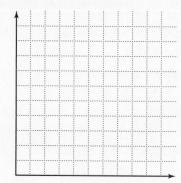

9. Write the polynomial expression
$5x - 2x^4 + 7x^2 - x^3 + 4$ in descending order.

_____

10. Evaluate $2x^4 - 5x^3 + 7x^2 - x + 6$ for $x = -1$.

10. _____

11. The surface area of a sphere is represented by the formula $S = 4\pi r^2$, where S = surface area and r = radius. Find the surface area of a soap bubble that is 4 inches in *diameter*. Use 3.14 for π.

11. _____

In 12–16, simplify the polynomial expression. Write each answer in descending order.

12. $(2a^3 - 7a^2 + 5) + (a^3 + 4a^2 - 2a)$

12. _____

13. $c^2 - 2c - 5$
  $+ \qquad 3c + 6$

13. _____

14. $(4q^2 + 3q + 9) - (3q^2 - 2q + 7)$

14. _____

15. $(3r^3 + 6r^2 - 5r + 7)$
  $- (r^3 + 6r^2 - \ r + 2)$

15. _____

16. $2v^3(7v^3 - 8v^2 + 4v)$

16. _____

17. Multiply $(3.2 \times 10^4) \cdot (5.6 \times 10^3)$. Write your answer in scientific notation.

17. _____

Give the letter of the correct answer. In 1 and 2, use the function machine.

Input ⟩ Divide by 5 and add 8 ⟩ Output

1. Find the output for an input of 20.

   A −4   **B** 12   **C** 92   **D** 108

1. _____

2. Find the input for an output of 35.

   A −5   **B** 15   **C** 135   **D** 215

2. _____

3. Which is a possible rule for the input and output shown in the table?

   A Multiply by 1.5.
   B Multiply by 2 and add 1.5.
   C Add 4.5.
   D Divide by 2 and add 5.5.

3. _____

Input	0	1	2	3	4
Output	1.5	3.5	5.5	7.5	9.5

4. Which graph represents the linear function $y = -2x + 3$?

4. _____

A
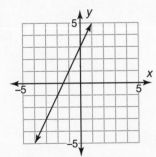

B
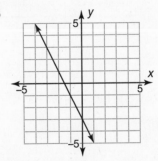

C
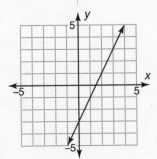

D
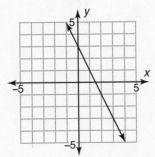

5. A parking fee is advertised as $2 plus $0.50 per hour. Which function represents this relationship?

5. _____

   A $y = 0.5x + 2$ **B** $y = 2x + 0.5$
   C $y = 2 = 0.5x$ **D** $2x + 0.5y = 0$

6. Which graph represents a quadratic function?

6. _____

A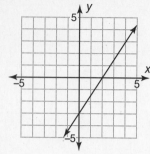

B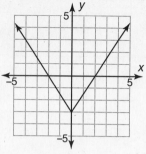

C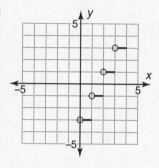

D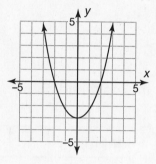

7. Which equation could represent the graph?

7. _____

A $y = x + 1$
B $y = -x^2 + 1$
C $y = x^2 + 1$
D $y = x^2 - 1$

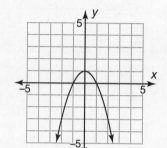

8. Which pair of graphs will *both* open upward?

8. _____

A $y = x^2 - 1$ and $y = x^2 + 2$
B $y = x^2 - 1$ and $y = -x^2 - 2$
C $y = -x^2 + 1$ and $y = x^2 - 2$
D $y = -x^2 + 1$ and $y = -x^2 + 2$

9. Which equation represents an exponential function?

9. _____

A $y = x + 6$ **B** $y = 6$ **C** $y = 6x^2 + 6$ **D** $y = 6^x$

Continued

10. Which graph represents $y = 3^x$?

10. _____

A
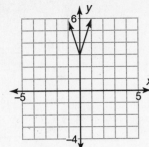

B
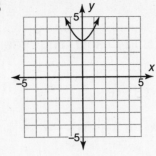

C
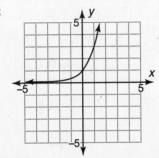

D
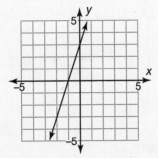

11. Marcy types students' papers to earn extra money. She charges $1 per typed page or any portion thereof. Which graph could represent the amount Marcy charges (y) to type a paper x pages in length?

11. _____

A
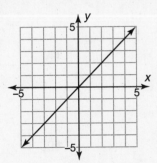

B
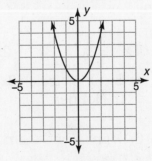

C
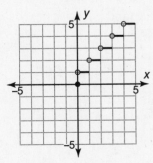

D
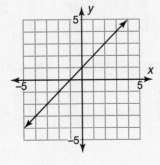

12. Evaluate $x^3 + x^2 - 2x + 4$ for $x = -2$.

12. _____

A -4 **B** 4 **C** 20 **D** 0

Name _____

13. What is the degree of the polynomial $3x - 7x^6 + 2x^2 + 9$?

 A 9   **B** 1   **C** 4   **D** 6

13. _____

14. Which of these polynomials is in descending order?

 A $5 + 3x + x^2$ **B** $8x + 5x^3 + 2 + x$
 C $2x^5 - 3x^3 + x - 1$ **D** Not here

14. _____

15. Simplify, if possible: $3x^4 + 2x^2 - 3 + 5x^4 - x^2 + 7$

 A $8x^4 + x^2 + 4$ **B** $8x^4 + 2x^2 + 4$
 C $8x^8 + x^4 + 4$ **D** Already simplified

15. _____

16. Find the sum: $(3m^2 + m - 8) + (4m^2 - 2m + 6)$

 A $7m^2 + 3m - 2$ **B** $7m^2 + m - 2$
 C $7m^2 - m - 14$ **D** $7m^2 - m - 2$

16. _____

17. Find the total area of the figure.

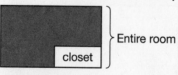

 A $3x^2 + 7x + 8$ **B** $3x^2 + 2x + 4$
 C $3x^2 + 8x + 8$ **D** $3x^2 + 2x - 4$

17. _____

18. What is the additive inverse of $x^4 + 2x^3 - 3x^2 + 2x + 1$?

 A $x^4 + 2x^3 - 3x^2 + 2x - 1$ **B** $-x^4 - 2x^3 + 3x^2 - 2x - 1$
 C $-x^4 - 2x^3 - 3x^2 - 2x - 1$ **D** Not here

18. _____

19. Subtract: $(4m^3 + 2m^2 - m + 6) - (m^3 - m^2 + 2m - 4)$

 A $3m^3 + 3m^2 - 3m + 2$ **B** $3m^3 + m^2 + m + 2$
 C $3m^3 + 3m^2 - 3m + 10$ **D** $3m^3 + m^2 - 3m + 10$

19. _____

20. Find the area of the room *not* taken up by the closet.

> Entire room

closet

Area of entire room
$A = 3x^2 + 5x + 8$
Area of closet
$A = x^2 + x + 1$

 A $4x^2 + 6x + 9$ **B** $2x^2 + 5x + 7$
 C $2x^2 + 4x + 9$ **D** Not here

20. _____

Continued

21. Multiply $7m^6 \cdot 8m$.

   A $56m^6$ **B** $56m^7$ **C** $54m^7$ **D** $54m^6$

21. _____

22. Multiply. Write the answer in scientific notation.
$(5.3 \times 10^6) \cdot (4.8 \times 10^3)$

   A 25.44×10^9 **B** 1.01×10^{10}
   C 2.544×10^{10} **D** 2.544×10^{19}

22. _____

23. Find the area of the rectangle.

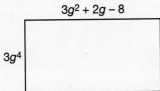

$3g^2 + 2g - 8$

$3g^4$

   A $9g^4 + 6g^3 - 24$ **B** $9g^6 + 6g^5 - 24g^4$
   C $9g^8 + 6g^4 - 24$ **D** Not here

23. _____

24. Denny (y) weighs 2 pounds less than 2.5 times the amount his sister, Vanessa (x), weighs. Denny weighs 118 pounds. How much does Vanessa weigh?

   A 25 lb   **B** $\frac{122}{2.5}$ lb   **C** 48 lb   **D** 303 lb

24. _____

Your school is thinking about starting a soap-making business. The planned selling price for each box of soap is $3.

Option 1

The school can rent the equipment needed to make the soap and the boxes for $200 per month. Materials for a 6-piece box of decorative soap cost $1 per box.

a. Complete the table for the income from the sale of x boxes. Write a rule in linear-equation form that can represent the income from the sales of x boxes.

b. Complete the table to show the cost of making x boxes of soap. Write a rule in linear-equation form that can be used to represent the cost of making x boxes.

Boxes	0	1	2	3	10	100
Income						

Boxes	0	1	2	3	10	100
Cost						

Rule: _____   **Rule:** _____

c. Graph the two sets of data on the same graph. What is the meaning of the point of intersection of the two lines?

Option 2

The school can buy the equipment needed to make the soap and the boxes for $2400. The materials can be bought in bulk at the following prices, based on the specified number of boxes.

Boxes	100	200	300	400	500	600	700	800	900	1000
Cost	100	190	270	340	400	450	490	520	540	550

d. Graph the cost of making x boxes of soap for this option. What kind of function does the *curve* of this graph resemble?

e. Choose which option you will recommend. Write a letter to your principal explaining which option you chose and why you chose that option. Be sure to support your choice by using the data you explored.

Teacher Notes

Concepts and Skills This activity requires students to:

- complete and interpret a table.
- make decisions based on data and real-world situations.
- write a linear equation and graph linear functions.
- compare a curve to a nonlinear function.
- prepare a written summary of results.

Guiding Questions

- Does the cost of renting equipment depend on how much of a product is to be made? Explain.
- Does the cost of the materials needed depend on how much of a product is to be made? Explain.

Answers

a. Income: 0; 3; 6; 9; 30; 300; $y = 3x$

b. Cost: 200; 201; 202; 203; 210; 300; $y = x + 200$

c.

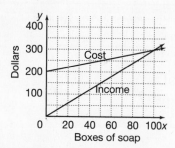

The point of intersection of the two lines is where the break-even occurs (profits = costs).

d.

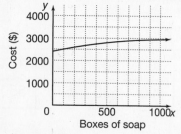

The curve resembles part of a quadratic function.

e. Answers will vary.

Extension

Have students plan a specific shape and size for the soap and box. Then have them design the box.

Evaluation

Level	Standard to be achieved for performance of specified level
4	The student demonstrates a clear understanding of the relationships between ordered pairs and functions. All calculations are accurate and complete. The graphs and letter are thorough, easy to read, and supported by data from this activity.
3	The student demonstrates a fundamental understanding of the relationships between ordered pairs and functions. The student does all necessary calculations but makes some minor errors. The graphs and letter are fairly well organized and easy to read.
2	The student has understanding of the relationship between ordered pairs and functions, but can only apply it with much assistance. There are several major errors in the calculations. The student attempts to prepare a graph and letter, but the results are poor.
1	The student demonstrates little if any understanding of the relationship between ordered pairs and functions. The student may attempt some calculations, but they are incomplete and misdirected. The student may attempt to graph random ordered pairs. The student may copy given information in a letter, but it is poorly organized or unreadable.

1. For the function machine shown, find the input for an output of 8.

Input | Multiply by 3 and add 2 | Output

   A $\frac{10}{3}$ **B** 18   **C** 2   **D** 30

1. _____

2. Write a possible rule for the input and output shown.

Input	0	1	2	3	4
Output	4	5	6	7	8

2. _____

3. When Kira took 1 step, James took 1 step. When Kira took 2 steps, James took 3 steps. When Kira took 3 steps, James took 5 steps. When Kira took 4 steps, James took 7 steps. Write a rule that fits this situation.

3. _____

_____

4. **a.** Complete the table for the rule $y = 2x + 5$.

4a.

Input (x)	−1	0	1	2	3
Output (y)					

   b. Graph the equation $y = 2x + 5$.

b.

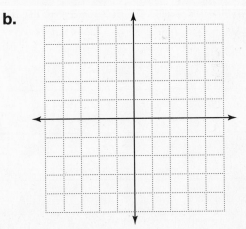

5. Complete the table of values for $y = 3x^2 − 5$.

5.

Input (x)	−3	−2	−1	0	1	2	3
Output (y)							

Continued **237**

6. Which linear
equation represents
the function shown?

A $y = -x - 4$
B $y = -x + 4$
C $y = x + 4$
D $y = x - 4$

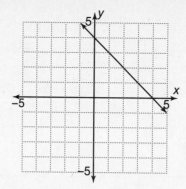

6. _____

7. Which function
describes the graph
shown?

A $y = -x^2 - 4$
B $y = x^2 - 4$
C $y = x^2 + 4$
D $y = -x^2 + 4$

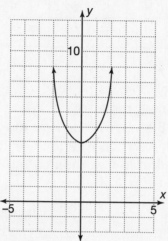

7. _____

8. Graph the set of functions and describe
the similarities and differences within the set.
$y = \frac{1}{2}x^2$, $y = \frac{1}{2}x^2 + 1$, $y = \frac{1}{2}x^2 - 1$

_____

_____

_____

8.

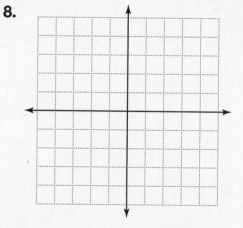

9. Which function
describes the
graph shown?

A $y = 6^x$
B $y = 6x$
C $y = 6x^2$
D $y = $ round x down
to the nearest
multiple of 6

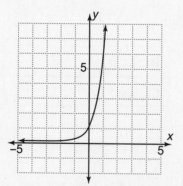

9. _____

Continued

10. Which type of function is $y = x$ rounded to the nearest five?

10. _____

    A Linear   **B** Step   **C** Quadratic   **D** Exponential

11. Which is the best way to describe the polynomial $x^2 + x - 6$?

11. _____

    A Monomial   **B** Binomial
    C Trinomial   **D** Not here

12. Evaluate the polynomial $3m^4 - 2m^3 + m^2 - m + 6$.

12. **a.** _____

    a. For $m = 2$
    b. For $m = -1$

b. _____

13. Simplify, if possible. $7x^3 + 3x^2 - 2x + x^3 - x^2 + x + 4$

_____

14. Give the sum in simplest form.
$(-y^3 + y^4 + 6y - 8) + (2y^4 - 3y^3 + y^2)$

14. _____

    A $y^4 - 4y^3 + y^2 + 6y - 8$
    B $-y^3 + 3y^4 - 3y^3 + y^2 + 6y - 8$
    C $2y^4 + 2y^3 + y^2 + 6y - 8$
    D $3y^4 - 4y^3 + y^2 + 6y - 8$

15. Draw a rectangular area model to show $(x^2 + 2x + 1) + (x^2 + 3)$. Give the final area for your model.

15. _____

16. Which of the following is the additive inverse of $-2x^2 + 7x - 8$?

16. _____

    A $2x^2 - 7x - 8$ **B** $2x^2 - 7x + 8$
    C $-2x^2 + 7x + 8$ **D** $2x^2 + 7x + 8$

17. Find the area of the wood showing on the floor. Write your answer in simplest form.

$A = 2v^3 - v^2 + 3v + 9$

Carpet
$A = v^3 + v^2 - v - 2$

17. _____

_____

        Continued **239**

Name _____

18. Draw a rectangular area model to show
$(x^2 + 4x + 5) - (x + 2)$. Give the final area
for your model.

18. _____

19. Which is the product of $-3x^4 \cdot -3x^4$?

A $9x^8$ **B** $9x^4$ **C** $-6x^8$ **D** $-6x^4$

19. _____

20. Performance Task Design a plan for a flower box.
Each flower should be planted in a 4 in. × 4 in., or
16 in^2, area of space. The height of the inside of the
box should be 6 in.

a. Make a table of values showing how much space (*y*) you
will need for (*x*) flowers. Show at least 5 pairs of values.

b. Look at the sketch of
this flower box. Write
an equation describing
how you will figure the
length (*y*) of one side
of the box.

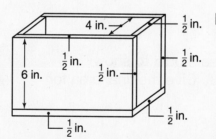

b. _____

c. Figure out how much wood you will need to build any size
flower box that holds *x* flowers. Draw a sketch of the box and
a net for the box. Label each side of the net with how much
wood you will need for a box with one row of flowers (*x*). Put
the dimensions of the wood needed for each side and the
bottom in simplest terms. Let the sides of the box rest
completely on the bottom.

— Computation —

1. For the function machine shown, find the output when the input is -2.

| Input | Multiply by 2 and add 4 | Output |

A 8   **B** 0   **C** -8 **D** Not here

1. _____

2. Add $(2m^3 - 3m^2 + 5m + 1) + (m^3 + 5m^2 - 2m - 6)$.

_____

3. Subtract $(3y^2 - 6y + 7) - (y^2 - 4y + 3)$.

3. _____

4. Multiply $-4t^6 \cdot -4t^6$.

4. _____

5. Multiply $5v^2(-v^2 + 7v - 4)$.

_____

6. Evaluate $5z^3 + 2z^2 - 3z + 1$ for $z = 2$.

6. _____

7. 52 is 40% of what number?

A 20.8   **B** 31.2   **C** 130   **D** 72.8

7. _____

8. Find the volume of a rectangular prism with edge lengths of 12 in., 8 in., and 6 in.

8. _____

9. Solve $\dfrac{x}{6.3} = 7.2$.

9. _____

10. Find the GCF and LCM of 24 and 36.

10. _____

— Concepts —

11. Which is the dependent variable in the equation $y = 8x - 9$?

A 8   **B** -9 **C** x **D** y

11. _____

Name _____

12. What is a possible rule for the input and output shown in the table?

Input	−1	0	1	2	3
Output	−1	1	3	5	7

A $y = x^2 - 2$ **B** $y = 2x - 1$
C $y = 2x + 1$ **D** Not here

12. _____

13. Which equation could represent the graph of the function shown?

A $y = 2x - 2$
B $y = 2^x$
C $y = x^2 - 2$
D $y =$ round x down to the next even number

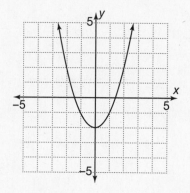

13. _____

14. Which equation could represent the graph of the function shown?

A $y = 4x$
B $y = 4^x$
C $y = 4x^2$
D $y =$ round x to the nearest ten

14. _____

15. When $7x^2 + -2x^2$ are added, which is the correct exponent?

A 2   **B** 2 + 2   **C** 2 × 2   **D** 2 ÷ 2

15. _____

16. What is the additive inverse of $-3m^2 + 6m - 8$?

16. _____

17. How many sides does a hexagon have?

A 5   **B** 6   **C** 7   **D** 9

17. _____

18. Which of these is a polynomial of degree 4?

A $3x^4 + 2x^2 - 8$ **B** $x^3 + 2x^2 + 5x + 1$
C $4x^2 + 4x - 4$ **D** Not here

18. _____

Continued

Name _____

━ Applications ━

19. During a particular exercise, a person can burn 8 calories per minute. Write an expression to show how many calories one could burn in x minutes.

19.

20. A rock is hurled into the air. The function $h = 20t - 2t^2 + 1$ models this situation, where h = height in ft and t = time in sec. What is the height of the rock at $t = 2$?

20.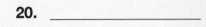

21. For a party, Rose is buying paper plates that come in packages of 25 for $1.25. Make a graph showing how much Rose will spend (y) on paper plates for x people.

21.

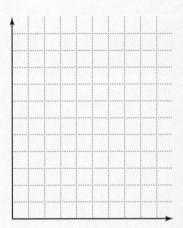

22. A company's income can be represented by the function $y = x^3 + 4x^2 - 2x + 500$. Its costs can be represented by the function $y = 2x^2 + x + 300$. If profit = income − costs, write a function to represent the company's profits.

_____

23. A flowering shrub that normally costs $15 is on sale for 15% off. If the sales tax is 7%, what is the total cost of the flowering shrub? Round up to the nearest cent.

23.

24. Bags of potato chips come 20 to a box. Apples come 8 to a bag. If you want to have the same number of bags of chips as you have of apples in order to pack school lunches, what is the minimum number of boxes of each you would have to buy?

_____

You will need a calculator and/or trigonometric tables.

1. The quadrilaterals are similar. Find the length represented by x.

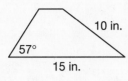

1. _____

2. Are the two quadrilaterals congruent? Explain.

_____

_____

3. State whether the triangles are congruent and the rule that justifies your answer.

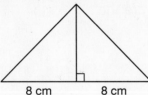

3. _____

_____

_____

4. Find the length represented by x.

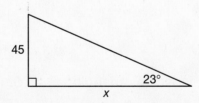

4. _____

5. A tree casts a shadow 80 feet long. A person sitting at the end of the shadow looks up 36° to the top of the tree. How tall is the tree?

5. _____

6. From the top of a vertical cliff, Shimona looks down at a cabin that she knows is 500 ft from the base of the cliff. If her line of sight and the cliff wall form a 30° angle, how tall is the cliff?

6. _____

7. **Test Prep** $\triangle ABC \cong \triangle DEF$. What is the length of $\overline{FE}$ in centimeters?

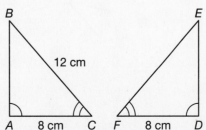

7. _____

A $\sqrt{80}$ **B** 20

C 12   **D** $\frac{16}{3}$

1. What transformation is shown?

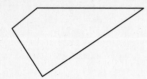

1. _____

2. List the corresponding
vertex coordinates of
the figure reflected
across the *x*-axis.

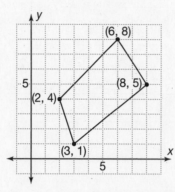

2. _____

  _____

3. A triangle with vertex coordinates (6, 9), (−3, −6),
and (3, 3) is reduced by a factor of $\frac{2}{3}$. What are the
vertex coordinates of the reduction?

3. _____

  _____

4. How many lines of
symmetry does the
figure have?

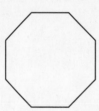

4. _____

5. Draw a tessellation using a right isosceles triangle.

5.

6. Test Prep After how
many degrees of rotation
does the figure rotate
onto itself?

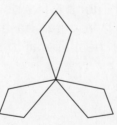

6. _____

A 120°   **B** 180°

C 90°   **D** 270°

© Scott Foresman Addison Wesley 8

You will need a calculator and/or trigonometric tables.

1. Are the figures similar?

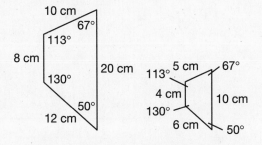

2. In the figure, the pentagons are congruent. Find the values of *x* and *y*.

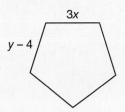 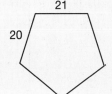

1. _____

2. _____

3. Are the triangles congruent? If so, state the rule that justifies your answer.

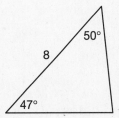

3. _____

   _____

4. Refer to the diagram below. How tall is the building?

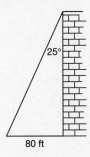

5. In the figure, △*MNQ* is similar to △*MOP*. If $\overline{MN}$ has length 16 cm, find the length of $\overline{MO}$.

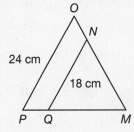

_____   _____

6. If △*ABC* is reflected across the *x*-axis to produce △*A'B'C'*, give the coordinates of:

   a. *A'*   **b.** *B'*   **c.** *C'*

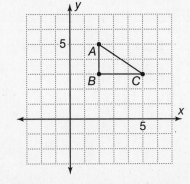

6. **a.** _____

   b. _____

   c. _____

© Scott Foresman Addison Wesley 8

Name _____

7. For a drawing that requires less detail, an architect has taken the drawing of a building and reduced it. Find the scale factor.

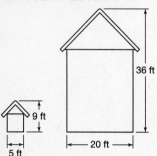

8. The illustration of tiles on a floor shows a tessellation based on what polygon?

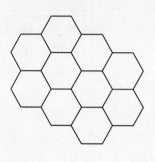

9. Find each trigonometric ratio.

a. sin 24°
b. cos 23°
c. tan 41°

9. a. _____

b. _____

c. _____

10. A figure has vertex coordinates X(0, 0), Y(2, 3), and Z(–1, 4). Find the coordinates of X′, Y′, and Z′ after each transformation.

a. Reflection across the y-axis
b. Rotation 180° clockwise

10. a. _____

_____

_____

11. How many lines of symmetry does this figure have? Draw them.

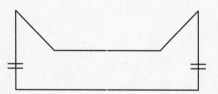

11. _____

You will need a calculator and/or trigonometric tables.

1. Are the rectangles similar?

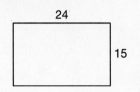

1. _____

2. In the figure, the quadrilaterals are congruent. Find the values of *x* and *y*.

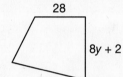

2. _____

3. Are the triangles congruent? If so, state the rule that justifies your answer.

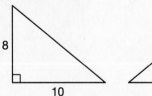
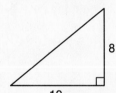

3. _____

_____

4. Refer to the figure. How tall is the tree?

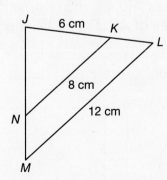

50 ft

4. _____

5. In the figure, △*JKN* is similar to △*JLM*. If $\overline{JK}$ has length 6 cm, find the length of $\overline{JL}$.

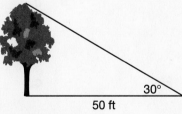

6 cm
K
L
8 cm
12 cm
N
M
J

5. _____

Name _____

6. If △*XYZ* is reflected across the *y*-axis to produce △*X'Y'Z'*, give the coordinates of:

a. *X'*   **b.** *Y'*   **c.** *Z'*

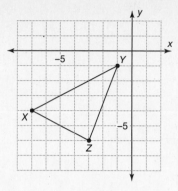

6. a. _____

b. _____

c. _____

7. The car diagram on the left was enlarged. Find the scale factor.

2.5 ft

6 ft

11.25 ft

27 ft

7. _____

8. What polygon(s) is the tessellation based on?

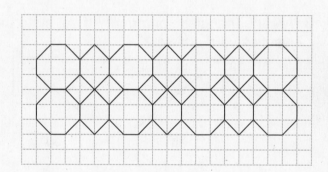

_____

_____

_____

9. Find each trigonometric ratio.

a. sin 52°
b. cos 52°
c. tan 14°

9. a. _____

b. _____

c. _____

10. A figure has vertex coordinates *A*(0, 0), *B*(3, −4), and *C*(−2, 6). Find the coordinates of *A'*, *B'*, and *C'* after each transformation.

a. Reflection across the *x*-axis _____

b. Rotation 180° counterclockwise _____

11. How many lines of symmetry does this figure have? Draw all lines of symmetry.

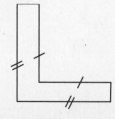

11. _____

You will need a calculator and/or trigonometric tables.

Give the letter of the correct answer.

1. The figures in which pair are similar?

1. _____

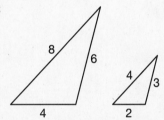

A

5
6

2
3

B

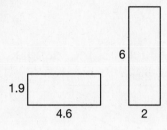

6

1.9
4.6

2

C

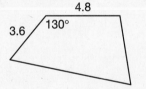

8   6
4

4   3
2

D

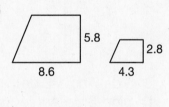

5.8
8.6

2.8
4.3

2. The quadrilaterals below are similar. Find x.

2. _____

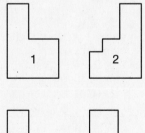

4.8
3.6   130°

x
1.8   130°

A 2.4   **B** 9.6   **C** 130°   **D** Not here

3. Two of the figures are congruent. Which are they?

3. _____

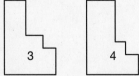

1   2

3   4

A 1 and 2   **B** 2 and 3   **C** 3 and 4   **D** 2 and 4

4. In the figure, the polygons are congruent. Find *x*.

4. _____

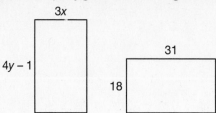

A 8   **B** 5.4   **C** 6   **D** 7.5

5. Which rule justifies the fact that the triangles are congruent?

5. _____

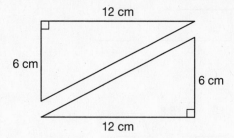

A Side-Side-Side   **B** Side-Angle-Side
C Angle-Side-Angle   **D** Side-Side-Angle

6. If the triangles are congruent, which rule justifies that fact?

6. _____

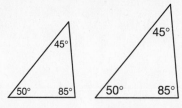

A Angle-Angle-Side   **B** Angle-Side-Angle
C Angle-Angle-Angle   **D** They are not necessarily congruent.

7. Find cosine *B* for the figure shown.

7. _____

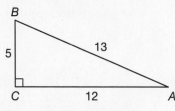

A $\dfrac{5}{13}$ **B** $\dfrac{12}{13}$ **C** $\dfrac{5}{12}$ **D** $\dfrac{13}{5}$

8. Find *x*.

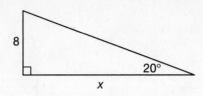

A ≈7.5   **B** ≈0.05   **C** ≈2.9   **D** ≈22

9. Find the length of $\overline{MN}$.

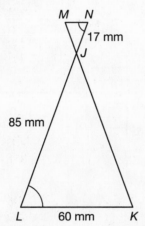

A 20.8 mm   **B** 104 mm   **C** 300 mm   **D** 12 mm

10. △*TVU* is similar to △*TWX*. If $\overline{WT}$ measures 18 cm, what does $\overline{VT}$ measure?

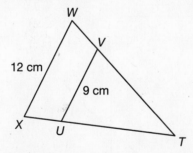

A 27 cm   **B** 13.5 cm   **C** 24 cm   **D** 6 cm

11. Find the coordinates of point *A* after the triangle has been translated right 3 units and down 2 units.

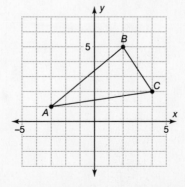

A (0, −1)   **B** (−6, −1)

C (−5, 4)   **D** (−5, 3)

12. Which is the reflection across the *x*-axis of the triangle shown in this figure?

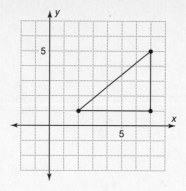

12. _____

A

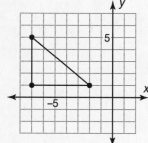

B

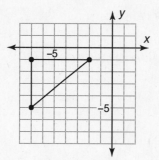

C

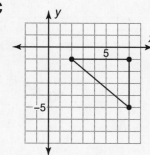

D

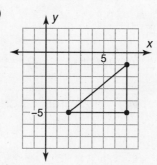

13. Use a scale factor of $\frac{2}{3}$ to dilate △*DKC*. Find the coordinates of point *D*.

A (−4, −3)   **B** (−9, −4.5)

C (4, 2)   **D** Not here

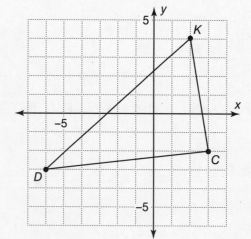

13. _____

Continued

14. Find the scale factor of the enlargement.

14. _____

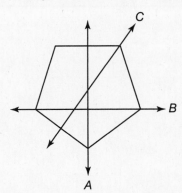

A 180   **B** $\frac{4}{5}$ **C** $\frac{5}{4}$ **D** $\frac{3}{2}$

15. Which line, if any, is *not* a line of symmetry?

15. _____

A *A*   **B** *B*   **C** *C*   **D** All are lines of symmetry.

16. Which rotation will give the same result as a rotation of 180° clockwise?

16. _____

A 180° counterclockwise   **B** 90° clockwise
C 90° counterclockwise   **D** 270° counterclockwise

17. Which of the following regular polygons will *not* tessellate?

17. _____

A Triangle   **B** Octagon   **C** Square   **D** Hexagon

18. Which transformation is *not* displayed by the tessellation shown?

18. _____

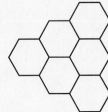

A Translation   **B** Rotation
C Reflection   **D** Not here

Find photographs of objects for which you can research and find actual measurements. Record the height of the object in the photograph and the actual height. Make sure both measurements are in the same unit.

Object	Height in Photo	Actual Height	Scale Factor

a. Find the scale factor for each object you have chosen.

b. Which of the objects in the photographs were smaller than the actual object? Which were larger than the actual object?

c. Are any of the photographs the same size as the object?

d. Explain how you can tell from the scale factor whether the object in a photograph is a reduction, an enlargement, or congruent to the actual object. Draw an example of a rectangle to show each of the three situations.

Teacher Notes

Concepts and Skills This activity requires students to:

- measure objects in a photograph.
- research to find actual measurements.
- convert units of measurement.
- find scale factors for dilations.
- decide if figures are similar or congruent.
- prepare a written summary of results, including sketching examples.

Guiding Questions

- Would a building in a photograph be larger or smaller than the actual building?
- Would an insect in a photograph be larger or smaller than the actual insect?
- For each of these cases, if you compare the size of the photo to the object's actual size, would you expect the scale factor to be less than, equal to, or greater than one?

Answers

a–d. Answers will vary.

Extension

Have students find photographs that include the scale factor used. Have them research the actual measurements as well as compute them using the scale factor given with the photograph. Are the numbers the same?

Evaluation

Level	Standard to be achieved for performance of specified level
4	The student demonstrates a clear understanding of dilations, similarity, and congruence, and a keen sense of the given situation. All calculations are accurate and complete. The explanation and sketched examples are thorough, well organized, and easy to read.
3	The student demonstrates a fundamental understanding of dilations, similarity, and congruence, and a sound grasp of the given situation. The student does all necessary calculations, but may make some minor errors. The explanation and sketched examples are fairly well organized, but reflect minor computational errors.
2	The student has some understanding of dilations, similarity, and congruence, but can apply them only to the given situation with a great deal of assistance. There are several major errors or omissions in the student's calculations. The student attempts to write an explanation and sketch the examples, but the results are jumbled and incomplete.
1	The student demonstrates little if any understanding of dilations, similarity, and congruence and, even when prompted, cannot apply them to the given situation. The student attempts some calculations, but they are superfluous or irrelevant. The student may prepare an explanation simply by copying given information, and there is no meaningful attempt to sketch examples.

You will need a calculator and/or trigonometric tables.

1. Are the rectangles similar?

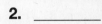
18.6

9.4

9.3
4.2

1. _____

2. The Johnsons and the Davises have similarly shaped triangular flower gardens. The figure shows some of the gardens' dimensions. Find *y*.

2. _____

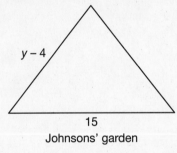

y − 4

15
Johnsons' garden

8

10
Davises' garden

A 12   **B** 16   **C** 24   **D** 28

3. In the figure, the polygons are congruent. Find *x*.

3. _____

22
18

3x + 1
18

A $\frac{23}{3}$ **B** $\frac{17}{3}$ **C** 7   **D** $\frac{19}{3}$

4. What rule justifies the fact that the triangles are congruent?

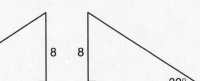
8   8
32°   32°

5. Maxine is experimenting with throwing a softball at different angles. She finds that she can throw it the farthest if she lets go of it so that its initial angle with respect to the ground is that shown by ∠A in the figure.

5. a. _____

b. _____

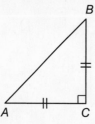

a. What is the value of ∠A?
b. What is the sine of ∠A?

6. Find the length represented by x.

6. _____

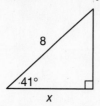

7. △ABC ~ △ADE. Find the length of $\overline{AD}$ if the length of $\overline{AB}$ is 6.

7. _____

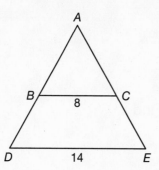

Continued

Name _____

8. Find the coordinates of point *A* after the triangle has been translated up 2 units and left 4 units.

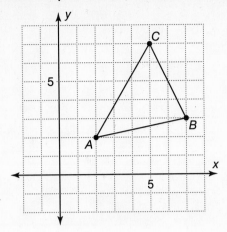

   A (4, −2)   **B** (2, 4)   **C** (6, 0)   **D** (−2, 4)

9. A scale factor of 2 is used to dilate a triangle. What are the new coordinates of point *A*(2, −4)?

   A (1, −2)   **B** (4, −8)   **C** (4, −4)   **D** (4, −2)

9. _____

10. Draw all lines of symmetry in the figure.

10.

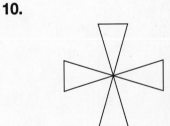

11. Performance Task Draw a tessellation using two different shapes.

11.

You will need a calculator and/or trigonometric tables.

— Computation —

1. The two figures are similar. Find x.

$2x - 4$ 9

20   10

A 11   **B** 13   **C** 6.5   **D** 4.25

1. _____

2. Jessie is devising a computer program. One of the instructions in the program is the rule "subtract 8." Find the output value that this part of the program will give for an input value of 15.

2. _____

3. In the figure, the polygons are congruent. Find the value of x.

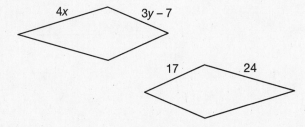

$4x$ $3y - 7$

17   24

3. _____

4. Write 2.36 as a mixed number in lowest terms.

A $2\frac{36}{100}$ **B** $\frac{59}{25}$ **C** $2\frac{9}{25}$ **D** $\frac{236}{100}$

4. _____

5. Multiply 2.8×3.46.

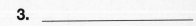
5. _____

6. Add $(2x^3 - 7x^2 + 5x - 1) + (3x^2 - 2x + 4)$.

— Concepts —

7. What rule tells you that the two triangles are congruent?

7. _____

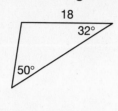

A Side-Side-Side   **B** Angle-Side-Angle
C Side-Angle-Side   **D** Angle-Angle-Side

8. Two alarms have been set to go off at different intervals. Alarm A rings every 18 hours. Alarm B rings every 24 hours. If they both are started running at the same time, after how many hours will they both ring at the same time?

8. _____

A 2   **B** 6   **C** 3   **D** 72

9. Find x.

9. _____

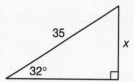

10. Find the length of $\overline{DE}$.

10. _____

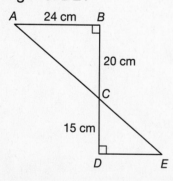

11. Find the coordinates of point $A(-2, 5)$ after it has been translated down 2 units and right 5 units.

11. _____

A $(-4, 10)$ **B** $(7, 10)$ **C** $(0, 0)$ **D** $(3, 3)$

12. A scale factor of 5 is used to dilate square $ABCD$. Find the coordinates of $A(4, 3)$ after the dilation.

12. _____

Continued

13. Which rotation will give the same results as a rotation 90° counterclockwise?

13. _____

A 90° clockwise   **B** 180° clockwise
C 270° clockwise   **D** 360° clockwise

— Applications —

14. Refer to the figure. How tall is the mountain?

14. _____

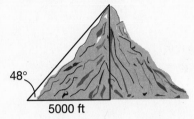

48°

5000 ft

15. Find the length of $\overline{DA}$.

15. _____

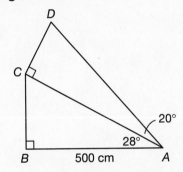

D

C

20°

28°

B   500 cm   A

16. Draw a tessellation by using 180° rotations around the midpoints of the sides.

16.

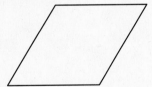

Evaluate the following.

1. $(11 - 6)!$

1. _____

2. $(4!)(3!)$

2. _____

3. $\dfrac{11!}{8!}$

3. _____

4. $\dfrac{8!}{3!(8 - 3)!}$

4. _____

5. Make a tree diagram showing the possible results of spinning the spinner on the left followed by spinning the spinner on the right.

5.

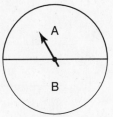

Spinner 1

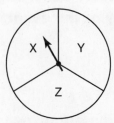

Spinner 2

6. In how many ways can the letters in the word STOVE be arranged if no letter is used twice? The letters do not have to form a word.

6. _____

In 7 and 8, assume that a school's cafeteria can make seven different kinds of soup and serves one kind of soup each day.

7. The cafeteria wants to serve a different soup on each of the first 7 school days of the year. In how many different ways can they arrange the daily soup choices?

7. _____

8. In how many different ways can they arrange the daily soup choices in any 5-day school week?

8. _____

9. At a salad bar, six possible ingredients are available to make a tossed salad. How many combinations of three different ingredients can be used?

9. _____

10. **Test Prep** There are 12 students in a class. In how many ways can a group of 5 students be selected from the class to serve on a prom committee?

10. _____

 A 12×5 **B** $12! \times 5!$ **C** $\dfrac{12!}{5! \times 7!}$ **D** $\dfrac{12!}{5!}$

In 1–9, use the spinner shown.

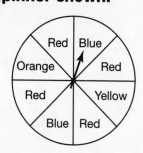

1. _____
   _____

1. Identify the sample space.

In 2 and 3, find the number of outcomes satisfying each event as well as the probability of the event.

2. Spinning orange

2. _____

3. Spinning blue

3. _____

In 4 and 5, find the probabilities indicated for two successive spins.

4. P(red then blue)

4. _____

5. P(orange then yellow)

5. _____

6. If you know the spinner did not land on red, what is the probability that it landed on blue?

6. _____

7. If the first of 2 spins lands on blue, what is the probability that the third spin will land on blue?

7. _____

8. Suppose the first spin of the spinner lands on red, and the second spin lands on blue. Are those *independent* or *dependent* events?

8. _____

9. Suppose that, after 100 spins, red has come up 55 times. What is the experimental probability of spinning red?

9. _____

10. **Test Prep** A box contains 3 red pencils and 2 blue pencils. Two pencils are taken at random from the box in succession, without replacement. If the first pencil is red, what is the probability that the second pencil is also red?

10. _____

    A $\frac{3}{5}$ **B** $\frac{2}{3}$ **C** $\frac{1}{2}$ **D** $\frac{1}{4}$

1. To upgrade his computer system with a new monitor, printer, and keyboard, Jon has a choice of a 256-color or monochrome (single-color) monitor; a choice of a dot-matrix, laser, or bubble-jet printer; and a choice of a standard, ergonomic, or extended keyboard. How many different ways can Jon upgrade his computer system?

1. _____

In 2–4, evaluate each expression.

2. 6!

2. _____

3. 8(7!)

3. _____

4. $\dfrac{8!}{4!(8-4)!}$

4. _____

5. How many ways can the letters of the word COMPUTE be arranged?

5. _____

6. After upgrading her computer system, Amy purchased 7 computer games. How many different ways can she arrange 4 games from among the 7?

6. _____

7. The computer store has 9 service technicians. Three service technicians work each shift. How many different 3-technician groups can be formed?

7. _____

8. A particular commercial appears on a half-hour television program. What is the probability that the commercial will be shown during the first 6 minutes of the program? Give your answer as a fraction, a decimal, and a percent.

8. _____

9. A computer disk is chosen at random from among 5 disks of a word-processing program, 4 disks of a drawing program, and 7 disks of a telecommunications program. How many outcomes are in the sample space? What is the probability that the chosen disk is a telecommunications program?

9. _____

© Scott Foresman Addison Wesley 8

Name _____

10. A family recorded the number of programs they watched on each of 5 different channels. Their results are shown. What is their experimental probability of watching a program on channel 56?

10.

Channel	5	11	56	73	116
Number of programs	12	15	8	10	5

11. At the computer store, games are displayed on the 3 sides of the display rack shown below. Find the probability that a game is displayed on the 20-inch side.

11. _____

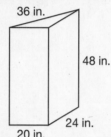

36 in.

48 in.

24 in.

20 in.

12. Find the probability that a game in Item 11 is *not* displayed on the 24-inch side.

12. _____

In 13–16, a box contains 20 computer programs for display. There are 6 word-processing programs, 5 drawing programs, and 9 communications programs.

13. A program is chosen at random. The program is returned to the box, the box of programs is "mixed," and a second program is chosen. Find the probability that both programs are drawing programs.

13. _____

14. Are the two events in Item 13 *independent* or *dependent* events?

14. _____

15. Now suppose that the first program is not replaced before selecting the second program. Then what is the probability that both programs are drawing programs?

15. _____

16. Are the two events in Item 15 *independent* or *dependent*?

16. _____

1. A video-rental store has a comedy-action-horror weekend special. You can select 3 videos for $5 if you select one of 5 comedies, one of 6 action movies, and one of 4 horror movies. In how many ways can the weekend-special movies be selected?

1. _____

In 2–4, evaluate each expression.

2. 4!

2. _____

3. $\dfrac{9!}{6!}$

3. _____

4. $\dfrac{5!}{3!(5-3)!}$

4. _____

5. In how many ways can you arrange the letters of the word TABLE?

5. _____

6. The video store has 9 "high-seas-adventure" movies. How many different ways can you arrange an "all-day show" of 4 of them?

6. _____

7. The video store offers 12 different kinds of "good-deal" coupons. How many different ways can you select 4 of the coupons?

7. _____

8. The video store has a list of 250 comedies, but 40 of them are already rented and not available. If you choose a comedy from the complete list, what is the probability that the tape is available? Give your answer as a fraction, a decimal, and a percent.

8. _____

9. A tool is selected at random from a box containing 8 screwdrivers, 4 hammers, and 7 wrenches. How many outcomes are in the sample space? What is the probability that the chosen tool is a hammer?

9. _____

10. A video store recorded the categories for 75 rental videos. Their results are shown. What is the experimental probability of renting an adventure video?

10. _____

Category	Comedy	Horror	Adventure	Animation	Documentary	Musical
Number of videos rented	17	18	20	12	3	5

11. The video store has a display wall for new titles, as shown in the figure below. Find the probability that a new title is displayed in Section D.

11. _____

2 ft	5 ft	4 ft	3 ft	
Section A	Section B	Section C	Section D	3 ft

12. Find the probability that the title in Item 11 is in Section B or Section C.

12. _____

In 13–16, a box contains 30 videotapes: 15 comedies, 10 action adventures, and 5 horror movies.

13. A tape is chosen at random. The tape is returned to the box, the tapes in the box are "mixed," and a second tape is chosen. Find the probability that both tapes are horror movies.

13. _____

14. Are the two events in Item 13 *independent* or *dependent* events?

14. _____

15. Suppose that the first tape is not replaced before selecting the second tape. Then find the probability that both tapes are horror movies.

15. _____

16. In Item 15, are the events *independent* or *dependent*?

16. _____

Give the letter of the correct answer.

1. To form a trio from the school band, the teacher needs to select one of the 3 drummers, one of the 6 tuba players, and one of the 4 flute players. In how many ways can a trio be selected?

   A 13   **B** 72   **C** 364   **D** 36

1. _____

2. At a banquet, diners had a choice of soup or salad; a choice of beef, fish, or chicken; a choice of cake, ice cream, or fruit; and a choice of tea, coffee, milk, or soft drink. In how many different ways could dinner be selected?

   A 13   **B** 16   **C** 22   **D** Not here

2. _____

In 3–5, evaluate each expression.

3. 8!

   A 40,320   **B** 5,040   **C** 56   **D** 36

3. _____

4. $\frac{5!}{3!}$

   A 120   **B** 40   **C** 20   **D** 2

4. _____

5. $\frac{9!}{5!(9-5)!}$

   A 362,880   **B** 15,120   **C** 3,024   **D** 126

5. _____

6. How many ways are there to arrange the letters in the word PENCIL?

   A 720   **B** 150   **C** 120   **D** 21

6. _____

7. Mr. MacDonald, the band teacher, is going to listen to each of the band's 8 flute players, one at a time. Today there is time to listen to 3 of the players. How many different ways can the teacher arrange the 3 players?

   A 3   **B** 8   **C** 24   **D** 336

7. _____

8. On the following day, Mr. MacDonald has time to listen to 2 of the remaining 5 flute players. Which expression represents the number of different ways the teacher can arrange 2 of the remaining flute players?

   A $\frac{5!}{3!}$ **B** $\frac{8!}{2!\,5!}$ **C** 5!   **D** 8!

8. _____

© Scott Foresman Addison Wesley 8

Name _____

In 9–12, there are 9 seniors in the band.

9. How many ways can Mr. MacDonald select a quartet (4 players) of seniors?

   A 362,880   **B** 15,120   **C** 3,024   **D** 126

9. _____

10. How many ways can he select a quintet (5 players) of seniors?

   A 362,880   **B** 15,120   **C** 3,024   **D** 126

10. _____

In 11 and 12, there are 12 juniors in the band.

11. Which expression tells the number of ways that Mr. MacDonald can select a duo (2 players) of juniors?

   A 12!   **B** 66   **C** $\frac{12!}{10!}$ **D** 12×11

11. _____

12. How many ways can he select a duo of 1 senior and 1 junior?

   A 144   **B** 81   **C** 108   **D** 54

12. _____

In 13–17, the school band has practiced 15 marches, 10 popular songs, and 5 college songs. One of those musical numbers is selected at random.

13. How many outcomes are in the sample space?

   A 3   **B** 3!   **C** 30   **D** 30!

13. _____

14. What is the probability that the selected number will be a march?

   A $\frac{1}{30}$ **B** $\frac{1}{15}$ **C** $\frac{1}{2}$ **D** $\frac{1}{3}$

14. _____

15. What is the probability that the selected number is *not* a college song?

   A $\frac{1}{2}$ **B** $\frac{5}{6}$ **C** $\frac{1}{5}$ **D** $\frac{1}{6}$

15. _____

16. The students are told that the next song will *not* be a march. What is the probability that it will be a college song?

   A $\frac{1}{10}$ **B** $\frac{1}{15}$ **C** $\frac{1}{3}$ **D** $\frac{2}{3}$

16. _____

17. The students never play the same song twice in a row. What is the probability that they play two marches in a row?

   A $\frac{7}{29}$ **B** $\frac{1}{9}$ **C** $\frac{1}{10}$ **D** $\frac{1}{225}$

17. _____

Name _____

**In 18 and 19, a dish is selected at random from a
shelf containing 2 dinner plates, 1 bread plate, and
3 dessert plates.**

18. What is the sample space?   18. _____

    A Dinner plates, bread plates, dessert plates
    B Dinner plate, dinner plate, bread plate, dessert plate,
       dessert plate, dessert plate
    C Plates
    D Not here

19. What is the probability that the selected dish is a dessert plate?   19. _____

    A $\frac{1}{3}$ **B** $\frac{1}{36}$ **C** $\frac{1}{2}$ **D** $\frac{1}{4}$

**In 20 and 21, a restaurant recorded the sizes of
45 groups that came to eat. The results are shown.**

Size of group	1	2	3	4	5	6	7	8
Number of groups	6	8	10	12	3	2	0	4

20. Give the experimental probability that the size of a group was   20. _____
    5 people.

    A $\frac{1}{9}$ **B** $\frac{3}{5}$ **C** $\frac{1}{5}$ **D** $\frac{1}{15}$

21. Give the experimental probability that the size of a group was   21. _____
    7 people.

    A $\frac{1}{7}$ **B** $\frac{7}{45}$ **C** 0   **D** Not here

22. The tables in a banquet room are arranged as shown in the   22. _____
    figure. Each table seats 8 diners. Diners are seated at random.
    What is the probability that a person will be seated at one of
    the three tables that are at the bottom?

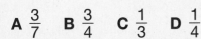

    A $\frac{3}{7}$ **B** $\frac{3}{4}$ **C** $\frac{1}{3}$ **D** $\frac{1}{4}$

23. Find the probability that the person in Item 22 is seated at a table that does not touch another table.

23. _____

   A $\frac{1}{2}$ **B** $\frac{2}{7}$ **C** $\frac{1}{7}$ **D** $\frac{1}{6}$

In 24 and 25, the school band has been preparing 5 different songs: Song A is 8 minutes long; Song B is 8 minutes long; Song C is 6 minutes long; Song D is 6 minutes long; Song E is 8 minutes long.

24. If the students know that the next song they will play is 8 minutes long, what is the probability that song E is the next song?

24. _____

   A $\frac{1}{5}$ **B** $\frac{1}{3}$ **C** $\frac{3}{5}$ **D** $\frac{2}{3}$

25. If the students know that the next song will be shorter than 8 minutes, what is the probability that song C is the next song?

25. _____

   A $\frac{1}{2}$ **B** 0   **C** $\frac{2}{3}$ **D** $\frac{1}{5}$

In 26–29, a silverware drawer contains 40 utensils: 15 knives, 12 spoons, and 13 forks.

26. A utensil is chosen at random, then returned to the drawer. Another person selects a utensil at random from the drawer. Find the probability that both utensils are spoons.

26. _____

   A $\frac{1}{3}$ **B** $\frac{1}{12}$ **C** $\frac{3}{10}$ **D** $\frac{9}{100}$

27. Are the two events in Item 26 independent or dependent events?

27. _____

   A Independent   **B** Dependent   **C** Neither   **D** Both

28. What would your answer to Item 26 be if the first utensil were not replaced in the drawer?

28. _____

   A $\frac{9}{100}$ **B** $\frac{3}{10}$ **C** $\frac{11}{130}$ **D** Not here

29. How would you then describe the two events in Item 28?

29. _____

   A Independent   **B** Dependent   **C** Neither   **D** Both

Date _____   Score _____

Suppose your school has a volleyball league with 4 teams. Here are their records in the middle of the season.

Team	A	B	C	D
Wins	9	7	8	12
Losses	9	11	10	6

a. Based on the teams' win-loss records, what is the probability that Team D will win both of its next two games?

b. Do you think Team D's chances of winning are affected by which team(s) it plays? Explain your answer.

You are planning a tournament in which each of the four teams will play two matches against each of the other teams.

c. How many matches will be necessary for the tournament? Make a list of all the matches.

d. There are two volleyball courts, so two matches can take place at the same time. Each match takes less than half an hour. Copy the chart below and use it to describe a plan for the matches in the tournament.

	Court 1	Court 2
Time	**Teams**	**Teams**
10:00 A.M.–10:30 A.M		
10:30 A.M.–11:00 A.M.		

Teacher Notes

Concepts and Skills This activity requires students to:
- read information from a table.
- record information in a table.
- calculate experimental probability.
- calculate the probability of a compound event.
- use the ideas of independent and dependent events.
- use the Counting Principle to determine all the possible outcomes of an event.

Guiding Questions
- How many games did each team play in all?
- How can you find the experimental probability that a team will win its next game?

Answers
a. $\frac{4}{9}$

b. Answers may vary. For example, based on the records so far, Team D seems to be the best, so it may have the best chance of winning its next game, regardless of its opponent. However, it may do better against some teams than others. It is likely that Team A may present more of a challenge than Team B would, but exceptions to this rule are fairly common in sports.

c. 12 matches: AB, AB, AC, AC, AD, AD, BC, BC, BD, BD, CD, CD

d. Answers may vary. Sample: at half-hour intervals
Court 1: AB, AC, AD, CD, BD, BC
Court 2: CD, BD, BC, AB, AC, AD

Extension
Ask students if they can come up with win-loss records for pairs of teams playing against each other that would result in the overall records shown at the beginning of Test Form D.

Sample answer:
A won 4, B won 2 of their matches.
A won 3, C won 3 of their matches.
A won 2, D won 4 of their matches.
B won 2, C won 4 of their matches.
B won 3, D won 3 of their matches.
C won 1, D won 5 of their matches.

Evaluation

Level	Standard to be achieved for performance of specified level
4	The student demonstrates a clear understanding of the Counting Principle and probability. The student is able to calculate the probability for Team D's next games, and provides clear reasons as to whether or not their chances depend on other teams. The list of matches is complete and organized.
3	The student demonstrates a sufficient understanding of the Counting Principle and probability. The student is able to calculate the probability for Team D's next games, but does not have clearly stated reasons as to whether their chances depend on other teams. The list of matches is complete but not well organized.
2	The student has some difficulty with either the Counting Principle or probability. The calculation of Team D's chances may not be accurate; the list of matches may not be complete; the schedule for the matches is disorganized.
1	The student demonstrates little if any understanding of either the Counting Principle or probability. They do not use the given information to find the total number of matches played and they do not provide a complete list of the matches for the tournament.

Name _____

Date _____ Score _____

1. Each member of a family on a vacation has to choose   1. _____
   1 of 3 tours for a morning activity, 1 of 4 games
   for an afternoon activity, and 1 of 2 movies as an
   evening activity. How many ways can each person
   choose the three activities?

2. A family member has already chosen her   2.
   morning activity. Make a tree diagram that
   shows her remaining choices.

In 3–5, evaluate each expression.

3. $\dfrac{9!}{7!(9-7)!}$ 3. _____

4. $\dfrac{10!}{3!(10-3)!}$ 4. _____

5. $\dfrac{6!}{4!(6-4)!}$ 5. _____

6. The family in Items 1 and 2 has 6 pieces of luggage   6. _____
   and is going to take 4 of the pieces on their vacation.
   Which expression gives the number of different
   ways they can choose the 4 pieces of luggage?

   A 6!   **B** 4!   **C** $\dfrac{6!}{4!\,2!}$ **D** Not here

7. There are 4 people in the family, and each person will   7. _____
   carry one piece of luggage. Which expression gives the
   number of different ways that the family members can carry
   the pieces of luggage? (Hint: Here, order matters, because
   it may be different, say, for the smallest person to carry the
   heaviest piece of luggage and the largest person to carry
   the lightest piece rather than vice versa, and so forth.)

   A 4   **B** $\dfrac{4!}{4!}$ **C** $4! \times 3! \times 1!$ **D** 4!

8. The maps and guidebooks are in one of the 4 pieces   8. _____
   of luggage. One piece of luggage is selected at
   random. What is the probability that the maps and
   guidebooks are in that piece of luggage?

   A $\dfrac{1}{2}$ **B** $\dfrac{1}{4}$ **C** 0   **D** Not here

9. The family is staying at a hotel with 8 floors. There are no guest rooms on the first two floors. What is the probability that the family's room is *not* on the top floor?

  A $\frac{5}{6}$ B $\frac{1}{8}$ C $\frac{7}{8}$ D $\frac{1}{6}$

9. _____

The hotel keeps a record of the number of guests on each floor. In 10 and 11, use their records for a particular day given in the table below.

Floor	3	4	5	6
Number of guests	35	25	18	42

10. A guest asks for a room key. What is the experimental probability that the key is for a room on the 4th floor?

10. _____

11. Another guest asks for a room key. If you know that the guest's room is not on the top two floors, what is the probability that the room is on the 4th floor?

11. _____

In the evening, the hotel staff leave mints in each guest room. In 12–14, the number of mints is a random number that could be 2, 3, or 4.

12. What is the probability that each of three particular rooms gets 2 mints?

12. _____

13. Suppose one room gets 3 mints. What is the probability that the next room gets either 2 or 4 mints?

13. _____

14. Are the two events in Item 13 *independent* or *dependent* events?

14. _____

15. **Performance Task** A hotel worker leaving mints has exactly 6 mints left for 3 rooms. List all the possible ways to distribute the mints if each room gets at least one mint. What is the total number of ways? Suppose that order is important.

_____

_____

_____

— Computation —

In 1–4, evaluate each expression.

1. $4! \times 3!$

1. _____

2. $\dfrac{6!}{3!}$

2. _____

3. $\dfrac{7!}{5!\,2!}$

3. _____

4. $(9 - 3)!$

4. _____

5. A sports center offers a selection of four activities each hour, and each hour's selections are unique. Use the Counting Principle to determine how many different ways a person who stays at the sports center for three hours can select activities.

5. _____

6. Draw a tree diagram to show all possible outcomes when a coin is tossed and then the spinner below is spun.

6.

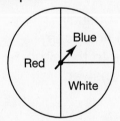

In 7–9, solve each inequality.

7. $3x + 5 \le 23$

7. _____

8. $\left(\dfrac{1}{4}\right)x - 3 < 5$

8. _____

9. $7x \ge -3$

9. _____

In 10–12, find the volume of each box with the given dimensions.

10. 5 in. by 8 in. by 12 in.

10. _____

11. 2.1 m by 3.2 m by 0.8 m

11. _____

12. 17 cm by 12 cm by 12 cm

12. _____

13. Find the dimensions and volume of the box in Item 12 after a dilation with scale factor 1.5.

_____

14. Find the volume of a cylinder with radius 7 cm and height 10 cm. Use 3.14 for π.

14. _____

15. Find the volume of a cone with diameter 2 m and height 0.75 m. Use 3.14 for π.

15. _____

▬ Concepts ▬

16. Annette has 3 uncles, Robert has 7 uncles, and Pedro has 5 uncles. If all their uncles are brought together in the same room, how many different personal introductions of one uncle to another would be required for all the uncles to be introduced to each other? Show the formula indicating how you got your answer.

_____

17. The Ace Cab Company has 15 cabs available. It usually likes to keep six of these cabs at the airport. In how many combinations can Ace send a group of six cabs to the airport? Show the formula indicating how you got your answer.

_____

18. In a softball game, the pitcher, Diane, throws a strike over home plate. The batter, Susan, hits it for a base hit. Are these events *independent* or *dependent*?

18. _____

19. In a softball game, Susan steals second base. Two plays later, the left fielder, Jerome, is injured. Are these events *independent* or *dependent*?

19. _____

20. A person has a choice of 4 flights leaving home and a choice of 6 flights returning. How many different ways can the person make the round trip?

A 2   **B** 10   **C** 24   **D** Not here

20. _____

Continued

21. The Brown Taxi Company has 3 taxis and 3 drivers. In how many ways can they assign their drivers to their taxis?

A 3   **B** 9   **C** 1   **D** Not here

21. _____

22. In Item 21, what is the probability that the most experienced driver drives the newest taxi?

A $\frac{1}{9}$ **B** $\frac{1}{3}$ **C** $\frac{2}{3}$ **D** Not here

22. _____

23. Of the 5 starting players on the basketball team, the coach wants to pick a group of 2 to serve as co-captains. Which expression gives the number of ways the coach can do this?

A $\frac{5!}{3!\,2!}$ **B** $\frac{5!}{2!}$ **C** 3!   **D** Not here

23. _____

In 24–26, a coin is tossed 3 times.

24. What is the probability that all 3 tosses result in heads?

24. _____

25. What is the probability that no toss results in heads?

25. _____

26. Suppose event *a* is "the first toss is heads" and event *b* is "the second toss is heads." Are these independent or dependent events?

26. _____

27. If you know that a person was born in a month whose name does not contain an R, what is the probability that the person was born in a month whose name begins with J?

27. _____

28. Is a triangle with sides 3 in., 4 in., and 5 in. similar to a triangle with sides 9 cm, 12 cm, and 15 cm?

28. _____

— Applications —

29. In her wallet, Gena has 3 ten-dollar bills, 4 five-dollar bills, and 4 one-dollar bills. How many different ways can she use 3 bills to come up with an amount of exactly $16?

29. _____

30. Gena reaches into her wallet and takes out 2 bills at random. What is the probability that both are five-dollar bills?

30. _____

31. Suppose both bills in Item 30 were five-dollar bills. If Gena reaches into the wallet and takes out another bill, what is the probability that it is a one-dollar bill?

31. _____

Gena works 6 hours, 8 hours, 14 hours, or 16 hours each week. She has kept a record of the numbers of weeks that she has worked each number of hours. In 32 and 33, use Gena's record in the table below.

Number of hours worked	6	8	14	16
Number of weeks	10	15	9	6

32. What is the experimental probability that Gena worked 6 hours in a given week?

32. _____

33. What is the experimental probability that Gena worked more than 10 hours in a week?

33. _____

You roll a number cube twice.

34. What is the probability that you will get a 3 on the first roll?

34. _____

35. If you get a 3 on the first roll, what is the probability that you will get an even number on the second roll?

35. _____

Name _____

Date _____ Score _____

Give the letter of the correct answer.

1. What is the mean of the data in this stem-and-leaf diagram?

Stem	Leaf
6	0 2 4 5 6
5	2 2 3 3 4 5
4	1 2 5 8 8

A 53   **B** 53.5   **C** 53.75   **D** Not here

1. _____

2. Which graph would be most appropriate to compare the salaries of college graduates with students who did not graduate from college over a span of 10 years?

A Line graph   **B** Bar graph
C Double line graph   **D** Double bar graph

2. _____

3. Mr. Wagner wants to find out how his neighbors would feel about having a swimming pool built in their neighborhood. Which sample is most representative?

A All the people mowing lawns on Saturday
B Every third house
C 25 neighbors at random
D Every other house

3. _____

4. Which of the following is correct?

A $-17 = -|-17|$ **B** $-3 > 0$
C $-10°F > -1°F$ **D** $-|-1| > 1$

4. _____

5. Marc lost $800 on 200 shares of stock. How much did each share of stock change in value?

A $4   **B** $-$4   **C** $-$40   **D** $400

5. _____

6. Which expression represents 2,457,000 in scientific notation?

A 2457×10^3 **B** 2.457×10^6
C 245.7×10^4 **D** 24.57×10^5

6. _____

7. Solve $x + 3.25 = 16.75$.

A 5.15   **B** 20   **C** 13.5   **D** Not here

7. _____

© Scott Foresman Addison Wesley 8

8. About $\frac{1}{2}$ of the students in a school purchase lunch in the cafeteria at least twice a week. Last week, 350 students purchased lunch at least twice a week. What is the best estimate of the number of students in the school?

   A 700   **B** 800   **C** 750   **D** 650

8. _____

9. $x \geq 5$ is a solution of which inequality?

   A $x + 2 \geq 8$ **B** $x + 3 \geq 8$
   C $x + 2 \leq 7$ **D** $15 - x \leq 8$

9. _____

10. A line having which slope would rise upward from left to right?

   A $-\frac{1}{2}$ **B** 4   **C** -2 **D** 0

10. _____

11. Which line is *not* parallel to the others?

   A $x - 2 = y$ **B** $x = y$
   C $x + 2 = y$ **D** $x = -y$

11. _____

12. Solve the proportion $\frac{5}{20} = \frac{12}{m}$.

   A $m = 3$ **B** $m = 48$ **C** $m = 1200$ **D** $m = 8.3$

12. _____

13. Chad pays $0.25 per week for club dues. What would his yearly payment be?

   A $13   **B** $3   **C** $12   **D** Not here

13. _____

14. If a 16-inch tall model were built to the scale $\frac{1}{3}$ in. = 1 ft, how tall would the actual figure be?

   A 48 in.   **B** 4.8 ft   **C** 48 ft   **D** 16 ft

14. _____

15. Which shows 7.75 expressed as a percent?

   A 7750%   **B** 7.75%   **C** 77.5%   **D** 775%

15. _____

16. Cousins Electronics buys a certain TV for $1000 and sells it for $1950. What is the percent increase?

   A 95%   **B** 9.5%   **C** 950%   **D** 0.95%

16. _____

Continued

17. Find the GCF for the numbers 90, 108, 630.　　　　　　　**17.** _____

　　A 36　**B** 108　**C** 54　**D** 18

18. Find the LCM for the numbers 32, 64, 80.　　　　　　　　**18.** _____

　　A 160　**B** 80　**C** 320　**D** 640

19. Calculate 5.35 cm × 4.7 cm and give the answer with the　**19.** _____
correct number of significant digits.

　　A 25.145 cm^2　**B** 25 cm^2　**C** 25.1 cm^2　**D** 25.15 cm^2

20. Which angle is complementary to 42.5°?　　　　　　　　**20.** _____

　　A 80°　**B** 47.5°　**C** 90°　**D** 137.5°

21. What is the area of this parallelogram?　　　　　　　　　**21.** _____

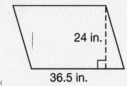

24 in.

36.5 in.

　　A 876 in^2　**B** 87.6 in^2　**C** 438 in^2　**D** 121 in^2

22. Vera received a gift in a box that measured　　　　　　　**22.** _____
14 cm by 12 cm by 10 cm. What is the surface area
of the box?

　　A 576 cm^2　**B** 428 cm^2　**C** 520 cm^2　**D** 856 cm^2

23. To the nearest 10 in^3, what is the volume of a cylinder　**23.** _____
with a diameter of 6 in. and a height of 9 in.?

　　A 254 in^3　**B** 300 in^3　**C** 250 in^3　**D** 254.3 in^3

24. $x^2 + 3x - 2$ is a polynomial known as a _____.　　　　**24.** _____

　　A Monomial　**B** Binomial　**C** Trinomial　**D** Not here

25. Which function does the graph show?

25. _____

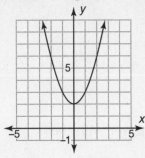

A $y = x^2$ **B** $y = x^2 + 2$ **C** $y = -x^2$ **D** $y = -x^2 - 2$

26. Which pair of terms are like terms?

26. _____

A $4x$ and 4 **B** x^2 and x **C** x^2 and $2x$ **D** x^3 and $5x^3$

27. These triangles are similar. Find the length represented by x.

27. _____

 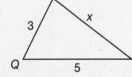

A 2.25   **B** 3   **C** 4.5   **D** 5

28. Which represents the sine of an angle in a right triangle?

28. _____

A $\dfrac{\text{opposite side}}{\text{adjacent side}}$ **B** $\dfrac{\text{adjacent side}}{\text{hypotenuse}}$

C $\dfrac{\text{hypotenuse}}{\text{opposite side}}$ **D** Not here

29. A submarine sandwich shop has two sizes of subs and 12 different kinds of subs. How many different choices of subs do you have?

29. _____

A 24   **B** 12   **C** 2   **D** Not here

30. Which of these estimates the probability that a person was *not* born on January 1?

30. _____

A .997   **B** 0.950   **C** 93%   **D** Not here

31. Kiri tossed a card into the air 200 times. The card landed on its red side 85 times and on its green side 115 times. What is the experimental probability of the card landing on its green side?

31. _____

A $\dfrac{17}{40}$ **B** $\dfrac{23}{40}$ **C** $\dfrac{23}{17}$ **D** $\dfrac{17}{23}$

Table of Contents for Answer Forms

Using Answer Forms

The answer forms in the *Assessment Sourcebook* can be used by students to answer test questions. There are two types of answer forms included in the sourcebook, Answer Form for Multiple-Choice Tests and Answer Form for Student-Produced Answers. Although both are formatted for machine scoring, they are easy to score by hand. The form for multiple-choice answers can be used for items with as many as four answer choices. The form for student-produced answers allows students to record numerical answers up to four digits, or up to three digits with decimal points and division bars. Using both these forms gives students practice in recording answers in the machine-scorable format that they will encounter when they take standardized tests.

Answer Form for Multiple-Choice Tests

Students use this form to record answers for multiple-choice tests with as many as 60 items. Have students fill in the correct information in the first three items at the top of the form before they begin the test. Make sure they know what the name of the test is. After tests are scored, you or the student can record the score in the fourth blank.

Be sure students understand that the numbers on the form next to the letter choices correspond to the numbers of the test items on the test. The letters in the circles correspond to the answer choices on the test. When fewer than four letter choices appear for a given test item, students should ignore the extra choices on the answer form. Explain that students are to mark each answer by filling in the lettered circle that corresponds to the answer they choose. They should use a number 2 pencil.

Explain to students that once they have completed the last item of the test, they should leave the rest of the item choices on the form blank.

Before students begin the test, you might want to guide them through the process of completing the form. Have students record the answer to a practice item in the row labeled Practice at the top of the form. Use this Practice item to make sure students understand how to mark their answers.

Caution students to:
- mark the answer in the correct row for each test item;
- fill in only one circle for each test item;
- fill in the answer circle completely.

Answer Form for Student-Produced Answers

This form is for recording numerical answers to problems that students calculate. The format is used for machine-score tests. Many standardized tests such as the SATs use this type of answer form.

Because students write their answers in the spaces at the top of each answer block, this form is also easily hand-scored.

The form can be used for answers expressed as decimals and fractions, as well as for whole numbers. However, it can only accommodate answers with four or fewer digits. If there are answers having fraction bars or decimals, the form can only accommodate three or fewer digits.

Have students fill in the correct information in the first three items at the top of the form before they begin the test. Make sure they know what the name of the test is. After tests are scored, you or the student can record the score in the fourth blank.

Make sure students understand that the number beside each answer block corresponds to the number of a test item. Then explain how to use the form, referring to the sample answer blocks on the next page. There are two steps to recording each answer as they calculate.

© Scott Foresman Addison Wesley 8

Example 1: Whole Numbers

Suppose the answer is 114.

Step 1: Write the answer in the empty row of marked spaces at the top of the appropriate answer block, one digit to a space. The digit farthest right in the answer goes in the farthest right space, and so on. Write 4 in the rightmost space, 1 in the second space from the right, and 1 in the third. For whole numbers, the space farthest left is the thousands place and the space farthest right is the ones place.

Step 2: Fill in the oval that corresponds to each digit in the column below it. Fill in oval 4 in the righthand column, oval 1 in the second column from the right, and oval 1 in the third column.

Explain that because the answer in Example 1 has only three digits, the leftmost space and the column below it are not marked.

Make sure students understand how to use the form to record answers in fractions and decimals.

Example 2: Decimals

Suppose the answer is 2.34.

Step 1: Write the digits of the answer in the empty spaces, as before, but also write the decimal point in the correct space. Stress to students that a decimal point uses one space. For 2.34, write 2 in the first space, a decimal point in the second space, 3 in the third space, and 4 in the last space as shown.

Step 2: Fill in the oval that corresponds to each digit, as before. For the decimal point, fill in the oval with the decimal point in the column under the space in which the decimal point appears.

Example 3: Fractions

Suppose the answer is $\frac{2}{13}$.

Step 1: Write the digits and the division bar in order in the empty spaces, allowing a full space for the division bar.

Step 2: Fill in the oval that corresponds to the division bar and to each digit.

Explain to students that once they have completed the last item of the test, they should leave the rest of the form blank.

Remind students to:
- write the answer in the correct answer block for each test item;
- carry out both steps 1 and 2 in recording their answers;
- fill in ovals for the decimal point and division bars where appropriate;
- fill in the ovals completely;
- make sure filled-in ovals correspond to the answer they have written above.

Answer Form for Multiple-Choice Tests

Student _____ Date _____

Name of Test _____ Score _____

Practice. (A) (B) (C) (D)

1. (A) (B) (C) (D)   21. (A) (B) (C) (D)   41. (A) (B) (C) (D)
2. (A) (B) (C) (D)   22. (A) (B) (C) (D)   42. (A) (B) (C) (D)
3. (A) (B) (C) (D)   23. (A) (B) (C) (D)   43. (A) (B) (C) (D)
4. (A) (B) (C) (D)   24. (A) (B) (C) (D)   44. (A) (B) (C) (D)
5. (A) (B) (C) (D)   25. (A) (B) (C) (D)   45. (A) (B) (C) (D)

6. (A) (B) (C) (D)   26. (A) (B) (C) (D)   46. (A) (B) (C) (D)
7. (A) (B) (C) (D)   27. (A) (B) (C) (D)   47. (A) (B) (C) (D)
8. (A) (B) (C) (D)   28. (A) (B) (C) (D)   48. (A) (B) (C) (D)
9. (A) (B) (C) (D)   29. (A) (B) (C) (D)   49. (A) (B) (C) (D)
10. (A) (B) (C) (D)   30. (A) (B) (C) (D)   50. (A) (B) (C) (D)

11. (A) (B) (C) (D)   31. (A) (B) (C) (D)   51. (A) (B) (C) (D)
12. (A) (B) (C) (D)   32. (A) (B) (C) (D)   52. (A) (B) (C) (D)
13. (A) (B) (C) (D)   33. (A) (B) (C) (D)   53. (A) (B) (C) (D)
14. (A) (B) (C) (D)   34. (A) (B) (C) (D)   54. (A) (B) (C) (D)
15. (A) (B) (C) (D)   35. (A) (B) (C) (D)   55. (A) (B) (C) (D)

16. (A) (B) (C) (D)   36. (A) (B) (C) (D)   56. (A) (B) (C) (D)
17. (A) (B) (C) (D)   37. (A) (B) (C) (D)   57. (A) (B) (C) (D)
18. (A) (B) (C) (D)   38. (A) (B) (C) (D)   58. (A) (B) (C) (D)
19. (A) (B) (C) (D)   39. (A) (B) (C) (D)   59. (A) (B) (C) (D)
20. (A) (B) (C) (D)   40. (A) (B) (C) (D)   60. (A) (B) (C) (D)

Answer Form for Student-Produced Answers

Student _____ Date _____

Name of Test _____ Score _____

Table of Contents for Answers

Answers

In 1–4, use the chart below, which lists how much four students spent on entertainment each month for 9 months during the school year.

Student	Sept	Oct	Nov	Dec	Jan	Feb	Mar	Apr	May
Irene	$14.00	$10.95	$ 8.95	$15.50	$11.95	$12.30	$25.00	$ 9.65	$10.25
Deepak	$ 7.00	$12.75	$ 5.80	$ 7.00	$16.40	$ 9.95	$ 8.30	$11.75	$ 7.00
Kim	$ 6.50	$ 8.10	$ 7.35	$ 5.25	$ 8.40	$ 6.25	$ 7.75	$ 9.00	$11.10
Stan	$12.35	$10.15	$ 8.05	$11.95	$ 7.85	$ 9.75	$ 8.50	$10.00	$ 9.20

1. Find the mean, the median, and the mode of Deepak's monthly entertainment costs.

1. **$9.55; $8.30; $7.00**

2. Make a box-and-whisker plot for all of Irene's monthly entertainment costs.

3. Construct a bar graph comparing the four monthly entertainment costs for February.

4. Draw a line graph that shows all of Stan's monthly entertainment costs.

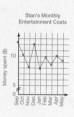

5. At a small, local airport, Beverly asked 75 people eating in the cafeteria if they like to fly. Did Beverly take a random sample for her survey?

No

---

6. Make a stem-and-leaf diagram for these biology test scores: 83, 67, 91, 85, 88, 78, 85, 95, 89, 85, 82

6.
Stem	Leaf
6	7
7	8
8	2 3 5 5 5 8 9
9	1 5

7. Jake recorded his weekly math test scores and the number of hours he studied for each test: 78–2 hours, 89–4 hours, 82–3 hours, 91–4.5 hours, 87–3.5 hours, 94–4 hours. Construct a scatterplot of Jake's data.

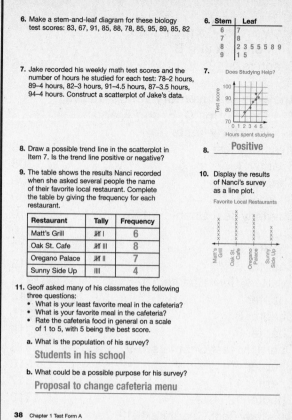

7.

8. Draw a possible trend line in the scatterplot in Item 7. Is the trend line positive or negative?

8. **Positive**

9. The table shows the results Nanci recorded when she asked several people the name of their favorite local restaurant. Complete the table by giving the frequency for each restaurant.

Restaurant	Tally	Frequency
Matt's Grill	卌 I	6
Oak St. Cafe	卌 III	8
Oregano Palace	卌 II	7
Sunny Side Up	IIII	4

10. Display the results of Nanci's survey as a line plot.

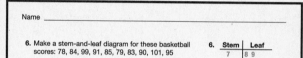

11. Geoff asked many of his classmates the following three questions:
- What is your least favorite meal in the cafeteria?
- What is your favorite meal in the cafeteria?
- Rate the cafeteria food in general on a scale of 1 to 5, with 5 being the best score.

a. What is the population of his survey?

Students in his school

b. What could be a possible purpose for his survey?

Proposal to change cafeteria menu

In 1–4, use the chart below, which lists how much time four students spent exercising or playing a sport for one week.

Student	Sun	Mon	Tues	Wed	Thurs	Fri	Sat
Paul	120 min	58 min	48 min	105 min	75 min	37 min	32 min
Suzanne	0 min	0 min	45 min	10 min	0 min	18 min	41 min
Mario	151 min	18 min	32 min	15 min	43 min	16 min	115 min
Elizabeth	12 min	15 min	12 min	15 min	12 min	15 min	41 min

1. Find the mean, the median, and the mode of Elizabeth's exercise times.

1. **17.4 min; 15 min; 12 min, 15 min**

2. Make a box-and-whisker plot for Suzanne's exercise times.

2.

3. Construct a bar graph comparing the four students' exercise times on Saturday.

3.

4. Construct a line graph of Mario's exercise time during the school week.

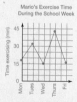

5. At a mall, Terry asked shoppers what kind of pet (or pets) they own. Did Terry take a random sample for his survey?

Yes

---

6. Make a stem-and-leaf diagram for these basketball scores: 78, 84, 99, 91, 85, 79, 83, 90, 101, 95

6.
Stem	Leaf
7	8 9
8	3 4 5
9	0 1 5 9
10	1

7. Patrick had his sister record the number of wrong notes he hit during 10-minute intervals as he practiced his piano recital piece: 1st interval–21 notes, 2nd interval–15 notes, 3rd interval–12 notes, 4th interval–9 notes, 5th interval–5 notes, 6th interval–3 notes. Construct a scatterplot of Patrick's data.

7.
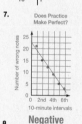

8. Draw a possible trend line in the scatterplot in Item 7. Is the trend positive or negative?

8. **Negative**

9. The table shows Lauren's results when she recorded how many people ordered the lunch specials at her family's restaurant. Complete the table by giving the frequency for each special.

Special	Tally	Frequency
"Spag" & Sauce	II	2
Tofu Cakes	IIII	4
Vegetable Bake	卌	5
Very Veggie Salad	III	3

10. Display Lauren's results as a line plot.

11. Kate asked many of her relatives the following three questions:
- What month is best for you to travel?
- Where should a reunion be held?
- What activities do you enjoy?

a. What is the population of her survey?

Kate's relatives

b. What could be a probable purpose for her survey?

Planning a family reunion

Chapter 2 Test Form A

Name _____

Date _____ Score _____

1. Order the following numbers from least to greatest:
−4, 3, 2, 0, −1.

1. $-4, -1, 0, 2, 3$

In 2–5, use >, <, or = to compare the numbers in each pair.

2. $9 \,\square\, -9$ 2. $>$

3. $-5 \,\square\, -4$ 3. $<$

4. $|-4| \,\square\, 4$ 4. $=$

5. $|11| \,\square\, |-13|$ 5. $<$

In 6–16, add or subtract.

6. $5 + (-1)$ 6. 4

7. $-1 + 5$ 7. 4

8. $22 + (-14)$ 8. 8

9. $-212 + 35$ 9. -177

10. $-125 + (-75)$ 10. -200

11. $6 - 31$ 11. -25

12. $-10 - 7$ 12. -17

13. $-12 - (-4)$ 13. -8

14. $-5 - (-15)$ 14. 10

15. $3 - (-11) + 17 + (-9) - 2$ 15. 20

16. $-45 - 18 - (-18) - (-45)$ 16. 0

17. Jared hiked from 132 feet above sea level to 6 feet below sea level. Give an integer to express his change in elevation.   17. -138 feet

In 18–20, multiply or divide.

18. -10×7 18. -70

19. $12(-2)$ 19. -24

20. $-20 \div 4$ 20. -5

In 21–24, evaluate.

21. $\dfrac{9(-4 + 6)}{3}$ 21. 6

22. $2 \cdot 3 - (-12) \div 6$ 22. 8

23. 8^2 23. 64

24. $(-3)^3$ 24. -27

In 25 and 26, use the grid below.

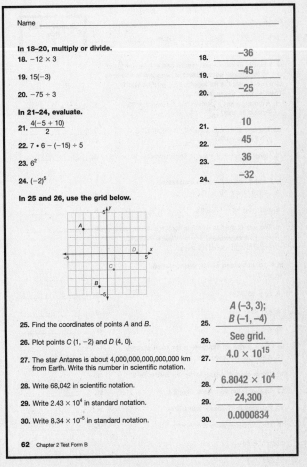

25. Find the coordinates of points A and B.   25. $A\,(-2, 2);$ $B\,(-4, -5)$

26. Plot points $C\,(3, -1)$ and $D\,(0, 1)$.   26. See grid.

27. Saturn is about 1,430,000,000 km from the sun. Write this distance in scientific notation.   27. 1.43×10^9 km

28. Write 112,648 in scientific notation.   28. 1.12648×10^5

29. Write 5.45×10^5 in standard notation.   29. $545,000$

30. Write 9.01×10^{-4} in standard notation.   30. 0.000901

Chapter 2 Test Form B

Name _____

Date _____ Score _____

1. Order the following numbers from least to greatest:
5, −7, −3, 2, 0

1. $-7, -3, 0, 2, 5$

In 2–4, use >, <, or = to compare the numbers in each pair.

2. $2 \,\square\, -2$ 2. $>$

3. $-24 \,\square\, -20$ 3. $<$

4. $|-1| \,\square\, 1$ 4. $=$

5. $|-7| \,\square\, |-4|$ 5. $>$

In 6–16, add or subtract.

6. $17 + (-9)$ 6. 8

7. $-9 + 17$ 7. 8

8. $18 + (-6)$ 8. 12

9. $-363 + (-36)$ 9. -399

10. $99 + (-55)$ 10. 44

11. $-75 - 21$ 11. -96

12. $-15 - (-6)$ 12. -9

13. $-30 - (-19)$ 13. -11

14. $-15 - (-6)$ 14. -9

15. $7 - (-4) + 28 + (-3) - 9$ 15. 27

16. $-65 - 27 - (-27) - (-65)$ 16. 0

17. The temperature fell from 28 degrees above 0 to 5 degrees below 0. Give an integer to express the change in temperature.   17. -33 degrees

In 18–20, multiply or divide.

18. -12×3 18. -36

19. $15(-3)$ 19. -45

20. $-75 \div 3$ 20. -25

In 21–24, evaluate.

21. $\dfrac{4(-5 + 10)}{2}$ 21. 10

22. $7 \cdot 6 - (-15) \div 5$ 22. 45

23. 6^2 23. 36

24. $(-2)^5$ 24. -32

In 25 and 26, use the grid below.

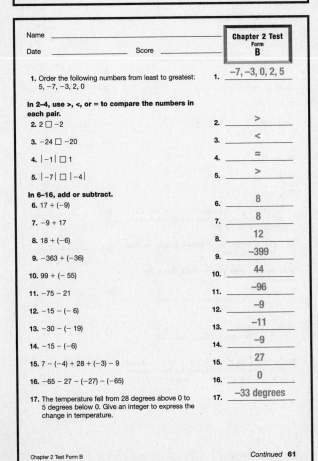

25. Find the coordinates of points A and B.   25. $A\,(-3, 3);$ $B\,(-1, -4)$

26. Plot points $C\,(1, -2)$ and $D\,(4, 0)$.   26. See grid.

27. The star Antares is about 4,000,000,000,000,000 km from Earth. Write this number in scientific notation.   27. 4.0×10^{15}

28. Write 68,042 in scientific notation.   28. 6.8042×10^4

29. Write 2.43×10^4 in standard notation.   29. $24,300$

30. Write 8.34×10^{-5} in standard notation.   30. 0.0000834

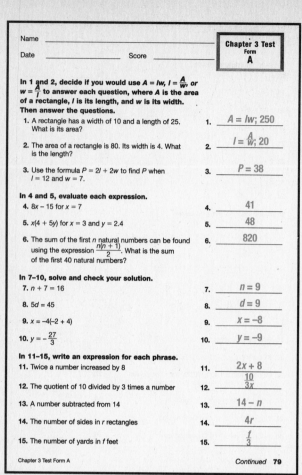

In 1 and 2, decide if you would use $A = lw$, $l = \frac{A}{w}$, or $w = \frac{A}{l}$ to answer each question, where A is the area of a rectangle, l is its length, and w is its width. Then answer the questions.

1. A rectangle has a width of 10 and a length of 25. What is its area?

1. $A = lw; 250$

2. The area of a rectangle is 80. Its width is 4. What is the length?

2. $l = \frac{A}{w}; 20$

3. Use the formula $P = 2l + 2w$ to find P when $l = 12$ and $w = 7$.

3. $P = 38$

In 4 and 5, evaluate each expression.

4. $8x - 15$ for $x = 7$

4. 41

5. $x(4 + 5y)$ for $x = 3$ and $y = 2.4$

5. 48

6. The sum of the first n natural numbers can be found using the expression $\frac{n(n + 1)}{2}$. What is the sum of the first 40 natural numbers?

6. 820

In 7–10, solve and check your solution.

7. $n + 7 = 16$

7. $n = 9$

8. $5d = 45$

8. $d = 9$

9. $x = -4(-2 + 4)$

9. $x = -8$

10. $y = -\frac{27}{3}$

10. $y = -9$

In 11–15, write an expression for each phrase.

11. Twice a number increased by 8

11. $2x + 8$

12. The quotient of 10 divided by 3 times a number

12. $\frac{10}{3x}$

13. A number subtracted from 14

13. $14 - n$

14. The number of sides in r rectangles

14. $4r$

15. The number of yards in f feet

15. $\frac{f}{3}$

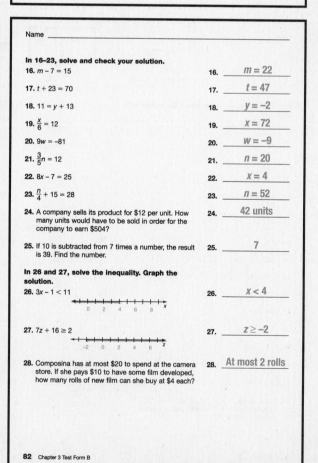

In 16–23, solve and check your solution.

16. $n + 10 = 18$

16. $n = 8$

17. $c - 12 = 7$

17. $c = 19$

18. $15 = x + 26$

18. $x = -11$

19. $\frac{n}{4} = 11$

19. $n = 44$

20. $7p = -105$

20. $p = -15$

21. $\frac{2}{5}y = 20$

21. $y = 50$

22. $6x - 11 = 13$

22. $x = 4$

23. $\frac{n}{8} + 10 = 21$

23. $n = 88$

24. A company sells its product for $16 per unit. How many units would have to be sold in order for the company to earn $528?

24. 33 units

25. If 15 is subtracted from 4 times a number, the result is 19. Find the number.

25. 8.5

In 26 and 27, solve the inequality. Graph the solution.

26. $2x - 3 < 5$

26. $x < 4$

27. $5z + 12 \geq 2$

27. $z \geq -2$

28. To pay for expenses, at least 500 copies of each issue of a school newspaper must be sold. If 450 copies go to subscribers, how many more copies must be sold so that the expenses are covered?

28. At least 50 copies

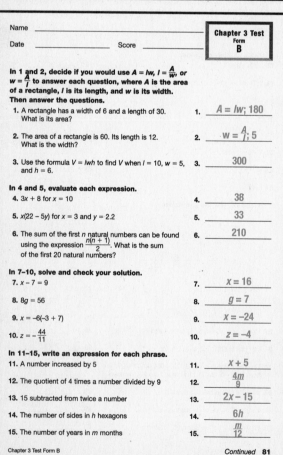

In 1 and 2, decide if you would use $A = lw$, $l = \frac{A}{w}$, or $w = \frac{A}{l}$ to answer each question, where A is the area of a rectangle, l is its length, and w is its width. Then answer the questions.

1. A rectangle has a width of 6 and a length of 30. What is its area?

1. $A = lw; 180$

2. The area of a rectangle is 60. Its length is 12. What is the width?

2. $w = \frac{A}{l}; 5$

3. Use the formula $V = lwh$ to find V when $l = 10$, $w = 5$, and $h = 6$.

3. 300

In 4 and 5, evaluate each expression.

4. $3x + 8$ for $x = 10$

4. 38

5. $x(22 - 5y)$ for $x = 3$ and $y = 2.2$

5. 33

6. The sum of the first n natural numbers can be found using the expression $\frac{n(n + 1)}{2}$. What is the sum of the first 20 natural numbers?

6. 210

In 7–10, solve and check your solution.

7. $x - 7 = 9$

7. $x = 16$

8. $8g = 56$

8. $g = 7$

9. $x = -6(-3 + 7)$

9. $x = -24$

10. $z = -\frac{44}{11}$

10. $z = -4$

In 11–15, write an expression for each phrase.

11. A number increased by 5

11. $x + 5$

12. The quotient of 4 times a number divided by 9

12. $\frac{4m}{9}$

13. 15 subtracted from twice a number

13. $2x - 15$

14. The number of sides in h hexagons

14. $6h$

15. The number of years in m months

15. $\frac{m}{12}$

In 16–23, solve and check your solution.

16. $m - 7 = 15$

16. $m = 22$

17. $t + 23 = 70$

17. $t = 47$

18. $11 = y + 13$

18. $y = -2$

19. $\frac{x}{6} = 12$

19. $x = 72$

20. $9w = -81$

20. $w = -9$

21. $\frac{3}{5}n = 12$

21. $n = 20$

22. $8x - 7 = 25$

22. $x = 4$

23. $\frac{n}{4} + 15 = 28$

23. $n = 52$

24. A company sells its product for $12 per unit. How many units would have to be sold in order for the company to earn $504?

24. 42 units

25. If 10 is subtracted from 7 times a number, the result is 39. Find the number.

25. 7

In 26 and 27, solve the inequality. Graph the solution.

26. $3x - 1 < 11$

26. $x < 4$

27. $7z + 16 \geq 2$

27. $z \geq -2$

28. Composina has at most $20 to spend at the camera store. If she pays $10 to have some film developed, how many rolls of new film can she buy at $4 each?

28. At most 2 rolls

Date _____ Score _____

1. Find the value of y when $x = 2$ in the equation $y = 3x$. **1.** $y = 6$

2. Find the rule that relates x and y in the table. Then find y when $x = 12$.

x	1	2	3	4	5
y	3	6	9	12	15

2. $y = 3x;\ y = 36$

3. The number of boys (y) on the softball team is equal to 4 less than the number of girls (x) on the team. Determine whether each is a solution of this situation: (6 girls, 2 boys); (7 girls, 11 boys); (1 girl, 4 boys).

3. Yes; No; No

4. Give two solutions for the equation $2x - 3y = 18$.

4. Possible answer: (9, 0), (0, −6)

5. Graph the ordered pairs in the table. Connect the points to determine if the graph is linear.

x	1	2	3	4	5
y	4	−3	2	−1	0

Not linear

6. Thom has a bucket of moss mixture for planting. The bucket weighs 6 ounces and each scoop of mixture weighs 2 ounces. Graph the weight of the bucket of mixture. Use x for the number of scoops of mixture.

6.

7. For each line, find the slope, the x-intercept, and the y-intercept.
  a. Line through A and B
  b. Line through B and C

7. a. $1;\ -5;\ 5$
   b. $-\frac{1}{2};\ 4;\ 2$

---

8. Graph the line $y = \frac{1}{2}x - 2$. Find the slope, the x-intercept, and the y-intercept.

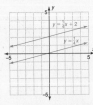

$\frac{1}{2};\ 4;\ -2$

9. Solve the system by graphing $y = x$ and $y = \frac{1}{2}x + 2$.

(4, 4)

10. Graph the equations $y = \frac{1}{4}x + 2$ and $y = \frac{1}{4}x$. Are these lines parallel? Explain.

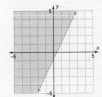

Yes; Slopes are equal so lines do not intersect.

11. Walter has x books. Lynda (y) has more than double this amount, minus 1. Graph the inequality.

Date _____ Score _____

1. Find the value of y when $x = 7$ in the equation $y = 2x + 2$. **1.** $y = 16$

2. Find the rule that relates x and y in the table. Then find y when $x = 9$.

x	1	2	3	4	5
y	6	7	8	9	10

2. $y = x + 5;\ y = 14$

3. The number of red cars (y) in the lot is equal to 3 times the number of blue cars (x) plus 1. Determine whether each is a solution of this situation: (1 blue car, 4 red cars); (6 blue cars, 18 red cars); (10 blue cars, 31 red cars).

3. Yes; No; Yes

4. Give two solutions for the equation $3x + 2y = 24$.

4. Possible answer: (8, 0), (0, 12)

5. Graph the ordered pairs in the table. Connect the points to determine if the graph is linear.

x	1	2	3	4	5
y	4	5	6	7	8

Linear

5.

6. Jill has yards of material wrapped around a board. The board weighs 12 ounces and each yard of material weighs 4 ounces. Graph the weight of the material and board. Use x for the number of yards of material.

6.

---

7. For each line, find the slope, the x-intercept, and the y-intercept.
  a. Line through A and B
  b. Line through B and C

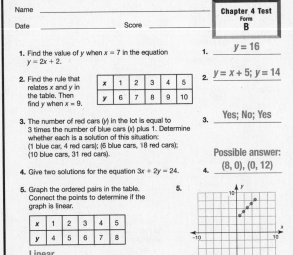

7. a. $-\frac{1}{2};\ 4;\ 2$
   b. $1;\ -5;\ 5$

8. Graph the line $y = \frac{1}{3}x + 1$. Find the slope, the x-intercept, and the y-intercept.

$\frac{1}{3};\ -3;\ 1$

9. Solve the system by graphing $y = x - 1$ and $y = 2x - 3$.

(2, 1)

10. Graph the equations $y = \frac{1}{2}x - 1$ and $y = \frac{1}{4}x$. Are these lines parallel? Explain.

No; The lines intersect.

11. Al makes x dollars per hour. Hal (y) makes *at most* twice that amount plus 3 dollars per hour more. Graph the inequality.

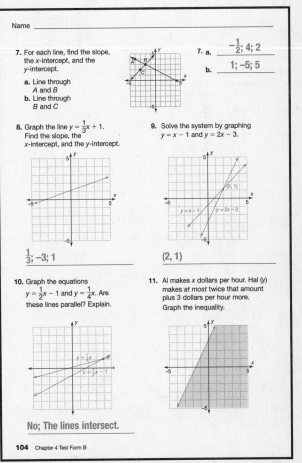

299

Name _____

Date _____ Score _____

1. Tammy was covering her bulletin board with pictures when a friend called to see how she was doing on the project. Estimate the ratio of the amount of bulletin board she covered to the amount of bulletin board she has left to do.

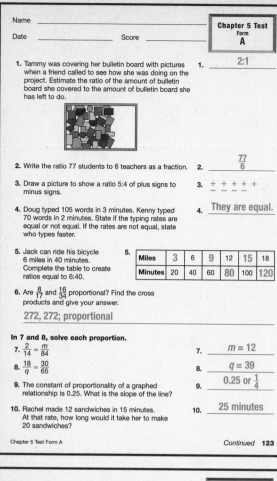

1. _____ 2:1

2. Write the ratio 77 students to 6 teachers as a fraction.

2. $\frac{77}{6}$

3. Draw a picture to show a ratio 5:4 of plus signs to minus signs.

3. + + + + +
      – – – – –

4. Doug typed 105 words in 3 minutes. Kenny typed 70 words in 2 minutes. State if the typing rates are equal or not equal. If the rates are not equal, state who types faster.

4. **They are equal.**

5. Jack can ride his bicycle 6 miles in 40 minutes. Complete the table to create ratios equal to 6:40.

Miles	3	6	9	12	15	18
Minutes	20	40	60	80	100	120

6. Are $\frac{8}{17}$ and $\frac{16}{34}$ proportional? Find the cross products and give your answer.

272, 272; proportional

In 7 and 8, solve each proportion.

7. $\frac{2}{14} = \frac{m}{84}$

7. $m = 12$

8. $\frac{18}{q} = \frac{30}{65}$

8. $q = 39$

9. The constant of proportionality of a graphed relationship is 0.25. What is the slope of the line?

9. 0.25 or $\frac{1}{4}$

10. Rachel made 12 sandwiches in 15 minutes. At that rate, how long would it take her to make 20 sandwiches?

10. **25 minutes**

Name _____

11. The graph at the right shows a bowler's total score after several games. What is the bowler's total score after playing $2\frac{1}{2}$ games?

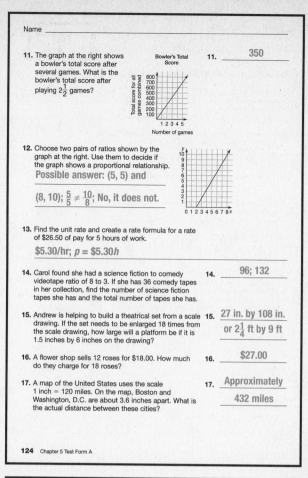

11. _____ 350

12. Choose two pairs of ratios shown by the graph at the right. Use them to decide if the graph shows a proportional relationship.

Possible answer: (5, 5) and

_____

(8, 10); $\frac{5}{5} \neq \frac{10}{8}$; **No, it does not.**

13. Find the unit rate and create a rate formula for a rate of $26.50 of pay for 5 hours of work.

$5.30/hr; $p = \$5.30h$

14. Carol found she had a science fiction to comedy videotape ratio of 8 to 3. If she has 36 comedy tapes in her collection, find the number of science fiction tapes she has and the total number of tapes she has.

14. **96; 132**

15. Andrew is helping to build a theatrical set from a scale drawing. If the set needs to be enlarged 18 times from the scale drawing, how large will a platform be if it is 1.5 inches by 6 inches on the drawing?

15. **27 in. by 108 in. or $2\frac{1}{4}$ ft by 9 ft**

16. A flower shop sells 12 roses for $18.00. How much do they charge for 18 roses?

16. **$27.00**

17. A map of the United States uses the scale 1 inch = 120 miles. On the map, Boston and Washington, D.C. are about 3.6 inches apart. What is the actual distance between these cities?

17. **Approximately 432 miles**

Name _____

Date _____ Score _____

1. Students at Carver Middle School voted for new band uniforms. Estimate the ratio of students choosing Uniform B to students choosing Uniform A.

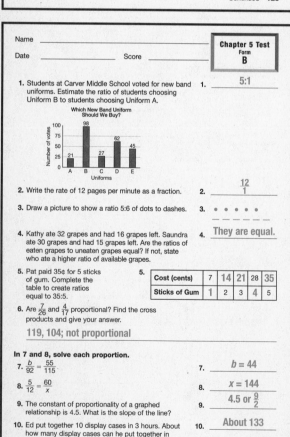

1. _____ 5:1

2. Write the rate of 12 pages per minute as a fraction.

2. $\frac{12}{1}$

3. Draw a picture to show a ratio 5:6 of dots to dashes.

3. • • • • •
      – – – – – –

4. Kathy ate 32 grapes and had 16 grapes left. Saundra ate 30 grapes and had 15 grapes left. Are the ratios of eaten grapes to uneaten grapes equal? If not, state who ate a higher ratio of available grapes.

4. **They are equal.**

5. Pat paid 35¢ for 5 sticks of gum. Complete the table to create ratios equal to 35:5.

Cost (cents)	7	14	21	28	35
Sticks of Gum	1	2	3	4	5

6. Are $\frac{7}{26}$ and $\frac{4}{17}$ proportional? Find the cross products and give your answer.

119, 104; not proportional

In 7 and 8, solve each proportion.

7. $\frac{b}{92} = \frac{55}{115}$

7. $b = 44$

8. $\frac{5}{12} = \frac{60}{x}$

8. $x = 144$

9. The constant of proportionality of a graphed relationship is 4.5. What is the slope of the line?

9. 4.5 or $\frac{9}{2}$

10. Ed put together 10 display cases in 3 hours. About how many display cases can he put together in 40 hours?

10. **About 133**

Name _____

11. The graph at the right shows the cost for various amounts (by weight) of bananas. How many pounds of bananas could you buy for $1.75?

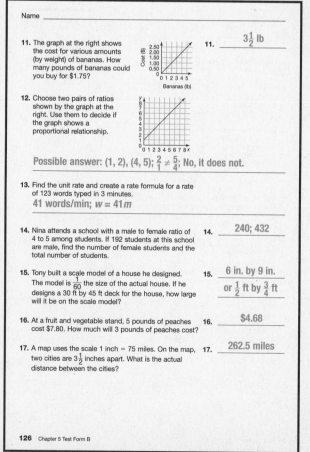

11. _____ $3\frac{1}{2}$ lb

12. Choose two pairs of ratios shown by the graph at the right. Use them to decide if the graph shows a proportional relationship.

Possible answer: (1, 2), (4, 5); $\frac{2}{1} \neq \frac{5}{4}$; No, it does not.

13. Find the unit rate and create a rate formula for a rate of 123 words typed in 3 minutes.

41 words/min; $w = 41m$

14. Nina attends a school with a male to female ratio of 4 to 5 among students. If 192 students at this school are male, find the number of female students and the total number of students.

14. **240; 432**

15. Tony built a scale model of a house he designed. The model is $\frac{1}{60}$ the size of the actual house. If he designs a 30 ft by 45 ft deck for the house, how large will it be on the scale model?

15. **6 in. by 9 in. or $\frac{1}{2}$ ft by $\frac{3}{4}$ ft**

16. At a fruit and vegetable stand, 5 pounds of peaches cost $7.80. How much will 3 pounds of peaches cost?

16. **$4.68**

17. A map uses the scale 1 inch = 75 miles. On the map, two cities are $3\frac{1}{2}$ inches apart. What is the actual distance between the cities?

17. **262.5 miles**

Chapter 6 Test Form A

Name _____

Date _____ Score _____

1. Write the fraction, decimal, and percent that describe how much of the figure is shaded.

1. $\frac{1}{2}$; 0.5; 50%

2. Write $\frac{3}{8}$ as a decimal and as a percent.

2. 0.375; 37.5%

3. Write 46% as a fraction in lowest terms and as a decimal.

3. $\frac{23}{50}$; 0.46

4. What number is 30% of 180?

4. 54

5. 50 is what percent of 25?

5. 200%

6. Thirty percent (84 students) of the eighth graders at Washington School ride a bus to school. How many eighth graders are in the school?

6. 280 eighth graders

7. Estimate the percent 27 is of 55.

7. 50%

8. Estimate 41% of 151.

8. 60

9. Estimate, to the nearest 10%, the percent that the shaded region represents.

9. 10%

In 10–13, find the percent increase or decrease for each and specify whether it is an increase or a decrease.

10. Old $30; new $40

10. 33% increase

11. Old $250; new $200

11. 20% decrease

12. Old $75; new $45

12. 40% decrease

13. Old $55; new $110

13. 100% increase

---

14. William bought roses at a wholesale store for $17.25 per dozen. He sold them in a booth for $25.00 per dozen. What was the percent increase?

14. 45%

15. Find the retail cost of a coat if the wholesale cost is $90 and the price increase is 58%.

15. $142.20

16. What is the wholesale price if the percent increase is 25% and the amount of increase is $15.65?

16. $62.60

17. The selling price for a bottle of cologne was $14.95. With her employee discount, Antonia was charged only $12.70 (before tax). What percent is her employee discount?

17. 15%

18. How much less will you pay for a CD priced at $12.99 if it is on sale for 15% off?

18. $1.95

19. What is the original price of a pair of boots if the percent discount is 20% and the sale price is $85?

19. $106.25

20. A shirt's selling price is marked up 50% and then decreased by 20%. If the shirt was originally $15, what is the new selling price?

20. $18

21. Perry made $20,000 per year. He took a 10% cut in wages for a new job. He soon received a promotion with a 20% increase in pay. What is his new salary?

21. $21,600

22. Joshua deposited $250 into a savings account that pays 6% simple interest per year. How much interest will Joshua have earned after 3 years?

22. $45

23. To open her restaurant, Ruth borrowed $40,000 for 3 years at 8% interest compounded annually. How much will she owe?

23. $50,388.48

Chapter 6 Test Form B

Name _____

Date _____ Score _____

1. Write the fraction, decimal, and percent that describe how much of the figure is shaded.

1. $\frac{3}{8}$; 0.375; 37.5%

2. Write $\frac{7}{50}$ as a decimal and as a percent.

2. 0.14; 14%

3. Write 45% as a fraction in lowest terms and as a percent.

3. $\frac{9}{20}$; 45%

4. What number is 40% of 260?

4. 104

5. 75 is what percent of 25?

5. 300%

6. Twenty percent (15 books) of Kayla's books are historical novels. How many books does Kayla have?

6. 75

7. Estimate 32% of 271.

7. 90

8. Estimate 40% of 59.

8. 24

9. Estimate, to the nearest 5%, the percent that the shaded region represents.

9. 25%

In 10–13, find the percent increase or decrease for each and specify whether it is an increase or a decrease.

10. Old 20; new 30

10. 50% increase

11. Old 300; new 250

11. $16\frac{2}{3}$% decrease

12. Old 200; new 100

12. 50% decrease

13. Old $350; new $385

13. 10% increase

---

14. Mona bought shorts that cost $18. With sales tax, she paid $19.44. What percent was charged for sales tax?

14. 8%

15. Find the retail cost of a jacket if the wholesale cost is $50 and the price increase is 75%.

15. $87.50

16. What is the wholesale price of a bicycle if the percent increase is 40% and the amount of increase is $50?

16. $125

17. Brad won a toaster worth $20. He preferred the one he had, so he sold the toaster at a garage sale for $8. What percent discount did the buyer receive?

17. 60%

18. How much weight will you lose altogether if you have already lost 2 pounds, and this is 20% of your goal?

18. 10 pounds

19. How much less will you pay for a videotape priced at $19.99 if it is on sale at 20% off?

19. $4.00

20. A pair of jeans priced at $25 is first marked down 20% when they go on sale and then marked up 20% after the sale. What is the final selling price of the jeans?

20. $24

21. Marlie worked 40 hours per week. Her hours got cut by 20%. Three months later, they were increased by 25%. How many hours did she work after the increase?

21. 40 hr/week

22. Jenna took out a loan of $500 for 5 years. If she pays 8% simple interest, what is the interest she must pay?

22. $200

23. The Hayes family borrowed $7000 for 2 years at 12% interest compounded annually. How much will they owe?

23. $8780.80

Chapter 7 Test
Form
A

1. Determine whether 360 is divisible by 2, 3, 4, 5, 6, 8, 9, or 10.

1. _____ 2, 3, 4, 5, 6, 8, 9, 10 _____

In 2 and 3, determine the prime factorization.

2. 425

2. _____ $5^2 \times 17$ _____

3. 890

3. _____ $2 \times 5 \times 89$ _____

4. Find the GCF of 40 and 64.

4. _____ 8 _____

5. Find the GCF of 24 and 120.

5. _____ 24 _____

In 6–8, write each fraction in lowest terms.

6. $\frac{56}{120}$

6. _____ $\frac{7}{15}$ _____

7. $\frac{840}{1260}$

7. _____ $\frac{2}{3}$ _____

8. $\frac{88}{132}$

8. _____ $\frac{2}{3}$ _____

9. Find the LCM of 18 and 24.

9. _____ 72 _____

10. Find the LCM of 30 and 96.

10. _____ 480 _____

11. Myra works every third day. Cassie works every fourth day, and Joel every sixth day. If all three work on the first of April, when will all three work together again?

11. _____ April 13 _____

12. Determine whether $\frac{5}{32}$ is a repeating or terminating decimal.

12. _____ Terminating _____

In 13 and 14, write >, =, or < to compare.

13. $\frac{3}{16}$ ☐ 0.2

13. _____ < _____

14. $\frac{9}{17}$ ☐ $\frac{12}{25}$

14. _____ > _____

15. Write $0.\overline{45}$ as a fraction in lowest terms.

15. _____ $\frac{5}{11}$ _____

16. Subtract 12.7429 − 4.86.

16. _____ 7.8829 _____

In 17–20, express the answer as a mixed number in lowest terms.

17. $3\frac{7}{8} + 4\frac{5}{6}$

17. _____ $8\frac{17}{24}$ _____

18. $4\frac{1}{2} \times 1\frac{1}{3}$

18. _____ 6 _____

19. $3\frac{3}{4} \div 1\frac{1}{2}$

19. _____ $2\frac{1}{2}$ _____

20. $8 - 4\frac{3}{4}$

20. _____ $3\frac{1}{4}$ _____

21. State whether 246 is a perfect square.

21. _____ No _____

22. Find the two closest perfect squares to 140.

22. _____ 121, 144 _____

23. Estimate the square root of 250.

23. _____ 15.8 _____

24. Find $\sqrt{\frac{50}{2}}$.

24. _____ 5 _____

25. Find $\sqrt{3} \times \sqrt{27}$.

25. _____ 9 _____

26. Use a calculator to find $\sqrt{88}$ and round to the nearest thousandth.

26. _____ 9.381 _____

27. Determine whether the lengths 5, 12, and 13 could form a right triangle.

27. _____ Yes _____

In 28 and 29, find the length of the missing side.

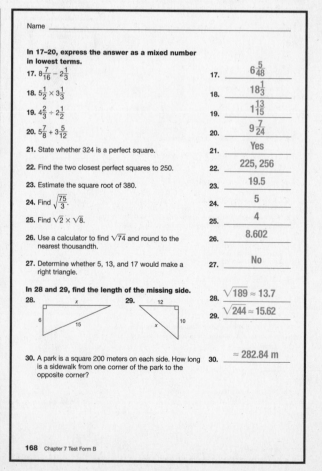

28. _____ $\sqrt{89} \approx 9.43$ _____

29. _____ $\sqrt{96} \approx 9.80$ _____

30. A football field is 53 yards wide and 100 yards long. What is the distance from one corner to the opposite corner?

30. _____ ≈ 113 yd _____

Chapter 7 Test
Form
B

1. Determine whether 350 is divisible by 2, 3, 4, 5, 6, 8, 9, or 10.

1. _____ 2, 5, 10 _____

In 2 and 3, determine the prime factorization.

2. 560

2. _____ $2^4 \times 5 \times 7$ _____

3. 3000

3. _____ $2^3 \times 3 \times 5^3$ _____

4. Find the GCF of 24 and 56.

4. _____ 8 _____

5. Find the GCF of 35 and 90.

5. _____ 5 _____

In 6–8, write each fraction in lowest terms.

6. $\frac{80}{124}$

6. _____ $\frac{20}{31}$ _____

7. $\frac{15}{90}$

7. _____ $\frac{1}{6}$ _____

8. $\frac{240}{720}$

8. _____ $\frac{1}{3}$ _____

9. Find the LCM of 24 and 40.

9. _____ 120 _____

10. Find the LCM of 30 and 36.

10. _____ 180 _____

11. Hot dogs come in packages of eight. Hot-dog buns come in packages of 12. Find the minimum number of each you need to buy to have the same number of hot dogs and hot-dog buns.

11. _____ Hot dogs: 3; Buns: 2 _____

12. Determine whether $\frac{5}{45}$ is a repeating or terminating decimal.

12. _____ Repeating _____

In 13 and 14, write >, =, or < to compare.

13. $\frac{9}{24}$ ☐ $\frac{6}{16}$

13. _____ = _____

14. $\frac{7}{12}$ ☐ $\frac{5}{9}$

14. _____ > _____

15. Write 0.71 as a fraction in lowest terms.

15. _____ $\frac{71}{100}$ _____

16. Add 15.42 + 9.7426.

16. _____ 25.1626 _____

In 17–20, express the answer as a mixed number in lowest terms.

17. $8\frac{7}{16} - 2\frac{1}{3}$

17. _____ $6\frac{5}{48}$ _____

18. $5\frac{1}{2} \times 3\frac{1}{3}$

18. _____ $18\frac{1}{3}$ _____

19. $4\frac{2}{3} \div 2\frac{1}{2}$

19. _____ $1\frac{13}{15}$ _____

20. $5\frac{7}{8} + 3\frac{5}{12}$

20. _____ $9\frac{7}{24}$ _____

21. State whether 324 is a perfect square.

21. _____ Yes _____

22. Find the two closest perfect squares to 250.

22. _____ 225, 256 _____

23. Estimate the square root of 380.

23. _____ 19.5 _____

24. Find $\sqrt{\frac{75}{3}}$.

24. _____ 5 _____

25. Find $\sqrt{2} \times \sqrt{8}$.

25. _____ 4 _____

26. Use a calculator to find $\sqrt{74}$ and round to the nearest thousandth.

26. _____ 8.602 _____

27. Determine whether 5, 13, and 17 would make a right triangle.

27. _____ No _____

In 28 and 29, find the length of the missing side.

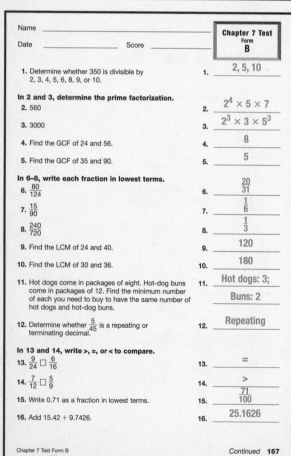

28. _____ $\sqrt{189} \approx 13.7$ _____

29. _____ $\sqrt{244} \approx 15.62$ _____

30. A park is a square 200 meters on each side. How long is a sidewalk from one corner of the park to the opposite corner?

30. _____ ≈ 282.84 m _____

Chapter 8 Test — Form A

Name _____

Date _____ Score _____

Chapter 8 Test Form A

You will need a ruler and a protractor.

1. What metric unit would you use for the distance to the moon?

   1. __kilometer__

2. Convert 19 ft 7 in. to inches.

   2. __235 in.__

3. Katie measured a distance as 0.25 mi. Elizabeth measured a distance to be 1319.5 ft. Whose measurement was more precise?

   3. __Elizabeth's__

4. Calculate 34.09 mL − 27.2 mL. Express the answer with the correct number of significant digits.

   4. __6.9 mL__

In 5–7, use the map of Montana.

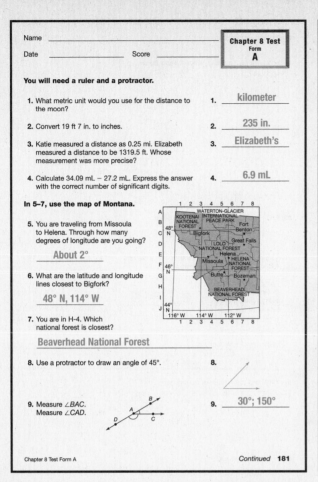

5. You are traveling from Missoula to Helena. Through how many degrees of longitude are you going?

   __About 2°__

6. What are the latitude and longitude lines closest to Bigfork?

   __48° N, 114° W__

7. You are in H-4. Which national forest is closest?

   __Beaverhead National Forest__

8. Use a protractor to draw an angle of 45°.

   8.

9. Measure ∠BAC.
   Measure ∠CAD.

   9. __30°; 150°__

Chapter 8 Test Form A   Continued 181

Name _____

10. Classify a 120° angle as right, straight, obtuse, or acute.

   10. __Obtuse__

11. Find the complementary and supplementary angles of 35°.

   11. __55°; 145°__

12. Draw a square with horizontal sides $\overline{AB}$ and $\overline{DC}$ (both read from left to right). Name two other parallel sides in the square.

   12. __$\overline{AD}$ and $\overline{BC}$__

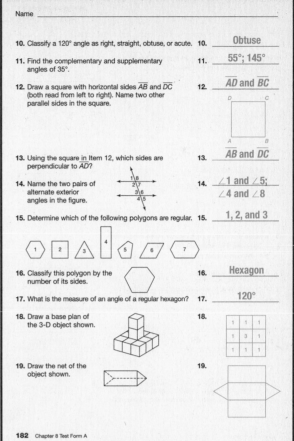

13. Using the square in Item 12, which sides are perpendicular to $\overline{AD}$?

   13. __$\overline{AB}$ and $\overline{DC}$__

14. Name the two pairs of alternate exterior angles in the figure.

   14. __∠1 and ∠5; ∠4 and ∠8__

15. Determine which of the following polygons are regular.

   15. __1, 2, and 3__

16. Classify this polygon by the number of its sides.

   16. __Hexagon__

17. What is the measure of an angle of a regular hexagon?

   17. __120°__

18. Draw a base plan of the 3-D object shown.

   18.

1	1	1
1	3	1
1	1	1

19. Draw the net of the object shown.

   19.

182 Chapter 8 Test Form A

Chapter 8 Test — Form B

Name _____

Date _____ Score _____

Chapter 8 Test Form B

You will need a ruler and a protractor.

1. What metric unit would you use for distance in track and field competitions?

   1. __meter__

2. Convert 4560 cm to km.

   2. __0.0456 km__

3. Ralph measured a distance as 21.34 m. Bobby measured a distance to be 0.125 km. Whose measurement was more precise?

   3. __Ralph's__

4. Calculate 56.9 km × 37.25 km. Express the answer with the correct number of significant digits.

   4. __2120 km²__

In 5–7, use the map of Montana.

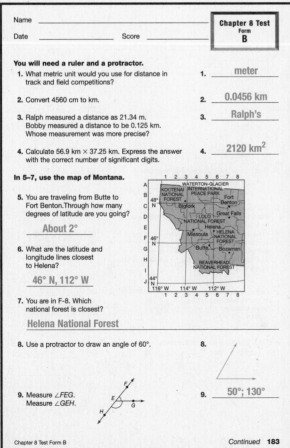

5. You are traveling from Butte to Fort Benton. Through how many degrees of latitude are you going?

   __About 2°__

6. What are the latitude and longitude lines closest to Helena?

   __46° N, 112° W__

7. You are in F-8. Which national forest is closest?

   __Helena National Forest__

8. Use a protractor to draw an angle of 60°.

   8.

9. Measure ∠FEG.
   Measure ∠GEH.

   9. __50°; 130°__

Chapter 8 Test Form B   Continued 183

Name _____

10. Classify 85° as a right, straight, obtuse, or acute angle.

   10. __Acute__

11. Find the complementary and supplementary angles of 49°.

   11. __41°; 131°__

12. Draw a rectangle with horizontal sides $\overline{EF}$ and $\overline{HG}$ (both read from left to right). Name two other parallel sides in the rectangle.

   12. __$\overline{EH}$; $\overline{FG}$__

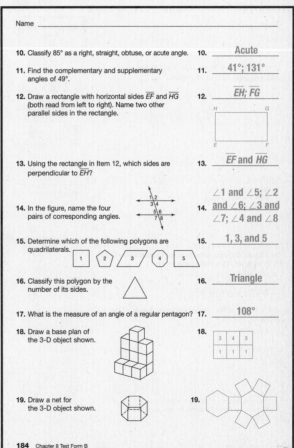

13. Using the rectangle in Item 12, which sides are perpendicular to $\overline{EH}$?

   13. __$\overline{EF}$ and $\overline{HG}$__

14. In the figure, name the four pairs of corresponding angles.

   14. __∠1 and ∠5; ∠2 and ∠6; ∠3 and ∠7; ∠4 and ∠8__

15. Determine which of the following polygons are quadrilaterals.

   15. __1, 3, and 5__

16. Classify this polygon by the number of its sides.

   16. __Triangle__

17. What is the measure of an angle of a regular pentagon?

   17. __108°__

18. Draw a base plan of the 3-D object shown.

   18.

   | 3 | 4 | 3 |
   | 1 | 1 | 1 |

19. Draw a net for the 3-D object shown.

   19.

184 Chapter 8 Test Form B

Name _____

Date _____ Score _____

In this test, use 3.14 for π. In 1 and 2, find the perimeter and area of the figure.

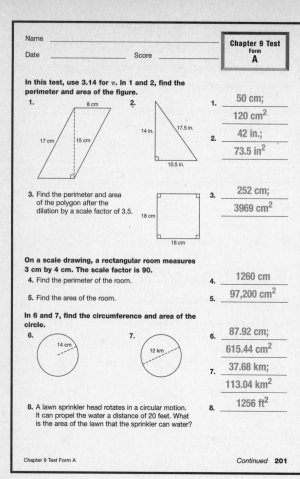

1.
2.

1. 50 cm; 120 cm²

2. 42 in.; 73.5 in²

3. Find the perimeter and area of the polygon after the dilation by a scale factor of 3.5.

3. 252 cm; 3969 cm²

On a scale drawing, a rectangular room measures 3 cm by 4 cm. The scale factor is 90.

4. Find the perimeter of the room.

4. 1260 cm

5. Find the area of the room.

5. 97,200 cm²

In 6 and 7, find the circumference and area of the circle.

6.   7.

6. 87.92 cm; 615.44 cm²

7. 37.68 km; 113.04 km²

8. A lawn sprinkler head rotates in a circular motion. It can propel the water a distance of 20 feet. What is the area of the lawn that the sprinkler can water?

8. 1256 ft²

Name _____

In 9–12, find the surface area of each figure.

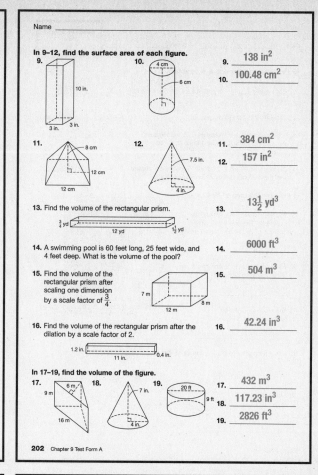

9.   10.

9. 138 in²

10. 100.48 cm²

11.   12.

11. 384 cm²

12. 157 in²

13. Find the volume of the rectangular prism.

13. $13\frac{1}{2}$ yd³

14. A swimming pool is 60 feet long, 25 feet wide, and 4 feet deep. What is the volume of the pool?

14. 6000 ft³

15. Find the volume of the rectangular prism after scaling one dimension by a scale factor of $\frac{3}{4}$.

15. 504 m³

16. Find the volume of the rectangular prism after the dilation by a scale factor of 2.

16. 42.24 in³

In 17–19, find the volume of the figure.

17.   18.   19.

17. 432 m³

18. 117.23 in³

19. 2826 ft³

Name _____

Date _____ Score _____

In this test, use 3.14 for π. In 1 and 2, find the perimeter and area of the figure.

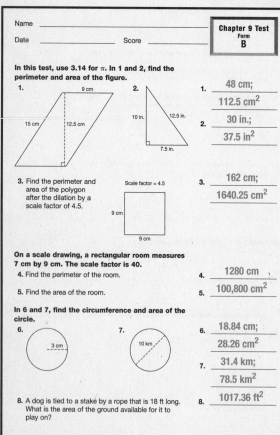

1.   2.

1. 48 cm; 112.5 cm²

2. 30 in.; 37.5 in²

3. Find the perimeter and area of the polygon after the dilation by a scale factor of 4.5.

Scale factor = 4.5

3. 162 cm; 1640.25 cm²

On a scale drawing, a rectangular room measures 7 cm by 9 cm. The scale factor is 40.

4. Find the perimeter of the room.

4. 1280 cm

5. Find the area of the room.

5. 100,800 cm²

In 6 and 7, find the circumference and area of the circle.

6.   7.

6. 18.84 cm; 28.26 cm²

7. 31.4 km; 78.5 km²

8. A dog is tied to a stake by a rope that is 18 ft long. What is the area of the ground available for it to play on?

8. 1017.36 ft²

Name _____

In 9–12, find the surface area of the figure.

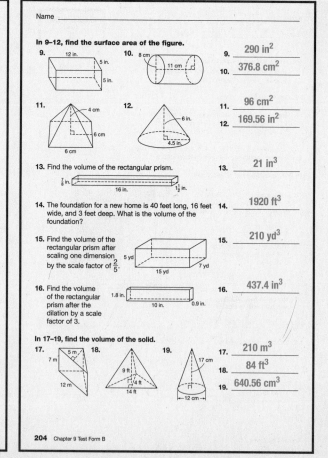

9.   10.

9. 290 in²

10. 376.8 cm²

11.   12.

11. 96 cm²

12. 169.56 in²

13. Find the volume of the rectangular prism.

13. 21 in³

14. The foundation for a new home is 40 feet long, 16 feet wide, and 3 feet deep. What is the volume of the foundation?

14. 1920 ft³

15. Find the volume of the rectangular prism after scaling one dimension by the scale factor of $\frac{2}{5}$.

15. 210 yd³

16. Find the volume of the rectangular prism after the dilation by a scale factor of 3.

16. 437.4 in³

In 17–19, find the volume of the solid.

17.   18.   19.

17. 210 m³

18. 84 ft³

19. 640.56 cm³

Name _____

Chapter 10 Test
Form
A

Name _____

Date _____ Score _____

In 1 and 2, use the function machine.

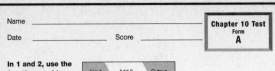

Input → Add 6 → Output

1. Find the output for an input of 6.

2. Find the input for an output of 60.

3. Complete the table of input and output values for $y = 2x + 3$. Then graph the equation. Does the equation describe a function?

1. _____ 12

2. _____ 54

3. _____ Yes

Input	Output
−4	−5
−3	−3
−2	−1
−1	1
0	3
1	5

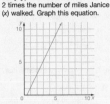

4. Larry (y) walked 1 mile less than 2 times the number of miles Janice (x) walked. Graph this equation.

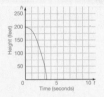

5. Graph the set of functions. Then describe the similarities and differences within the set of graphs.
$y = x^2$, $y = x^2 + 1$, $y = x^2 − 1$

6. A ball is dropped from a height of 200 feet. Ignoring air resistance, the function $h = −16t^2 + 200$, where t is the time in seconds and h is the height in feet, will model the situation. Graph this function. Estimate when the ball will hit the ground.

The graphs have the same general shapes, but they all have different y-values for each x-value.

Between 3 and 4 seconds

Name _____

7. Graph $y = 2.5^x$.

8. Arthur's telephone company rounds each long-distance call to the next whole minute. The rate is 15 cents per minute. Graph how much it will cost (y) if Arthur makes a long-distance telephone call for x minutes.

9. Write the polynomial expression $−2x + 3x^4 + 6 + 4x^2 − 2x^3$ in descending order.

$3x^4 − 2x^3 + 4x^2 − 2x + 6$

10. Evaluate $3x^4 − 2x^3 + 7x^2 − 5x + 1$ for $x = 3$.

10. _____ 238

11. The volume of a sphere is represented by the formula $V = \frac{4}{3}\pi r^3$, where V = volume and r = radius. Find the volume of air (to the nearest tenth) inside a soap bubble that is 4 inches in *diameter*. Use 3.14 for π.

11. _____ 33.5 in^3

In 12–16, simplify the polynomial expression. Write each answer in descending order.

12. $(3b^2 + 7b − 1) + (b^2 − 4b + 6)$

12. _____ $4b^2 + 3b + 5$

13. $2q^3 − q + 3$
    $+ \quad 7q + 9$

13. _____ $2q^3 + 6q + 12$

14. $(2a^2 + 5a + 3) − (a^2 + 4a + 1)$

14. _____ $a^2 + a + 2$

15. $(3v^3 + 2v^2 − v + 1)$
    $− (2v^3 + 2v^2 − 3v − 8)$

15. _____ $v^3 + 2v + 9$

16. $3u^2(2u^4 + u^3 − 2u)$

16. _____ $6u^6 + 3u^5 − 6u^3$

17. Multiply $(2.3 \times 10^3) \cdot (4.1 \times 10^2)$. Write your answer in scientific notation.

17. _____ 9.43×10^5

Name _____

Chapter 10 Test
Form
B

Date _____ Score _____

In 1 and 2, use the function machine.

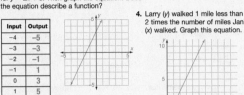

Input → Subtract 1 → Output

1. Find the output for an input of 20.

2. Find the input for an output of 5.

3. Complete the table of input and output values for $y = −x + 5$. Then graph the equation. Does the equation describe a function?

1. _____ 19

2. _____ 6

3. _____ Yes

Input	Output
5	0
4	1
3	2
2	3
1	4
0	5

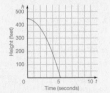

4. Regina (y) read 4 less than 3 times the number of books Tony (x) read. Graph this equation.

5. Graph the set of functions. Then describe the similarities and differences within the set of graphs.
$y = −x^2$, $y = −2x^2$, $y = −3x^2$

6. A ball is dropped from a height of 450 feet. Ignoring air resistance, the function $h = −16t^2 + 450$, where t is the time in seconds and h is the height in feet, will model the situation. Graph this function. Estimate when the ball will hit the ground.

The graphs have the same general shapes, but each has a different y-value for a given x-value.

Between 5 and 6 seconds

Name _____

7. Graph $y = 2^x$.

8. Al charges to the next higher half hour for baby-sitting. He charges $3.00 per half hour for baby-sitting the Miller children. Graph how much Al will charge (y) for baby-sitting the Miller children for x half hours.

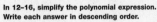

9. Write the polynomial expression $5x − 2x^4 + 7x^2 − x^3 + 4$ in descending order.

$−2x^4 − x^3 + 7x^2 + 5x + 4$

10. Evaluate $2x^4 − 5x^3 + 7x^2 − x + 6$ for $x = −1$.

10. _____ 21

11. The surface area of a sphere is represented by the formula $S = 4\pi r^2$, where S = surface area and r = radius. Find the surface area of a soap bubble that is 4 inches in *diameter*. Use 3.14 for π.

11. _____ 50.24 in^2

In 12–16, simplify the polynomial expression. Write each answer in descending order.

12. $(2a^3 − 7a^2 + 5) + (a^3 + 4a^2 − 2a)$

12. _____ $3a^3 − 3a^2 − 2a + 5$

13. $c^2 − 2c − 5$
    $+ \quad 3c + 6$

13. _____ $c^2 + c + 1$

14. $(4q^2 + 3q + 9) − (3q^2 − 2q + 7)$

14. _____ $q^2 + 5q + 2$

15. $(3r^3 + 6r^2 − 5r + 7)$
    $− (r^3 + 6r^2 − r + 2)$

15. _____ $2r^3 − 4r + 5$

16. $2v^3(7v^3 − 8v^2 + 4v)$

16. _____ $14v^6 − 16v^5 + 8v^4$

17. Multiply $(3.2 \times 10^4) \cdot (5.6 \times 10^3)$. Write your answer in scientific notation.

17. _____ 1.792×10^8

Name _____

Date _____ **Score** _____

You will need a calculator and/or trigonometric tables.

1. Are the figures similar?

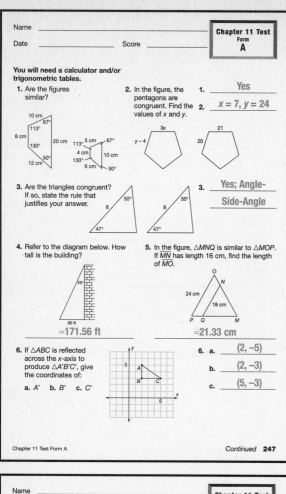

1. _____ Yes

2. In the figure, the pentagons are congruent. Find the values of x and y.

2. _____ $x = 7, y = 24$

3. Are the triangles congruent? If so, state the rule that justifies your answer.

3. _____ Yes; Angle-Side-Angle

4. Refer to the diagram below. How tall is the building?

5. In the figure, $\triangle MNQ$ is similar to $\triangle MOP$. If $\overline{MN}$ has length 16 cm, find the length of $\overline{MO}$.

≈171.56 ft

≈21.33 cm

6. If $\triangle ABC$ is reflected across the x-axis to produce $\triangle A'B'C'$, give the coordinates of:

a. A' b. B' c. C'

6. a. _____ $(2, -5)$

b. _____ $(2, -3)$

c. _____ $(5, -3)$

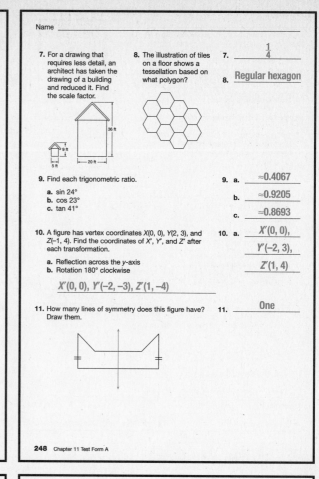

7. For a drawing that requires less detail, an architect has taken the drawing of a building and reduced it. Find the scale factor.

7. _____ $\frac{1}{4}$

8. The illustration of tiles on a floor shows a tessellation based on what polygon?

8. _____ Regular hexagon

9. Find each trigonometric ratio.

a. sin 24°
b. cos 23°
c. tan 41°

9. a. _____ ≈0.4067

b. _____ ≈0.9205

c. _____ ≈0.8693

10. A figure has vertex coordinates $X(0, 0)$, $Y(2, 3)$, and $Z(-1, 4)$. Find the coordinates of X', Y', and Z' after each transformation.

a. Reflection across the y-axis
b. Rotation 180° clockwise

$X'(0, 0), Y'(-2, -3), Z'(1, -3)$

10. a. _____ $X'(0, 0),$
$Y'(-2, 3),$
$Z'(1, 4)$

11. How many lines of symmetry does this figure have? Draw them.

11. _____ One

Name _____

Date _____ **Score** _____

You will need a calculator and/or trigonometric tables.

1. Are the rectangles similar?

1. _____ No

2. In the figure, the quadrilaterals are congruent. Find the values of x and y.

2. _____ $x = 7, y = 4$

3. Are the triangles congruent? If so, state the rule that justifies your answer.

3. _____ Yes; Side-Angle-Side

4. Refer to the figure. How tall is the tree?

4. _____ ≈28.87 ft

5. In the figure, $\triangle JKN$ is similar to $\triangle JLM$. If $\overline{JK}$ has length 6 cm, find the length of $\overline{JL}$.

5. _____ 9 cm

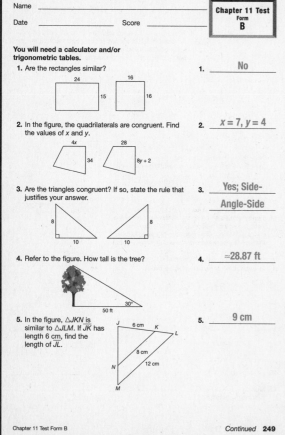

---

6. If $\triangle XYZ$ is reflected across the y-axis to produce $\triangle X'Y'Z'$, give the coordinates of:

a. X' b. Y' c. Z'

6. a. _____ $(7, -4)$

b. _____ $(1, -1)$

c. _____ $(3, -6)$

7. The car diagram on the left was enlarged. Find the scale factor.

7. _____ 4.5

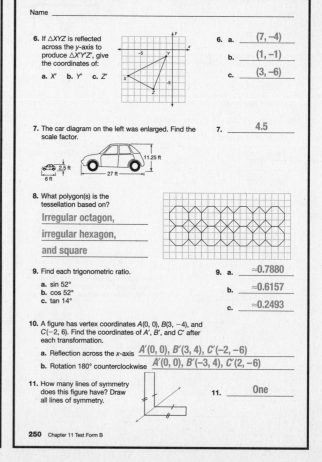

8. What polygon(s) is the tessellation based on?

Irregular octagon, irregular hexagon, and square

9. Find each trigonometric ratio.

a. sin 52°
b. cos 52°
c. tan 14°

9. a. _____ ≈0.7880

b. _____ ≈0.6157

c. _____ ≈0.2493

10. A figure has vertex coordinates $A(0, 0)$, $B(3, -4)$, and $C(-2, 6)$. Find the coordinates of A', B', and C' after each transformation.

a. Reflection across the x-axis
b. Rotation 180° counterclockwise

a. $A'(0, 0), B'(3, 4), C'(-2, -6)$
b. $A'(0, 0), B'(-3, 4), C'(2, -6)$

11. How many lines of symmetry does this figure have? Draw all lines of symmetry.

11. _____ One

Name _____

Date _____ Score _____

1. To upgrade his computer system with a new monitor, printer, and keyboard, Jon has a choice of a 256-color or monochrome (single-color) monitor; a choice of a dot-matrix, laser, or bubble-jet printer; and a choice of a standard, ergonomic, or extended keyboard. How many different ways can Jon upgrade his computer system?

1. **18 ways**

In 2–4, evaluate each expression.

2. 6!

2. **720**

3. 8(7!)

3. **40,320**

4. $\frac{8!}{4!(8-4)!}$

4. **70**

5. How many ways can the letters of the word COMPUTE be arranged?

5. **5040 ways**

6. After upgrading her computer system, Amy purchased 7 computer games. How many different ways can she arrange 4 games from among the 7?

6. **840**

7. The computer store has 9 service technicians. Three service technicians work each shift. How many different 3-technician groups can be formed?

7. **84 groups**

8. A particular commercial appears on a half-hour television program. What is the probability that the commercial will be shown during the first 6 minutes of the program? Give your answer as a fraction, a decimal, and a percent.

8. **$\frac{1}{5}$; 0.2; 20%**

9. A computer disk is chosen at random from among 5 disks of a word-processing program, 4 disks of a drawing program, and 7 disks of a telecommunications program. How many outcomes are in the sample space? What is the probability that the chosen disk is a telecommunications program?

9. **16; $\frac{7}{16}$**

Name _____

10. A family recorded the number of programs they watched on each of 5 different channels. Their results are shown. What is their experimental probability of watching a program on channel 56?

Channel	5	11	56	73	116
Number of programs	12	15	8	10	5

10. **$\frac{4}{25}$**

11. At the computer store, games are displayed on the 3 sides of the display rack shown below. Find the probability that a game is displayed on the 20-inch side.

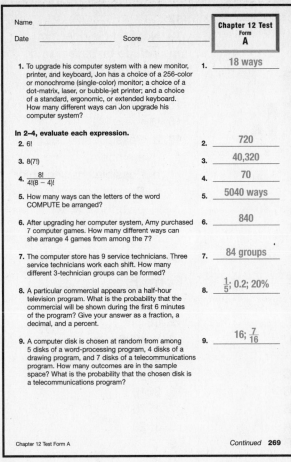

11. **$\frac{1}{4}$**

12. Find the probability that a game in Item 11 is *not* displayed on the 24-inch side.

12. **$\frac{7}{10}$**

In 13–16, a box contains 20 computer programs for display. There are 6 word-processing programs, 5 drawing programs, and 9 communications programs.

13. A program is chosen at random. The program is returned to the box, the box of programs is "mixed," and a second program is chosen. Find the probability that both programs are drawing programs.

13. **$\frac{1}{16}$**

14. Are the two events in Item 13 *independent* or *dependent* events?

14. **Independent**

15. Now suppose that the first program is not replaced before selecting the second program. Then what is the probability that both programs are drawing programs?

15. **$\frac{1}{19}$**

16. Are the two events in Item 15 *independent* or *dependent*?

16. **Dependent**

Name _____

Date _____ Score _____

1. A video-rental store has a comedy-action-horror weekend special. You can select 3 videos for $5 if you select one of 5 comedies, one of 6 action movies, and one of 4 horror movies. In how many ways can the weekend-special movies be selected?

1. **120**

In 2–4, evaluate each expression.

2. 4!

2. **24**

3. $\frac{9!}{6!}$

3. **504**

4. $\frac{5!}{3!(5-3)!}$

4. **10**

5. In how many ways can you arrange the letters of the word TABLE?

5. **120 ways**

6. The video store has 9 "high-seas-adventure" movies. How many different ways can you arrange an "all-day show" of 4 of them?

6. **3024**

7. The video store offers 12 different kinds of "good-deal" coupons. How many different ways can you select 4 of the coupons?

7. **495**

8. The video store has a list of 250 comedies, but 40 of them are already rented and not available. If you choose a comedy from the complete list, what is the probability that the tape is available? Give your answer as a fraction, a decimal, and a percent.

8. **$\frac{21}{25}$; 0.84; 84%**

9. A tool is selected at random from a box containing 8 screwdrivers, 4 hammers, and 7 wrenches. How many outcomes are in the sample space? What is the probability that the chosen tool is a hammer?

9. **19; $\frac{4}{19}$**

10. A video store recorded the categories for 75 rental videos. Their results are shown. What is the experimental probability of renting an adventure video?

10. **$\frac{4}{15}$**

Category	Comedy	Horror	Adventure	Animation	Documentary	Musical
Number of videos rented	17	18	20	12	3	5

Name _____

11. The video store has a display wall for new titles, as shown in the figure below. Find the probability that a new title is displayed in Section D.

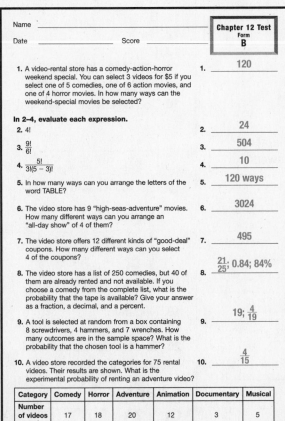

11. **$\frac{3}{14}$**

12. Find the probability that the title in Item 11 is in Section B or Section C.

12. **$\frac{9}{14}$**

In 13–16, a box contains 30 videotapes: 15 comedies, 10 action adventures, and 5 horror movies.

13. A tape is chosen at random. The tape is returned to the box, the tapes in the box are "mixed," and a second tape is chosen. Find the probability that both tapes are horror movies.

13. **$\frac{1}{36}$**

14. Are the two events in Item 13 *independent* or *dependent* events?

14. **Independent**

15. Suppose that the first tape is not replaced before selecting the second tape. Then find the probability that both tapes are horror movies.

15. **$\frac{2}{87}$**

16. In Item 15, are the events *independent* or *dependent*?

16. **Dependent**

Answers

Inventory Test

1. A	**20.** D
2. A	**21.** D
3. B	**22.** B
4. C	**23.** C
5. B	**24.** B
6. C	**25.** C
7. A	**26.** A
8. D	**27.** A
9. C	**28.** B
10. D	**29.** D
11. D	**30.** A
12. B	**31.** D
13. A	**32.** A
14. B	**33.** C
15. C	**34.** B
16. D	**35.** C
17. C	**36.** D
18. B	**37.** D
19. A	**38.** A

Chapter 1

Quiz 1A

1. Main Use of the Home Computer

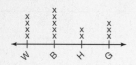

2.

Stem	Leaf
4	7 8 8 9
5	0 1 2 2 5 6

3. ≈ 19.4; 17.5; 23

4.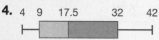
4   9   17.5   32   42

5. March; May

6. 35%

7. B

Quiz 1B

1. After-School Chorus; No

2. Number of CDs or Tapes
Purchased by Students

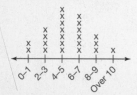

3. Number of CDs or Tapes
Puchased by Students

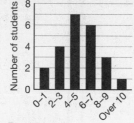

4. Positive

5. Negative

6. Possible answer: Juice manufacturer

7. B

Chapter 1 Test
Form C

1. B	**14.** C
2. C	**15.** D
3. A	**16.** A
4. D	**17.** C
5. A	**18.** C
6. C	**19.** B
7. D	**20.** A
8. D	**21.** B
9. B	**22.** D
10. C	**23.** B
11. C	**24.** C
12. B	**25.** D
13. A	**26.** A

Chapter 1 Test
Form D

See the back of Chapter 1 Test Form D for answers.

Chapter 1 Test
Form E

1. C

2. 6; 6

3. C

4. B

5. 118.2

6. 116

7. Yes; 114

8.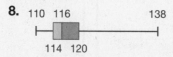
110   116   138
       114   120

9. 110–138, or 28

10. A

11. B

12. C

13. No; Sample does not include taxpayers who have no children in school.

14. C

15. No trend

16. D

17. a. Possible answer: club members

b. Possible answer: color

c. Possible answer: line plot; to show what most club members prefer

Chapter 1 Test
Form F

1. 87.3

2. 88

3. Yes; 88

4. 8, 7, 11, 9, 12, 8, 7

5. 31

6. 3010

7. 1575

8. 5, 23

9. C

10. B

11. B

12. B

13. C

14. 678, 768, 786, 876

15. 201, 2001, 2010, 2100

16. October Baby-sitting Days

17. Heart Rate Workouts

18. Negative

19. C

20. To determine people's sports-watching habits

Chapter 2
Quiz 2A

1. −78 ft, −27 ft, −10 ft, 8 ft, 66 ft

2. >
3. 1
4. 23
5. On the 1st step
6. 177
7. −25
8. −20
9. −12
10. $1\frac{1}{2}$ gal/hr; 216 gal
11. $3 \times 2 + 3 \times 5$
12. $(2 + 8)$
13. −3
14. A

Quiz 2B

1. (−2, −1)
2. (0, 4)
3. (3, 2)
4. (2, −5)
5.

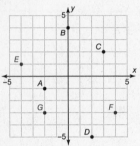

6. See grid.
7. See grid.
8. 343
9. 625
10. 4
11. 29,000
12. 582,600,000
13. 2.2×10^{-2}
14. D

Chapter 2 Test
Form C

1. B	**13.** D
2. A	**14.** C
3. C	**15.** B
4. D	**16.** D
5. B	**17.** A
6. C	**18.** C
7. B	**19.** D
8. C	**20.** C
9. D	**21.** D
10. D	**22.** D
11. A	**23.** B
12. B	**24.** D

25. B	**32.** B
26. B	**33.** C
27. B	**34.** B
28. D	**35.** C
29. A	**36.** B
30. D	**37.** D
31. A	**38.** C

Chapter 2 Test
Form D

See the back of Chapter 2
Test Form D for answers.

Chapter 2 Test
Form E

1. −21, −11, 0, 12, 27
2. I−13I, I5I, I0I
3. C
4. D
5. 10
6. $19
7. 246
8. −20 − (−5) − (−3)
9. 3 degrees
10. $8; $96
11. 0
12. 10
13. C
14. C
15. D
16. 4^3
17. 4.202×10^3
18. B
19. 9.91×10^{-2}
20. B
21. a. 2×10^{-4} m
6×10^{-5} m
8×10^{-5} m
9×10^{-4} m
2.6×10^{-6} m
b. 2.5 times
The size of Cell A is
2×10^{-4} m. The size of
the microscope slide is
2×10^{-2} m. The cell
would fit on the slide.

Chapter 2 Test
Form F

1. D
2. C

3. 1
4. 729
5. 5.2010916×10^7
6. 9.922×10^{-4}
7. A
8. C
9. $(-6 \bullet 5) + (-6 \bullet 3)$
10. M
11. D
12. C
13. I−14I
14. In the center of town
15. $43 + (−$7) + (−$2) + (−$4)
= $30
16. A
17. B
18. D
19.

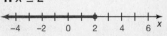

Chapter 3
Quiz 3A

1. 18.84
2. 28.26
3. 58
4. 15
5. 77
6. 51
7. $a = 18$
8. $g = 9$
9. $x = 21$
10. $y = -8$
11. $c + 12$
12. $8z$
13. $10 - 2x$
14. $\frac{d}{7}$
15. B

Quiz 3B

1. $h = 22$
2. $c = 25$
3. $x = -14$
4. $b = 40$
5. $n = -5$
6. $y = 40$
7. $x = 4$
8. $a = 60$
9. 24 pounds
10. 6
11. $x \le 2$

12. $n > -4$

13. At least 8 hr
14. \$5
15. B

Chapter 3 Test
Form C

1. C	**14.** B
2. D	**15.** A
3. D	**16.** D
4. B	**17.** D
5. A	**18.** B
6. C	**19.** A
7. B	**20.** C
8. D	**21.** A
9. D	**22.** B
10. A	**23.** B
11. C	**24.** A
12. C	**25.** C
13. B	**26.** C

Chapter 3 Test
Form D

See the back of Chapter 3 Test Form D for answers.

Chapter 3 Test
Form E

1. 27
2. B
3. $x = -10$
4. C
5. A
6. C
7. $24 \div x$
8. $2a - 1$
9. D
10. D
11. B
12. $n = -12$
13. $b = -18$
14. B
15. $w = 63$
16. $x \geq 2$

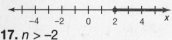

17. $n > -2$

18. At least 32 min
19. $d = 90$ miles
20. Possible answers:
$\frac{x}{3} + 5 = 9; x = 12$
$2x - 3 > 1; x > 2$

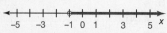

Chapter 3 Test
Form F

1. D
2. 16
3. 63
4. C
5. 5
6. −10
7. $x = -42$
8. $y = 7$
9. $n = 24$
10. $z = -4$
11. $w = -7.5$
12. $k = -12$
13. $a = -18$
14. $w = 3$
15. C
16. $2n - 10$
17. 4 times the sum of n and 8
18. 7 less than the product of 3 and x
19. D
20. $x \geq -1$

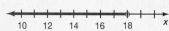

21. $x < 18$

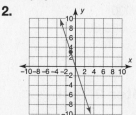

22. 82; 81
23. $\frac{1}{4}x - 3 = 9$; 48 points
24. C
25. 24 m
26. C
27. 5000 ft

Quarterly Test
Chapters 1–3

1. A	**7.** C
2. C	**8.** D
3. B	**9.** A
4. C	**10.** A
5. D	**11.** D
6. A	**12.** B

13. D	**23.** C
14. B	**24.** C
15. A	**25.** D
16. C	**26.** B
17. B	**27.** A
18. C	**28.** D
19. C	**29.** C
20. B	**30.** B
21. B	**31.** A
22. C	**32.** C

Chapter 4
Quiz 4A

1. $y = 2$
2. $y = 14$
3.

x	0	1	2	3	4
y	1	3	5	7	9

4. No
5. Yes
6. $y = 2x + 3$
7.

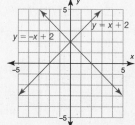

8. C

Quiz 4B

1. −1; 3; 3
2.

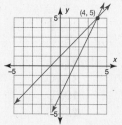

3. −3; 0; 0
4.

5.

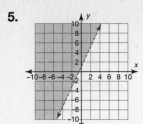

6. 4 hours

7. D

Chapter 4 Test
Form C

1. B	**12.** D
2. C	**13.** B
3. A	**14.** C
4. D	**15.** D
5. B	**16.** D
6. C	**17.** A
7. D	**18.** D
8. D	**19.** B
9. D	**20.** B
10. B	**21.** A
11. A	

Chapter 4 Test
Form D

See the back of Chapter 4 Test Form D for answers.

Chapter 4 Test
Form E

1. $y = 2$

2. A

3. Possible answer: (12, 0), (0, −8)

4.

x	0	1	2	3	4	5
y	6	8	10	12	14	16

5. C

6.

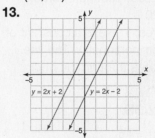

7. A

8.

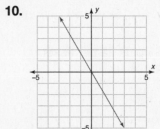

9. B

10.

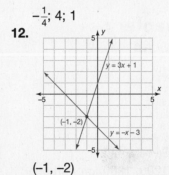

11.

$-\frac{1}{4}$; 4; 1

12.

(−1, −2)

13.

Yes; The slopes are equal so the lines do not intersect.

14.

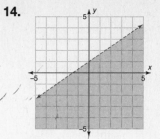

15. Possible answer:
(1, \$3000), (2, \$5000) 2;
$y = 2x + 1$
Week 2
It is true according to the graph, but would not be true in real life. In real life, a business would not make an income before it started.
Probably not. A business might show an initial high growth in income as people first try it, but as time went by business would probably become steady or at least show a slower rate of growth.

Chapter 4 Test
Form F

1. $y = 0$

2. Possible answer:
(−6, 0), (0, 4)

3.

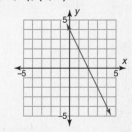

−2; 2; 4

4. B

5. D

6. $t = 36$

7. $y = 3$

8. $y = 3x − 2$

9. A

10.

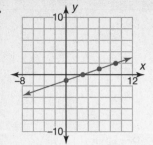

11.

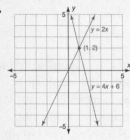

(1, 2)

12.

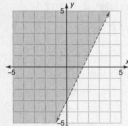

No; The lines intersect.

13.

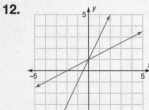

14. B

15. 2x + 4

16.

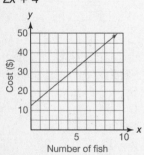

$40

17.

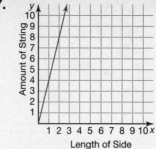

y = 4x

18. y = 0.15x + 1.50

19. $\frac{1}{10}$

20. $5 plus $2 per ticket

21. 9.3 × 10⁷

22.

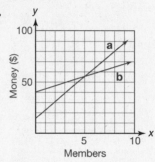

c. 5 members

Chapter 5
Quiz 5A

1. 3:1

2. 1:4

3. $\frac{\$21}{hour}$

4. $\frac{8}{20}$

5. 8, 14, 21, 32

6. 1200, 1200; proportional

7. 20

8. Yes; There is a constant of proportionality. The line goes through the origin.

9. D

Quiz 5B

1. m = 45

2. p = 3.5

3. 160 packs

4. 42 words/min

5. $3.95/lb

6. 212 votes

7. a = 144; c = 13

8. 2187.5 miles

9. 3.5 inches

10. C

Chapter 5 Test
Form C

1. C   **13.** D

2. A   **14.** B

3. D   **15.** D

4. B   **16.** B

5. C   **17.** C

6. D   **18.** B

7. A   **19.** C

8. C   **20.** C

9. C   **21.** C

10. A   **22.** A

11. A   **23.** C

12. A   **24.** A

Chapter 5 Test
Form D

See the back of Chapter 5 Test Form D for answers.

Chapter 5 Test
Form E

1. 5:3

2. A

3. Neil

4. B

5. 10, 15, 16, 20, 30

6. 78 photographs

7. No; 61.50, 62.25

8. C

9. 1, 2, 6, 8, 5

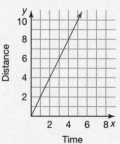

Slope = 2

10. D

11. $0.25

12. 352.5 minutes

13. A

14. $\frac{150}{5} = \frac{400}{x}$

15. A

16. 120 miles

17. 14.5 feet

18. 40 cm

20 cm

No; The cross products are not equal.

15.00, 17.50, 20.00, 22.50, 25.00, 27.50, 30.00, 32.50

Actual values are A: $10.77, B: $20.40, and C: $30.27.

Chapter 5 Test

Form F

1. 55 miles/hour
2. C
3. 3, $2.80, $4.20, 12, $7.00
4. 245, 245; proportional
5. $\frac{2}{5}$
6. $x = 22$
7. B
8. $y = -8$
9. $x = 60$
10.

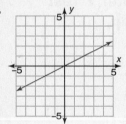

11. $\frac{10}{10}$
12. C
13. A
14. A
15. B
16. $\frac{20}{x} = \frac{4}{\$0.99}$ or $\frac{20}{4} = \frac{x}{\$0.99}$
17. B
18. Shape
19. C
20. 1
21. C
22. Baseball and basketball
23. 5 dogs and 5 cats
24. 2, 4, 6, 8, 10, 12, 14, 16

16 feet
25. Pecans
26. **a.** 13.5 minutes

b. 1250 words
27. 22 RBIs
28. 42 miles

Chapter 6

Quiz 6A

1. $\frac{27}{100}$; 0.27; 27%
2. 180%
3. 0.2; $\frac{1}{5}$
4. 248
5. 25%
6. 30
7. 25%
8. 40
9. $110
10. B

Quiz 6B

1. 50%	7. $15.50
2. 40%	8. 105
3. $40	9. $6.30
4. 6%	10. $180
5. 60%	11. $5290
6. $200	12. C

Chapter 6 Test

Form C

1. C	17. A
2. A	18. D
3. D	19. B
4. C	20. C
5. B	21. B
6. D	22. D
7. C	23. A
8. A	24. B
9. B	25. A
10. D	26. B
11. B	27. C
12. A	28. B
13. B	29. C
14. C	30. B
15. D	31. A
16. C	32. D

Chapter 6 Test

Form D

See the back of Chapter 6 Test Form D for answers.

Chapter 6 Test

Form E

1. B
2. $\frac{7}{8}$; 0.875

3. 112
4. 890
5. A
6. 25%
7. 15% increase
8. 20% decrease
9. 4% decrease
10. $40
11. $17.15
12. B
13. $40.71
14. $22.49
15. A
16. B
17. $560
18. C
19. **a.** $864

b. He should wait; an $800 car with a price increase of 23% followed by a price decrease of 20% will cost $787.20.

c. First option: $960; Second option: $933.12

Chapter 6 Test

Form F

1. 212.5
2. $\frac{11}{20}$; 0.55
3. B
4. D
5. $x = 5$
6. 70%
7. 12.5%
8. 37.5%
9. 2
10. B
11. C
12. Neither; they both result in a selling price of $108.
13. B
14. $40
15. $1.20
16. $11.50
17. D
18. $375
19. Healthy Hearts
20. $20
21. C

Quarterly Test
Chapters 1–6

1. D	17. A
2. C	18. C
3. B	19. A
4. C	20. D
5. A	21. B
6. D	22. B
7. B	23. C
8. A	24. A
9. C	25. C
10. D	26. D
11. D	27. A
12. B	28. C
13. C	29. A
14. D	30. B
15. B	31. D
16. B	

Chapter 7
Quiz 7A

1. 2, 3, 5, 6, 10
2. Prime
3. 2, 3, 6
4. $2^3 \times 5 \times 13$
5. $2^2 \times 71$
6. $2^4 \times 5$
7. 3
8. 6
9. 25
10. 21
11. 72
12. 100
13. B

Quiz 7B

1. –2.1, –0.5, 1.6
2. $\frac{3}{4}, \frac{13}{16}, \frac{5}{6}$
3. 1.7, $1\frac{3}{4}$, $2\frac{1}{3}$
4. $\frac{16}{25}$; Terminating
5. $\frac{35}{99}$; Repeating
6. $5\frac{11}{12}$
7. $8\frac{1}{6}$
8. $1\frac{11}{30}$
9. $1\frac{1}{9}$
10. $\frac{3}{8}$
11. $3\frac{1}{3}$
12. B

Quiz 7C

1. Yes
2. 9, 10
3. $-\frac{11}{15}$
4. Irrational
5. 28.653
6. ≈ 9.06 in.
7. $\sqrt{52} \approx 7.21$
8. $\sqrt{80} \approx 8.94$
9. 9
10. C

Chapter 7 Test
Form C

1. D	19. C
2. A	20. B
3. C	21. A
4. B	22. B
5. B	23. A
6. D	24. C
7. C	25. D
8. C	26. B
9. D	27. C
10. B	28. D
11. B	29. A
12. B	30. C
13. A	31. A
14. D	32. B
15. C	33. C
16. C	34. A
17. B	35. D
18. A	

Chapter 7 Test
Form D

See the back of Chapter 7 Test Form D for answers.

Chapter 7 Test
Form E

1. B
2. $2 \times 5^2 \times 17$
3. A
4. $\frac{5}{6}$
5. D
6. Every 12 days
7. $\frac{12}{37}$
8. C
9. $7\frac{7}{15}$
10. A
11. $10\frac{1}{2}$
12. C
13. D
14. 121, 144
15. Irrational
16. B
17. no
18. $\sqrt{164} \approx 12.81$
19. $\sqrt{363} \approx 19.05$
20. a. $2^2 \times 3^4 \times 7^2$; Find the square root of each factor: $2 \times 3^2 \times 7 = 126 = \sqrt{15,876}$
 b. $2^2 \times 5^4$; Find the square root of each factor: $2 \times 5^2 = 50 = \sqrt{2500}$
 c. $2^2 \times 3^4 \times 5^2$; Find the square root of each factor: $2 \times 3^2 \times 5 = 90 = \sqrt{8100}$

Chapter 7 Test
Form F

1. B
2. $5\frac{1}{24}$
3. $2\frac{7}{24}$
4. 4
5. $\frac{3}{4}$
6. C
7. $x = -1$
8. D
9. $-\frac{2}{3}$
10. B
11. 1
12. 120
13. D
14. $-1.2, -\frac{3}{4}, \frac{2}{3}, \frac{5}{6}$
15. 5.2, $5\frac{1}{6}$, 5.16, $5\frac{1}{8}$
16. C
17. 19.3
18. A
19. $y = 2x - 3$
20. $\sqrt{57} \approx 7.55$
21. $\sqrt{125} \approx 11.18$
22. 9 by 12, 36 by 6
23. 50%
24. $7\frac{3}{8}$ lb
25. $15\frac{5}{8}$ mi

Chapter 8

Quiz 8A

1. miles
2. cm^2
3. 0.25 m
4. 2.25 lb
5. 0.8 cm
6. 5.5 in.
7. 15.9 g
8. 28 ft^2
9. About 4.5°
10. D-3
11. A

Quiz 8B

1. Obtuse
2. 87.5°
3. 65°
4.

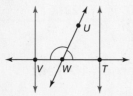

5. ∠3 and ∠6; ∠4 and ∠5
6. 62°
7. Yes
8. No
9.

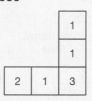

10. D

Chapter 8 Test

Form C

1. B	16. B
2. C	17. C
3. D	18. A
4. A	19. D
5. B	20. C
6. D	21. B
7. A	22. A
8. C	23. B
9. C	24. D
10. B	25. D
11. A	26. A
12. C	27. C
13. A	28. C
14. A	29. D
15. D	

Chapter 8 Test

Form D

See the back of Chapter 8 Test Form D for answers.

Chapter 8 Test

Form E

1. Ounce
2. C
3. C
4. 70 mi
5. 33° N, 97° W
6. D
7. About 5°
8.

9. 40°
10. 140°
11. D
12. 65°; 155°
13. ∠1 and ∠7, ∠2 and ∠8
14. C
15. Right, or 90°
16. A
17. Octagon
18. 1080°
19.

20. B
21. Answers will vary. Check students' work.

Chapter 8 Test

Form F

1. 95
2. $\frac{11}{30}$
3. A
4. C
5. 81
6. A
7. B
8. 194 in.
9. 2
10. D

11. Meter
12. 0.685 ft
13. Obtuse

14. 85°; 95°
15. A
16. Side AC
17. C
18. B
19. Square
20.

21. 34° N, 118° W
22. About 2°
23. San Luis Obispo

Chapter 9

Quiz 9A

1. 42 in.; 84 in^2
2. 126 mm; 810 mm^2
3. 62.8 mm; 314 mm^2
4. 76.5 ft^2
5. 163.3 cm^2
6. 96 ft^2
7. 282.6 mm^2
8. D

Quiz 9B

1. 75 cm^3
2. 176 in^3
3. 48 ft^3
4. 213.52 cm^3
5. 50 m^3
6. 75.36 cm^3
7. D

Chapter 9 Test

Form C

1. B	9. A
2. A	10. A
3. C	11. C
4. C	12. B
5. C	13. A
6. B	14. B
7. D	15. A
8. B	16. C

17. B   **21.** D
18. A   **22.** A
19. C   **23.** D
20. C

Chapter 9 Test
Form D

See the back of Chapter 9 Test Form D for answers.

Chapter 9 Test
Form E

1. 48 in.; 120 in^2
2. 150.72 mm; 1808.64 mm^2
3. 2336.16 cm^2
4. 800 m^2
5. 1280 m^3
6. 703.36 mm^2; 1230.88 mm^3
7. 276 cm^2; 228 cm^3
8. 549.5 in^3; 376.8 in^2
9. C
10. A
11. B
12. C
13. D
14. Possible answer: Designing or purchasing moving boxes; Sketches will vary.

Chapter 9 Test
Form F

1. 20 in.; 25 in^2
2. C
3. D
4. 15%
5. B
6. 62 in^2; 30 in^3
7. D
8. C
9. B
10. 20.41 ft^2
11. 1130.4 cm^2; 2512 cm^3
12. 2; (–2, 0); (0, 4)
13. 112.5 cm^3
14. 207.24 cm^2; 226.08 cm
15. 8192 ft^3
16. 25%
17. 119.32 ft
18. 6480 in^3, or 3.75 ft^3

---

19. 8, 18, 43, 78
20. 80 questions

Quarterly Test
Chapters 1–9

1. D   **17.** D
2. B   **18.** A
3. C   **19.** D
4. A   **20.** B
5. C   **21.** B
6. D   **22.** A
7. A   **23.** C
8. B   **24.** D
9. C   **25.** A
10. C   **26.** C
11. A   **27.** B
12. B   **28.** C
13. C   **29.** A
14. A   **30.** C
15. C   **31.** B
16. B

Chapter 10
Quiz 10A

1. One
2. –6
3. 5
4. Exponential
5. Quadratic
6.

Functional		
Input	Rule	Output
x	$5x - 2$	y
–1	$5(-1) - 2$	–7
0	$5(0) - 2$	–2
1	$5(1) - 2$	3

7.

Functional		
Input	Rule	Output
x	$2x^2 - 1$	y
–1	$2(-1)^2 - 1$	1
0	$2(0)^2 - 1$	–1
1	$2(1)^2 - 1$	1

8. 5
9. B

Quiz 10B

1. Binomial
2. 4
3. 64 cm^3
4. $9m^2 + 6m - 1$
5. $5u^2 - 4u + 8$
6. $9c^3 - c^2 - 9c + 15$

---

7. $v^2 + 2v - 6$
8. $-18y^5$
9. $8x^3 + 12x^2 - 4x$
10. $5x^2 + 4x + 1$
    58 ft^2
11. C

Chapter 10 Test
Form C

1. B   **13.** D
2. C   **14.** C
3. B   **15.** A
4. D   **16.** D
5. A   **17.** C
6. D   **18.** B
7. B   **19.** C
8. A   **20.** D
9. D   **21.** B
10. C   **22.** C
11. C   **23.** B
12. B   **24.** C

Chapter 10 Test
Form D

See the back of Chapter 10 Test Form D for answers.

Chapter 10 Test
Form E

1. C
2. Add 4
3. Multiply by 2 and subtract 1
4. a. 3, 5, 7, 9, 11
   b.

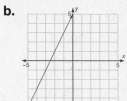

5. 22, 7, –2, –5, –2, 7, 22
6. B
7. C
8. All are parabolas. One is one unit up from $y = \frac{1}{2}x^2$, one is one unit down from $y = \frac{1}{2}x^2$.
9. A
10. B
11. C

12. **a.** 40
b. 13
13. $8x^3 + 2x^2 - x + 4$
14. D
15. $2x^2 + 2x + 4$
16. B
17. $v^3 - 2v^2 + 4v + 11$
18. $x^2 + 3x + 3$
19. A
20. **a.** Answers will vary. Values should fit the equation $y = 16x$. No negative values should be given.
b. $y = 4x + 1$
c. Long sides of the box should have dimensions of $6 \times (4x + 1)$. Short sides of the box should have dimensions of 6×4. The bottom of the box should have dimensions of $5 \times (4x + 1)$.

Chapter 10 Test
Form F
1. B
2. $3m^3 + 2m^2 + 3m - 5$
3. $2y^2 - 2y + 4$
4. $16t^{12}$
5. $-5v^4 + 35v^3 - 20v^2$
6. 43
7. C
8. 576 in^3
9. $x = 45.36$
10. 12;72
11. D
12. C
13. C
14. B
15. A
16. $3m^2 - 6m + 8$
17. B
18. A
19. $y = 8x$
20. 33 ft

21.

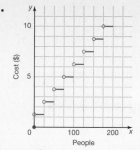

22. $y = x^3 + 2x^2 - 3x + 200$
23. $13.65
24. 2 boxes; 5 bags

Chapter 11
Quiz 11A
1. 6 in.
2. They are not congruent. They have the same shape but not the same size.
3. They are congruent by Side-Angle-Side.
4. ≈ 106.01
5. ≈ 58.12 ft
6. ≈ 866 ft
7. C

Quiz 11B
1. Translation
2. (2, −4), (3, −1), (8, −5), (6, −8)
3. (4, 6), (−2, −4), (2, 2)
4. 8
5. Possible answer:

6. A

Chapter 11 Test
Form C
1. C	10. B
2. A	11. A
3. B	12. C
4. C	13. D
5. B	14. C
6. D	15. B
7. A	16. A
8. D	17. B
9. D	18. D

Chapter 11 Test
Form D
See the back of Chapter 11 Test Form D for answers.

Chapter 11 Test
Form E
1. No
2. B
3. C
4. Side-Angle-Side
5. **a.** 45°
b. ≈ 0.7071
6. ≈ 6.04
7. 10.5
8. D
9. B
10.

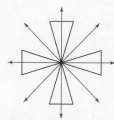

11. Possible answer:

Chapter 11 Test
Form F
1. A
2. 7
3. 6
4. C
5. 9.688
6. $2x^3 - 4x^2 + 3x + 3$
7. D
8. D
9. ≈ 18.55
10. 18 cm
11. D
12. (20, 15)
13. C
14. ≈ 5553 ft
15. ≈ 602.63 cm
16.

Chapter 12

Quiz 12A

1. 120
2. 144
3. 990
4. 56
5.

6. 5! = 120
7. 5040
8. 2520
9. 20
10. C

Quiz 12B

1. Orange, blue, blue, red, red, red, red, yellow
2. 1; $\frac{1}{8}$
3. 2; $\frac{1}{4}$
4. $\frac{1}{8}$
5. $\frac{1}{64}$
6. $\frac{1}{2}$
7. $\frac{1}{4}$
8. Independent
9. $\frac{11}{20}$
10. C

Chapter 12 Test

Form C

1. B
2. D
3. A
4. C
5. D
6. A
7. D
8. A
9. D
10. D
11. B
12. C
13. C
14. C
15. B
16. C
17. A
18. B
19. C
20. D
21. C
22. A
23. B
24. B
25. A
26. D
27. A
28. C
29. B

Chapter 12 Test

Form D

See the back of Chapter 12 Test Form D for answers.

Chapter 12 Test

Form E

1. 24
2.

3. 36
4. 120
5. 15
6. C
7. D
8. B
9. A
10. $\frac{5}{24}$
11. $\frac{5}{12}$
12. $\frac{1}{27}$
13. $\frac{2}{3}$
14. Independent
15. 1, 1, 4; 1, 2, 3; 1, 3, 2; 1, 4, 1; 2, 1, 3; 2, 2, 2; 2, 3, 1; 3, 1, 2; 3, 2, 1; 4, 1, 1. There is a total of 10 ways.

Chapter 12 Test

Form F

1. 144
2. 120
3. 21
4. 720
5. 64
6.

Heads — Red, Blue, White
Tails — Red, Blue, White

7. $x \le 6$
8. $x < 32$
9. $x \ge -\frac{3}{7}$
10. 480 in³

11. 5.376 m³
12. 2448 cm³
13. 25.5 cm x 18 cm x 18 cm; 8262 cm³
14. 1538.6 cm³
15. 0.785 m³
16. $\frac{15!}{2!\,(15-2)!} = 105$
17. $\frac{15!}{6!\,(15-6)!} = 5005$
18. Dependent
19. Independent
20. C
21. D
22. B
23. A
24. $\frac{1}{8}$
25. $\frac{1}{8}$
26. Independent
27. $\frac{1}{2}$
28. Yes
29. 1
30. $\frac{6}{55}$
31. $\frac{4}{9}$
32. $\frac{1}{4}$
33. $\frac{3}{8}$
34. $\frac{1}{6}$
35. $\frac{1}{2}$

Quarterly Test

Chapters 1–12

1. C
2. D
3. C
4. A
5. B
6. B
7. C
8. A
9. B
10. B
11. D
12. B
13. A
14. C
15. D
16. A
17. D
18. C
19. B
20. B
21. A
22. D
23. C
24. C
25. B
26. D
27. C
28. D
29. A
30. A
31. B

Table of Contents for Management Forms

Using Management Forms

There are several types of forms included in the *Assessment Sourcebook*. Some forms can be used to record results of student assessment. Other forms offer at-a-glance information about content objectives. Also included is a Percent Table that provides assistance in scoring formal assessments. Each type of form is described below.

Item Analysis for Individual Assessment: Inventory Test

The Inventory Test can be used as a baseline assessment at the beginning of the school year. The Item Analysis Form for this test can be used to plan activities and assignments that address the strengths and weaknesses of individual students.

> "Together, assessment and instruction can build on students' understanding, interests, and experiences."
>
> —NCTM Assessment Standards for School Mathematics

Item Analysis for Individual Assessment: Chapters 1–12

Item Analysis Forms for the variety of chapter tests can be used to evaluate student understanding of specific objectives. The forms can also be used to look for patterns in class performance on specific objectives.

These Item Analysis Forms also provide suggestions for Review Options for specific objectives. Options for the Student Edition are listed, along with pages from the Practice and Reteaching Components.

Item Analysis for Individual Assessment: Quarterly Tests

Use the Item Analysis Form for Quarterly Tests to assess student and group performance and plan instruction for the following quarter.

Class Test Record Form

This two-page form may be used for recording Chapter Test scores and Quarterly Test scores for the whole class for an entire year.

Percent Table for Scoring Tests

This table, found on page 345, can be used to convert a raw test score to a percent score for any test containing up to 53 items.

Item Analysis for Individual Assessment

Inventory Test

Student Name _____ **See page 345 for scoring.**

Place a ✔ in the column if the student has answered some or all of the questions correctly.

Objectives from Grade 7	Inventory Test		Review Options in Grade 7 Supplements	
	Test Item	✔ if correct	Practice (pages)	Reteaching (pages)
to make a stem-and-leaf diagram	1		3	3
to find the mean, median, mode, and range for a set of data	2		4	4
to recognize relationships in data	3		7	6
to use the order of operations to find the value of expressions	4		12	9
to translate words and phrases into algebraic expressions	5		16	12
to solve multiplication and division equations using inverse operations	6		18	14
to round to the nearest place	7		23	17
to write large numbers in scientific notation	9		26	20
to find sums and differences of fractions	10		36	27
to find sums and differences of mixed numbers	11		37	28
to multiply mixed numbers	8, 12		40	30
to find the angle sum of polygons	13		47	35
to find a square root	14		50	37
to learn the Pythagorean Theorem	15		51	38
to make comparisons to one unit	16		58	43
to find equivalent ratios and rates	17		59	44
to use unit rates to solve a proportion	20		64	48
to use cross multiplication to solve a proportion	18		65	49
to estimate distances from maps using scales	19		68	50
to solve problems involving conversion of rates	21		75	56
to use equations to solve problems involving percents	24		87	64
to solve problems involving percent increase and percent decrease	22, 23		89	66
to graph points on a coordinate plane	25		94	69
to add integers	26		96	70
to multiply integers	27		98	72
to write an equation from a table of values	28		105	77
to solve addition and subtraction equations involving positive and negative integers	29		112	82

Continued on next page.

Item Analysis for Individual Assessment

Inventory Test (continued)

Student Name _____   See page 345 for scoring.

Place a ✔ in the column if the student has answered some or all of the questions correctly.

Objectives from Grade 7	Inventory Test		Review Options in Grade 7 Supplements	
	Test Item	✔ if correct	Practice (pages)	Reteaching (pages)
to solve two-step equations involving positive and negative integers	30		114	84
to name polyhedrons	31		118	86
to find the volume of a prism	32		121	89
to make circle graphs	33		123	90
to find the area of a circle	34		125	92
to count the number of ways items can be arranged	35		135	99
to calculate the number of ways to choose some items out of a larger group when the order is unimportant	36		136	100
to find the probability of an event	37		139	102
to find the probabilities of dependent and independent events	38		141	104

Item Analysis for Individual Assessment: Chapter 1

Chapter 1: Data Analysis

Student Name _____

Place a ✔ in the column if the student has answered some or all of the questions correctly.

For Test Form D, check all the objectives that are reflected in the student's response.

Quiz or Test Form	Score	Date

Review Options in Student Edition
- Section A Review, page 30
- Section B Review, page 52
- Chapter 1 Summary and Review, page 54
- Chapter 1 Assessment, page 56

Lesson	Objectives	Quizzes Items	✔	Chapter Test Forms A & B Items	✔	Chapter Test Form C Items	✔	Chapter Test Form D ✔	Chapter Test Form E Items	✔	Chapter Test Form F Items	✔	Review Options in Supplements: Practice and Reteaching Masters (pages)
Section A													
1-1	how to understand data with line plots and stem-and-leaf diagrams	1, 2		6, 10		1–4			1–4		8, 16		P(1); R(1)
1-2	how to analyze and represent data using mean, median, and mode	3, 7		1		5–7, 23, 24		d	5–7		1–3		P(2); R(2)
1-3	how to analyze and represent the spread and distribution of data using box-and-whisker plots	4		2		8–10			8, 9		9, 10		P(3); R(3)
1-4	how to understand data using bar graphs and line graphs	5, 6		3, 4		11–14			10–12		11, 12		P(4); R(4)
Section B													
1-5	to understand surveys and consider how a sample affects survey results	1		5		15, 21, 26		a, e, f	13, 16		13, 20		P(6); R(5)
1-6	to organize data and choose an appropriate method of organization	2, 3		9, 10		17, 18, 25		b, c	10, 14		4		P(7); R(6)
1-7	to make scatterplots and determine trends shown in the scatterplots	4, 5		7, 8		19, 20			15		17, 18		P(8); R(7)
1-8	to design a survey and to decide the purpose and population of a survey	6, 7		11		16, 21, 22			16, 17		13, 19, 20		P(9); R(8)

Item Analysis for Individual Assessment: Chapter 2

Chapter 2: Integers

Student Name _____

Place a ✔ in the column if the student has answered some or all of the questions correctly.

For Test Form D, check all the objectives that are reflected in the student's response.

Quiz or Test Form	Score	Date

Review Options in Student Edition

- Section A Review, page 88
- Section B Review, page 112
- Chapter 2 Summary and Review, page 114
- Chapter 2 Assessment, page 116

Quizzes and Tests from the Assessment Sourcebook

Lesson	Objectives	Quizzes Items	✔	Chapter Test Forms A & B Items	✔	Chapter Test Form C Items	✔	Chapter Test Form D	✔	Chapter Test Form E Items	✔	Chapter Test Form F Items	✔	Review Options in Supplements — Practice and Reteaching Masters (pages)
Section A														
2-1	to compare and order integers	1, 2		1–3		1–3		c, d		1–3, 21		7, 8		P(12); R(9)
	to find the absolute value of integers	3		4, 5		4–6				2, 4		13		
2-2	to add integers	4, 5		6–10, 15, 17		7–11				5, 6		14, 15		P(13); R(10)
2-3	to subtract integers	6, 7		11–16		12–15		c, d		7, 8		14		P(14); R(11)
2-4	to multiply and divide integers	8–10		18–20		16–19		b, e, f		9, 10, 21		1, 2		P(15); R(12)
2-5	to evaluate expressions involving integers and to use the distributive property	11–14		21, 22		20–22				11–13		9		P(16); R(13)
Section B														
2-6	to plot pairs of integers on a coordinate grid	1–7		25, 26		23–25				14, 15		10		P(18); R(14)
2-7	to change numbers from standard to exponential notation, and vice versa	8–11, 14		23, 24		26–30				12, 16		3, 4, 11		P(19); R(15)
2-8	to convert large numbers between standard notation and scientific notation	12		27–29		31, 32, 35, 36		a		17, 18		5		P(20); R(16)
2-9	to convert small numbers between standard notation and scientific notation	13		30		33, 34, 37, 38				19–21		6		P(21); R(17)

Item Analysis for Individual Assessment: Chapter 3

Chapter 3: The Language of Algebra: Variables, Expressions, and Equations

Student Name _____

Place a ✓ in the column if the student has answered some or all of the questions correctly.

For Test Form D, check all the objectives that are reflected in the student's response.

Quiz or Test Form	Score	Date

Review Options in Student Edition
- Section A Review, page 138
- Section B Review, page 162
- Chapter 3 Summary and Review, page 164
- Chapter 3 Assessment, page 166

Lesson	Objectives	Quizzes Items	✓	Chapter Test Forms A & B Items	✓	Chapter Test Form C Items	✓	Chapter Test Form D	✓	Chapter Test Form E Items	✓	Chapter Test Form F Items	✓	Practice and Reteaching Masters (pages)
Section A														
3-1	how to use familiar formulas as an introduction to algebra	1–3		1–3		1–3		g		1, 19		1, 25, 26		P(24); R(18)
3-2	how to apply algebraic expressions in a wide variety of situations	11–13		11–15		9, 13		h		2, 10, 14		23, 24, 26, 27		P(25); R(19)
	how to solve simple equations	1–10		7–10		14–6				4, 11–13, 15		4, 5		
3-3	how to translate verbal expressions into algebraic expressions	14		11–15		6, 10–12		a, b, e, f, h		6–9		16–18		P(26); R(20)
Section B														
3-4	how to solve equations by undoing addition or subtraction	1–3		7, 16, 18		14, 15		a, f		10, 11, 15		9, 10, 15, 16		P(28); R(21)
3-5	how to solve equations by undoing multiplication or division	4–6, 9, 13		8, 19–21, 24		4, 5, 7, 8, 17–19		d		4, 10, 12–14, 18		11, 12, 15, 16		P(29); R(22)
3-6	how to solve equations by undoing operations in two steps	7, 8, 10, 14		4–6, 22, 23, 25, 28		20–23		h		2, 3, 9, 14, 15, 20		2, 3, 6, 7, 8, 13–16, 24		P(30); R(23)
3-7	how to solve inequalities	11, 12, 15		26, 27		24–26		c		5, 16, 17, 19		20, 21		P(31); R(24)

Quizzes and Tests from the Assessment Sourcebook — *Review Options in Supplements*

Chapter 4: Algebra: Linear Equations and Inequalities

Student Name _____

Place a ✔ in the column if the student has answered some or all of the questions correctly.

For Test Form D, check all the objectives that are reflected in the student's response.

Quiz or Test Form	Score	Date

Review Options in Student Edition
- Section A Review, page 188
- Section B Review, page 212
- Chapter 4 Summary and Review, page 214
- Chapter 4 Assessment, page 216

Lesson	Objectives	Quizzes		Chapter Test Forms A & B		Chapter Test Form C		Chapter Test Form D	Chapter Test Form E		Chapter Test Form F		Review Options in Supplements: Practice and Reteaching Masters (pages)
		Items	✔	Items	✔	Items	✔	✔	Items	✔	Items	✔	
Section A													
4-1	to describe patterns produced by relationships between two variables	1-3, 6		1, 2		1-3		a, b	1, 2, 4		1, 8, 16		P(34); R(25)
4-2	to determine whether a pair of values is a solution of a two-variable equation	4, 5, 8		3, 4		4, 5, 15, 18			3, 5		2, 4		P(35); R(26)
4-3	to graph a two-variable relationship	7		5, 6		8, 9, 21		c	6, 8-10		9, 10, 22a, 22b		P(36); R(27)
Section B													
4-4	to find the slope of a line	1, 3, 7		7, 8		6, 9, 10, 19			10, 11, 15		18		P(38); R(28)
4-5	to graph an equation and then find the slope and the intercepts	1-3		7, 8, 10		7, 10-12			7, 11, 13		3, 12		P(39); R(29)
4-6	to find a single solution of a pair of linear equations	4, 6		9		13, 14, 20		c	12, 15		11, 22c		P(40); R(30)
4-7	to express two-variable inequalities graphically	5		11		16, 17		d	14		13		P(41); R(31)

Quizzes and Tests from the Assessment Sourcebook

Item Analysis for Individual Assessment: Chapter 5

Chapter 5: Ratio and Proportion

Student Name _____

Quiz or Test Form	Score	Date

Place a ✔ in the column if the student has answered some or all of the questions correctly.

For Test Form D, check all the objectives that are reflected in the student's response.

Review Options in Student Edition

- Section A Review, page 240
- Section B Review, page 264
- Chapter 5 Summary and Review, page 266
- Chapter 5 Assessment, page 268

Lesson	Objectives	Quizzes Items	✔	Chapter Test Forms A & B Items	✔	Chapter Test Form C Items	✔	Chapter Test Form D ✔	Chapter Test Form E Items	✔	Chapter Test Form F Items	✔	Practice and Reteaching Masters (pages)
Section A													
5-1	to estimate ratios and rates from pictures and data	1, 2		1		1, 2, 3		b	1, 2		21, 22		P(44); R(32)
	to use ratios and rates to compare quantities	3		2, 3, 14		4, 5			3		1, 23		
5-2	to create and identify equal ratios and rates	4, 9		4		6, 7		c, d	4, 15		2, 11		P(45); R(33)
	to express equal ratios and rates in tables	5		5		8, 9		e	5, 18		3, 24		
	to test for proportionality	6		6, 12		10, 11			7, 18		4, 12		
5-3	to differentiate proportional and nonproportional relationships graphically	8		11, 12		12, 13			8		13, 14		P(46); R(34)
	to link the constant of proportionality to slope	7		9		14, 15			9		5, 15		
Section B													
5-4	to use mental math and cross multiplication to solve proportions	1–3, 11		7, 8, 10		16, 17, 21, 22			10, 14		6, 16		P(48); R(35)
5-5	to find unit rates and use rate formulas to solve proportion problems	4, 5		10, 13		18–20			11, 16		17, 25		P(49); R(36)
5-6	to solve problems with rates and proportions	6, 7		14, 16		21, 22		c, d	6, 12		26a, b		P(50); R(37)
5-7	to use scales and create scale drawings	7–9		15, 17		23, 24		a, c	13, 17, 18		7, 18		P(51); R(38)

Quizzes and Tests from the Assessment Sourcebook

Review Options in Supplements

Item Analysis for Individual Assessment: Chapter 6

Chapter 6: Percent

Student Name _____

Place a ✔ in the column if the student has answered some or all of the questions correctly.

For Test Form D, check all the objectives that are reflected in the student's response.

Quiz or Test Form	Score	Date

Review Options in Student Edition
- Section A Review, page 292
- Section B Review, page 314
- Chapter 6 Summary and Review, page 316
- Chapter 6 Assessment, page 318

Lesson	Objectives	Quizzes Items	✔	Chapter Test Forms A & B Items	✔	Chapter Test Form C Items	✔	Chapter Test Form D ✔	Chapter Test Form E Items	✔	Chapter Test Form F Items	✔	Practice and Reteaching Masters (pages)
Section A													
6-1	to convert among fractions, decimals, and percents	1–3		1–3		1–3			1–3		2		P(54); R(39)
6-2	to use proportions and equations to solve percent problems	4–6, 9		4–6		4–7, 29, 30			4		1, 6		P(55); R(40)
6-3	to estimate percents of numbers, and what percent one number is of another	7, 8, 10		7–9		8–10			5, 6		3		P(56); R(41)
Section B													
6-4	to find the percent increase of a number	1, 2, 4		10, 13, 14		11, 14, 16, 32			7		7, 10		P(58); R(42)
	to find the result or the original number given the percent increase	3		15, 16		17, 18, 19, 31		a, c	10, 11		15, 16, 20		
6-5	to find the percent decrease of a number	5, 12		11, 12, 17		12, 13, 15			8, 9, 12		8, 11		P(59); R(43)
	to find the result or the original number given the percent decrease	6, 7		18, 19		20–22		d	13, 14, 19		14, 18		
6-6	to use and apply percent increase and decrease	8, 9		20, 21		23–25		b, e	15, 16		12		P(60); R(44)
	to calculate simple and compound interest	10, 11		22, 23		26–28			17, 18		17, 21		

Item Analysis for Individual Assessment: Chapter 7

Chapter 7: Number Sense, Rational Numbers, and Irrational Numbers

Student Name _____

Place a ✔ in the column if the student has answered some or all of the questions correctly.

For Test Form D, check all the objectives that are reflected in the student's response.

Quiz or Test Form	Score	Date

Review Options in Student Edition
- Section A Review, page 342
- Section B Review, page 362
- Section C Review, page 380
- Chapter 7 Summary and Review, page 382
- Chapter 7 Assessment, page 384

		Quizzes and Tests from the Assessment Sourcebook											Review Options in Supplements
Lesson	Objectives	Quizzes		Chapter Test Forms A & B		Chapter Test Form C		Chapter Test Form D	Chapter Test Form E		Chapter Test Form F		Practice and Reteaching Masters (pages)
		Items	✔	Items	✔	Items	✔	✔	Items	✔	Items	✔	
Section A													
7-1	to use rules for determining whether a number is divisible by another number	1–6		1–3		1–3		b, c	1, 2, 20		1, 22		P(63); R(45)
7-2	to find the GCF of two or more numbers	7–9		4, 5		4–6		d, e, f	3, 4		10, 11		P(64); R(46)
7-3	to find the LCM of two or more numbers	10–13		6–11		7–9		a, e, f	5, 6		12, 13, 22		P(65); R(47)
Section B													
7-4	to compare and order rational numbers	1–5		12–15		10–12			7, 8		14, 15		P(67); R(48)
7-5	to add and subtract rational numbers	6, 8, 10, 12		16, 17, 20		13–17, 34, 35			9, 10		2, 3, 24		P(68); R(49)
7-6	to multiply and divide rational numbers	7, 9, 11		18, 19		18–21, 33		a, b, e, f	11, 12		4, 5, 25		P(69); R(50)
Section C													
7-7	to take square roots and identify perfect squares	1, 3		21–25		22–24			13, 14, 20		6, 16		P(71); R(51)
7-8	to identify square roots that are irrational numbers	2, 4–6		26		25–27			15, 16		17, 18		P(72); R(52)
7-9	to use the Pythagorean theorem with right triangles	7–10		27–30		28–32			17, 18, 19		20, 21		P(73); R(53)

Item Analysis for Individual Assessment: Chapter 8

Chapter 8: Geometry and Measurement

Student Name _____

Place a ✔ in the column if the student has answered some or all of the questions correctly.

For Test Form D, check all the objectives that are reflected in the student's response.

Quiz or Test Form	Score	Date

Review Options in Student Edition
- Section A Review, page 408
- Section B Review, page 434
- Chapter 8 Summary and Review, page 436
- Chapter 8 Assessment, page 438

		Quizzes		Quizzes and Tests from the Assessment Sourcebook										Review Options in Supplements
Lesson	Objectives			Chapter Test Forms A & B		Chapter Test Form C		Chapter Test Form D		Chapter Test Form E		Chapter Test Form F		Practice and Reteaching Masters (pages)
		Items	✔	Items	✔	Items	✔		✔	Items	✔	Items	✔	
Section A														
8-1	to choose an appropriate unit of measurement	1–4		1, 2		1–5				1, 2		8, 11		P(76); R(54)
8-2	to identify more precise measurements	5–8, 11		3, 4		6–9				3, 4		9, 12		P(77); R(55)
8-3	to locate places using map coordinates and latitude and longitude	9, 10		5–7		10–13		c, d		5–7		21–23		P(78); R(56)
Section B														
8-4	to draw, measure, and identify angles	1–3		8–11		14–18		b		8–12, 21		13, 14		P(80); R(57)
8-5	to recognize and construct parallel and perpendicular lines	4–6		12–14		19–22		a, d		13–15		15, 16		P(81); R(58)
8-6	to classify polygons	7, 8		15–17		23–26				16–18		17–19		P(82); R(59)
8-7	to represent three-dimensional shapes in a drawing	9, 10		18, 19		27–29				19, 20		20		P(83); R(60)

Item Analysis for Individual Assessment: Chapter 9

Chapter 9: Area and Volume

Student Name _____

Quiz or Test Form	Score	Date

Place a ✔ in the column if the student has answered some or all of the questions correctly.

For Test Form D, check all the objectives that are reflected in the student's response.

Review Options in Student Edition
• Section A Review, page 474
• Section B Review, page 498
• Chapter 9 Summary and Review, page 500
• Chapter 9 Assessment, page 502

Lesson	Objectives	Quizzes Items	✓	Chapter Test Forms A & B Items	✓	Chapter Test Form C Items	✓	Chapter Test Form D	✓	Chapter Test Form E Items	✓	Chapter Test Form F Items	✓	Practice and Reteaching Masters (pages)
Section A														
9-1	to find the area and perimeter of polygons	1, 8		1, 2		1, 2, 3				1		1, 2, 8		P(86); R(61)
9-2	to dilate rectangles and predict the resulting perimeters and areas	2		3–5		4, 5, 20, 21				9, 10		3		P(87); R(62)
9-3	to find the area and circumference of circles	3		6–8		6, 7				2		17		P(88); R(63)
9-4	to find the surface area of prisms and cylinders	4, 5		9, 10		8, 9		a		3, 7, 8, 11, 14		6, 10, 14		P(89); R(64)
9-5	to find the surface area of pyramids and cones	6, 7		11, 12		10, 11		a		4, 6		10		P(90); R(65)
Section B														
9-6	to determine the volume of rectangular prisms	1		13, 14		12, 13		a, b		12, 14		18		P(92); R(66)
9-7	to dilate rectangular prisms and predict their volume	3, 7		15, 16		14, 15				13		7, 15		P(93); R(67)
9-8	to find the volume of prisms and cylinders	2, 4		A 17, 19 B 17		16, 17, 22		a, b		7, 8		6, 14		P(94); R(68)
9-9	to find the volume of pyramids and cones	5, 6		A 18, B 18, 19		18, 19, 22		a, b		5, 6		9, 11, 13		P(95); R(69)

Quizzes and Tests from the Assessment Sourcebook

Review Options in Supplements

Item Analysis for Individual Assessment: Chapter 10

Chapter 10: Algebra: Functions and Relationships

Student Name _____

Place a ✔ in the column if the student has answered some or all of the questions correctly.

For Test Form D, check all the objectives that are reflected in the student's response.

Quiz or Test Form	Score	Date

Review Options in Student Edition

- Section A Review, page 530
- Section B Review, page 554
- Chapter 10 Summary and Review, page 556
- Chapter 10 Assessment, page 558

Lesson	Objectives	Quizzes Items	✔	Chapter Test Forms A & B Items	✔	Chapter Test Form C Items	✔	Chapter Test Form D	✔	Chapter Test Form E Items	✔	Chapter Test Form F Items	✔	Practice and Reteaching Masters (pages)
Section A														
10-1	to recognize a function and to find the input and output values of a function	1-3, 8		1, 2		1, 2, 5, 24		a, b		1-3		1, 6		P(98); R(70)
10-2	to represent functions using tables, graphs, and equations	4-7		3-8		3, 4		a, b, c		4, 6		12		P(99); R(71)
10-3	to represent quadratic functions as graphs, tables, and equations	5, 7		5, 6		6-8		d		5, 7, 8		13		P(100); R(72)
10-4	to graph and evaluate other types of functions	4, 6, 9		7, 8		9-11				9, 10		14, 21		P(101); R(73)
Section B														
10-5	to evaluate polynomials	1-3, 10		9-11		12-14				11, 12		12, 18, 20		P(103); R(74)
10-6	to add polynomials	4, 5, 10		12, 13		15-17				13-15		2, 15		P(104); R(75)
10-7	to subtract polynomials	6, 7		14, 15		18-20				16-18		3, 16, 22		P(105); R(76)
10-8	to multiply polynomials and monomials	8, 9, 11		16, 17		21-23				19, 20		4, 5		P(106); R(77)

Quizzes and Tests from the Assessment Sourcebook
Review Options in Supplements

Item Analysis for Individual Assessment: Chapter 11

Chapter 11: Similarity, Congruence, and Transformations

Student Name _____

Place a ✔ in the column if the student has answered some or all of the questions correctly.

For Test Form D, check all the objectives that are reflected in the student's response.

Quiz or Test Form	Score	Date

Review Options in Student Edition

- Section A Review, page 592
- Section B Review, page 616
- Chapter 11 Summary and Review, page 618
- Chapter 11 Assessment, page 620

Quizzes and Tests from the Assessment Sourcebook / **Review Options in Supplements**

Lesson	Objectives	Quizzes Items	✔	Chapter Test Forms A & B Items	✔	Chapter Test Form C Items	✔	Chapter Test Form D ✔	Chapter Test Form E Items	✔	Chapter Test Form F Items	✔	Practice and Reteaching Masters (pages)
Section A													
11-1	to identify similar figures	1		1		1, 2			1, 2		1		P(109); R(78)
11-2	to identify congruent figures	2		2		3, 4			3		3		P(110); R(79)
11-3	to identify congruent triangles	3, 7		3		5, 6			4		7		P(111); R(80)
11-4	to use ratios in order to find missing side lengths of a right triangle	4		4		7, 8			5, 6		9, 10, 15		P(112); R(81)
11-5	to apply your knowledge of geometry and trigonometric ratios	5, 6		5, 9		9, 10			7		14		P(113); R(82)
Section B													
11-6	to move all the points of a figure and still have a congruent shape	1, 2, 6		6, 10		11, 12			8		11		P(115); R(83)
11-7	to transform a figure and have a shape that is similar to but not congruent to the original	3		7		13, 14		a, b, c, d	9		12		P(116); R(84)
11-8	to recognize several types of symmetry	4		11		15, 16			10		13		P(117); R(85)
11-9	to create endless patterns using transformations	5		8		17, 18			11		16		P(118); R(86)

Item Analysis for Individual Assessment: Chapter 12

Chapter 12: Counting and Probability

Student Name _____

Place a ✔ in the column if the student has answered some or all of the questions correctly.

For Test Form D, check all the objectives that are reflected in the student's response.

Quiz or Test Form	Score	Date

Review Options in Student Edition

- Section A Review, page 644
- Section B Review, page 670
- Chapter 12 Summary and Review, page 672
- Chapter 12 Assessment, page 674

Quizzes and Tests from the Assessment Sourcebook

Lesson	Objectives	Quizzes Items	✔	Chapter Test Forms A & B Items	✔	Chapter Test Form C Items	✔	Chapter Test Form D ✔	Chapter Test Form E Items	✔	Chapter Test Form F Items	✔	Review Options in Supplements Practice and Reteaching Masters (pages)
Section A													
12-1	to use tree diagrams and develop counting methods	5		1, 9		1, 2		c, d	1, 2, 15		5, 6, 20, 30		P(121); R(87)
12-2	to develop ways of counting in situations for which order of items is important	1–3, 6–8		2, 3, 5, 6		3, 4, 6–8			7		1, 2, 4, 21		P(122); R(88)
12-3	to recognize unordered selections as combinations and to develop ways of counting in situations for which the order of items is unimportant	4, 9, 10		4, 7, 8		5, 7, 9–12			3–6		3, 15, 16, 23		P(123); R(89)
Section B													
12-4	to compare probability	1–3		8, 9		13–19			8, 9		22, 24, 25, 31		P(125); R(90)
12-5	to use experiments to find probabilities	9		10–12		20–23		a	10, 11		32, 33		P(126); R(91)
12-6	to understand what affects the probability of an event	4–6		13, 14		24–26, 28		b	12, 13		27, 32		P(127); R(92)
12-7	to recognize an independent event	7, 8, 10		15, 16		27, 29		b	14		18, 19, 26		P(128); R(93)

Item Analysis for Individual Assessment

Quarterly Test, Chapters 1–3

Student Name _____   **See page 345 for scoring.**

Place a ✔ in the column if the student has answered some or all of the questions correctly.

Objectives	Lesson	Test Item	✔ if correct	Practice (pages)	Reteaching (pages)
		Quarterly Test Chapters 1–3		**Review Options in Supplements**	
how to understand data with line plots and stem-and-leaf diagrams	1-1	1, 2, 3, 4		1	1
how to analyze and represent data using mean, median, and mode	1-2	3, 4		2	2
how to analyze and represent the spread and distribution of data using box-and-whisker plots	1-3	5		3	3
how to understand data using bar graphs and line graphs	1-4	6		4	4
to understand surveys and consider how a sample affects survey results	1-5	7, 8		6	5
to organize data and choose an appropriate method of organization	1-6	9		7	6
to make scatterplots and determine trends shown in the scatterplots	1-7	10		8	7
to design a survey and to decide the purpose and population of a survey	1-8	8		9	8
to compare and order integers	2-1	11		12	9
to find the absolute value of integers	2-1	12, 13		12	9
to subtract integers	2-3	14		14	11
to multiply and divide integers	2-4	15, 16		15	12
to evaluate expressions involving integers and to use the distributive property	2-5	17		16	13
to plot pairs of integers on a coordinate grid	2-6	18		18	14
to change numbers from standard to exponential notation, and vice versa	2-7	19, 20		19	15
to convert small numbers between standard notation and scientific notation	2-9	21		21	17
how to use familiar formulas as an introduction to algebra	3-1	22, 23, 24, 25		24	18
how to solve simple equations	3-2	27, 29, 30		25	19
how to translate verbal expressions into algebraic expressions	3-3	26, 28		26	20
how to solve equations by undoing addition or subtraction	3-4	30		28	21
how to solve equations by undoing multiplication or division	3-5	29		29	22
how to solve inequalities	3-7	31, 32		31	24

Item Analysis for Individual Assessment

Quarterly Test, Chapters 1–6

Student Name _____

See page 345 for scoring.

Place a ✔ in the column if the student has answered some or all of the questions correctly.

Objectives	Lesson	Test Item	✔ if correct	Practice (pages)	Reteaching (pages)
		Quarterly Test Chapters 1–6		**Review Options in Supplements**	
how to understand data with line plots and stem-and-leaf diagrams	1-1	1, 2		1	1
how to analyze and represent data using mean, median, and mode	1-2	2		2	2
how to analyze and represent the spread and distribution of data using box-and-whisker plots	1-3	3		3	3
how to understand data using bar graphs and line graphs	1-4	4		4	4
to understand surveys and consider how a sample affects survey results	1-5	5		6	5
to compare and order integers	2-1	6		12	9
to add integers	2-2	7		13	10
to multiply and divide integers	2-4	8		15	12
to evaluate expressions involving integers and to use the distributive property	2-5	9		16	13
to convert small numbers between standard notation and scientific notation	2-9	10		21	17
how to use familiar formulas as an introduction to algebra	3-1	11		24	18
how to translate verbal expressions into algebraic expressions	3-3	12		26	20
how to solve equations by undoing multiplication or division	3-5	13, 14		29	22
to describe patterns produced by relationships between two variables	4-1	15		34	25
to determine whether a pair of values is a solution of a two-variable equation	4-2	16		35	26
to graph a two-variable relationship	4-3	17		36	27
to find the slope of a line	4-4	18		38	28
to graph an equation and then find the slope and the intercepts	4-5	19		39	29
to find a single solution of a pair of linear equations	4-6	20		40	30
to express two-variable inequalities graphically	4-7	21		41	31
to estimate ratios and rates from pictures and data	5-1	25		44	32
to test for proportionality	5-2	22		45	33
to link the constant of proportionality to slope	5-3	23		46	34

Continued on next page.

© Scott Foresman Addison Wesley 8

Item Analysis for Individual Assessment

Quarterly Test, Chapters 1–6 (continued)

Student Name _____   **See page 345 for scoring.**

Place a ✔ in the column if the student has answered some or all of the questions correctly.

Objectives	Lesson	Test Item	✔ if correct	Practice (pages)	Reteaching (pages)
		Quarterly Test Chapters 1–6		**Review Options in Supplements**	
to use mental math and cross multiplication to solve proportions	5-4	24		48	35
to use scales and create scale drawings	5-7	26		51	38
to convert among fractions, decimals, and percents	6-1	27		54	39
to use proportions and equations to solve percent problems	6-2	28, 30, 31		55	40
to find the percent increase of a number	6-4	29		58	42

Item Analysis for Individual Assessment

Quarterly Test, Chapters 1–9

Student Name _____   See page 345 for scoring.

Place a ✔ in the column if the student has answered some or all of the questions correctly.

Objectives	Lesson	Quarterly Test Chapters 1–9		Review Options in Supplements	
		Test Item	✔ if correct	Practice (pages)	Reteaching (pages)
how to understand data with line plots and stem-and-leaf diagrams	1-1	1		1	1
how to analyze and represent data using mean, median, and mode	1-2	1		2	2
how to analyze and represent the spread and distribution of data using box-and-whisker plots	1-3	2		3	3
to understand surveys and consider how a sample affects survey results	1-5	3		6	5
to compare and order integers	2-1	4		12	9
to add integers	2-2	5		13	10
to evaluate expressions involving integers and to use the distributive property	2-5	6		16	13
to convert large numbers between standard notation and scientific notation	2-8	7		20	16
how to use familiar formulas as an introduction to algebra	3-1	8		24	18
how to solve simple equations	3-2	10		25	19
how to translate verbal expressions into algebraic expressions	3-3	9		26	20
how to solve equations by undoing multiplication or division	3-5	10		29	22
how to solve inequalities	3-7	11		31	24
to find the slope of a line	4-4	12		38	28
to graph an equation and then find the slope and the intercepts	4-5	13		39	29
to find a single solution of a pair of linear equations	4-6	14		40	30
to test for proportionality	5-2	15		45	33
to link the constant of proportionality to slope	5-3	16		46	34
to find unit rates and use rate formulas to solve proportion problems	5-5	17		49	36
to use proportions and equations to solve percent problems	6-2	18, 19, 20		55	40
to use rules for determining whether a number is divisible by another number	7-1	21		63	45
to identify square roots that are irrational numbers	7-8	22		72	52
to use the Pythagorean theorem with right triangles	7-9	23		73	53
to choose an appropriate unit of measurement	8-1	24		76	54
to identify more precise measurements	8-2	25		77	55

Continued on next page.

© Scott Foresman Addison Wesley 8

Item Analysis for Individual Assessment

Quarterly Test, Chapters 1–9 (continued)

Student Name _____

See page 345 for scoring.

Place a ✔ in the column if the student has answered
some or all of the questions correctly.

Objectives	Lesson	Quarterly Test Chapters 1–9		Review Options in Supplements	
		Test Item	✔ if correct	Practice (pages)	Reteaching (pages)
to recognize and construct parallel and perpendicular lines	8-5	26		81	58
to classify polygons	8-6	27		82	59
to dilate rectangles and predict the resulting perimeters and areas	9-2	28		87	62
to find the area and circumference of circles	9-3	29		88	63
to find the surface area of pyramids and cones	9-5	30		90	65
to determine the volume of rectangular prisms	9-6	31		92	66

Item Analysis for Individual Assessment

Quarterly Test, Chapters 1–12

Student Name _____   See page 345 for scoring.

Place a ✔ in the column if the student has answered some or all of the questions correctly.

Objectives	Lesson	Quarterly Test Chapters 1–12		Review Options in Supplements	
		Test Item	✔ if correct	Practice (pages)	Reteaching (pages)
how to understand data with line plots and stem-and-leaf diagrams	1-1	1		1	1
how to analyze and represent data using mean, median, and mode	1-2	1		2	2
how to understand data using bar graphs and line graphs	1-4	2		4	4
to organize data and choose an appropriate method of organization	1-6	2		7	6
to design a survey and to decide the purpose and population of a survey	1-8	3		9	8
to compare and order integers	2-1	4		12	9
to multiply and divide integers	2-4	5		15	12
to convert large numbers between standard notation and scientific notation	2-8	6		20	16
how to solve simple equations	3-2	7		25	19
how to translate verbal expressions into algebraic expressions	3-3	8		26	20
how to solve equations by undoing addition or subtraction	3-4	7		28	21
how to solve equations by undoing multiplication or division	3-5	8		29	22
how to solve inequalities	3-7	9		31	24
to graph a two-variable relationship	4-3	11		36	27
to find the slope of a line	4-4	10		38	28
to use mental math and cross multiplication to solve proportions	5-4	12		48	35
to find unit rates and use rate formulas to solve proportion problems	5-5	13		49	36
to use scales and create scale drawings	5-7	14		51	38
to convert among fractions, decimals, and percents	6-1	15		54	39
to find the percent increase of a number	6-4	16		58	42
to find the GCF of two or more numbers	7-2	17		64	46
to find the LCM of two or more numbers	7-3	18		65	47
to identify more precise measurements	8-2	19		77	55
to draw, measure, and identify angles	8-4	20		80	57
to find the area and perimeter of polygons	9-1	21		86	61

Continued on next page.

Item Analysis for Individual Assessment

Quarterly Test, Chapters 1–12 (continued)

Student Name _____   **See page 345 for scoring.**

Place a ✔ in the column if the student has answered some or all of the questions correctly.

Objectives	Lesson	Quarterly Test Chapters 1–12		Review Options in Supplements	
		Test Item	✔ if correct	Practice (pages)	Reteaching (pages)
to find the surface area of prisms and cylinders	9-4	22		89	64
to find the volume of prisms and cylinders	9-8	23		94	68
to graph and evaluate other types of functions	10-4	25		101	73
to evaluate polynomials	10-5	24		103	74
to add polynomials	10-6	26		104	75
to use ratios in order to find missing side lengths of a right triangle	11-4	27, 28		112	81
to use tree diagrams and develop counting methods	12-1	29		121	87
to compare probability	12-4	30		125	90
to use experiments to find probabilities	12-5	31		126	91

Class Test Record Form: Chapters 1–6

Students	Tests							
	Chapter			Quarterly	Chapter			Quarterly
	1	2	3	Ch. 1–3	4	5	6	Ch. 1–6
1.								
2.								
3.								
4.								
5.								
6.								
7.								
8.								
9.								
10.								
11.								
12.								
13.								
14.								
15.								
16.								
17.								
18.								
19.								
20.								
21.								
22.								
23.								
24.								
25.								
26.								
27.								
28.								
29.								
30.								
31.								
32.								
33.								
34.								
35.								

Class Test Record Form: Chapters 7–12

Students	Tests							
	Chapter			Quarterly	Chapter			Quarterly
	7	8	9	Ch. 1–9	10	11	12	Ch. 1–12
1.								
2.								
3.								
4.								
5.								
6.								
7.								
8.								
9.								
10.								
11.								
12.								
13.								
14.								
15.								
16.								
17.								
18.								
19.								
20.								
21.								
22.								
23.								
24.								
25.								
26.								
27.								
28.								
29.								
30.								
31.								
32.								
33.								
34.								
35.								

Percent Table for Scoring Tests

This table will help you quickly convert a raw test score to a percent score for any test continuing up to 53 items.

Directions for using the table

Example: There are 28 items on a test, and a student correctly answers 22 of them.

1. Find the number of items, 28, along the left side of the table.
2. Place a rule or a strip of paper under the row for 28.
3. Find the column for 22, the number of items correctly answered.
4. Go down the column for 22 until you come to the row for 28. The number 79 is the percent score.

Number Correct

Number of Items	1	2	3	4	5	6	7	8	9	10	11	12	13	14	15	16	17	18	19	20	21	22	23	24	25	26	27	28	29	30	31	32	33	34	35	36	37	38	39	40	41	42	43	44	45	46	47	48	49	50	51	52	53
1	100																																																				
2	50	100																																																			
3	33	67	100																																																		
4	25	50	75	100																																																	
5	20	40	60	80	100																																																
6	17	33	50	67	83	100																																															
7	14	29	43	57	71	86	100																																														
8	13	25	38	50	63	75	88	100																																													
9	11	22	33	44	56	67	78	89	100																																												
10	10	20	30	40	50	60	70	80	90	100																																										
11	9	18	27	36	45	55	64	73	82	91	100																																									
12	8	17	25	33	42	50	58	67	75	83	92	100																																								
13	8	15	23	31	38	46	54	62	69	77	85	92	100																																							
14	7	14	21	29	36	43	50	57	64	71	79	86	93	100																																						
15	7	13	20	27	33	40	47	53	60	67	73	80	87	93	100																																					
16	6	13	19	25	31	38	44	50	56	63	69	75	81	88	94	100																																				
17	6	12	18	24	29	35	41	47	53	59	65	71	76	82	88	94	100																																			
18	6	11	17	22	28	33	39	44	50	56	61	67	72	78	83	89	94	100																																		
19	5	11	16	21	26	32	37	42	47	53	58	63	68	74	79	84	89	95	100																																	
20	5	10	15	20	25	30	35	40	45	50	55	60	65	70	75	80	85	90	95	100																																
21	5	10	14	19	24	29	33	38	43	48	52	57	62	67	71	76	81	86	90	95	100																															
22	5	9	14	18	23	27	32	36	41	45	50	55	59	64	68	73	77	82	86	91	95	100																														
23	4	9	13	17	22	26	30	35	39	43	48	52	57	61	65	70	74	78	83	87	91	96	100																													
24	4	8	13	17	21	25	29	33	38	42	46	50	54	58	63	67	71	75	79	83	88	92	96	100																												
25	4	8	12	16	20	24	28	32	36	40	44	48	52	56	60	64	68	72	76	80	84	88	92	96	100																											
26	4	8	12	15	19	23	27	31	35	38	42	46	50	54	58	62	65	69	73	77	81	85	88	92	96	100																										
27	4	7	11	15	19	22	26	30	33	37	41	44	48	52	56	59	63	67	70	74	78	81	85	89	93	96	100																									
28	4	7	11	14	18	21	25	29	32	36	39	43	46	50	54	57	61	64	68	71	75	79	82	86	89	93	96	100																							
29	3	7	10	14	17	21	24	28	31	34	38	41	45	48	52	55	59	62	66	69	72	76	79	83	86	90	93	97	100																						
30	3	7	10	13	17	20	23	27	30	33	37	40	43	47	50	53	57	60	63	67	70	73	77	80	83	87	90	93	97	100																					
31	3	6	10	13	16	19	23	26	29	32	35	39	42	45	48	52	55	58	61	65	68	71	74	77	81	84	87	90	94	97	100																				
32	3	6	9	13	16	19	22	25	28	31	34	38	41	44	47	50	53	56	59	63	66	69	72	75	78	81	84	88	91	94	97	100																			
33	3	6	9	12	15	18	21	24	27	30	33	36	39	42	45	48	52	55	58	61	64	67	70	73	76	79	82	85	88	91	94	97	100																		
34	3	6	9	12	15	18	21	24	26	29	32	35	38	41	44	47	50	53	56	59	62	65	68	71	74	76	79	82	85	88	91	94	97	100																	
35	3	6	9	11	14	17	20	23	26	29	31	34	37	40	43	46	49	51	54	57	60	63	66	69	71	74	77	80	83	86	89	91	94	97	100																
36	3	6	8	11	14	17	19	22	25	28	31	33	36	39	42	44	47	50	53	56	58	61	64	67	69	72	75	78	81	83	86	89	92	94	97	100															
37	3	5	8	11	14	16	19	22	24	27	30	32	35	38	41	43	46	49	51	54	57	59	62	65	68	70	73	76	78	81	84	86	89	92	95	97	100														
38	3	5	8	11	13	16	18	21	24	26	29	32	34	37	39	42	45	47	50	53	55	58	61	63	66	68	71	74	76	79	82	84	87	89	92	95	97	100													
39	3	5	8	10	13	15	18	21	23	26	28	31	33	36	38	41	44	46	49	51	54	56	59	62	64	67	69	72	74	77	79	82	85	87	90	92	95	97	100												
40	2	5	8	10	13	15	18	20	23	25	28	30	33	35	38	40	43	45	48	50	53	55	58	60	63	65	68	70	73	75	78	80	83	85	88	90	93	95	98	100											
41	2	5	7	10	12	15	17	20	22	24	27	29	32	34	37	39	41	44	46	49	51	54	56	59	61	63	66	68	71	73	76	78	80	83	85	88	90	93	95	98	100										
42	2	5	7	10	12	14	17	19	21	24	26	29	31	33	36	38	40	43	45	48	50	52	55	57	60	62	64	67	69	71	74	76	79	81	83	86	88	90	93	95	98	100									
43	2	5	7	9	12	14	16	19	21	23	26	28	30	33	35	37	40	42	44	47	49	51	53	56	58	60	63	65	67	70	72	74	77	79	81	84	86	88	91	93	95	98	100							
44	2	5	7	9	11	14	16	18	20	23	25	27	30	32	34	36	39	41	43	45	48	50	52	55	57	59	61	64	66	68	70	73	75	77	80	82	84	86	89	91	93	95	98	100						
45	2	4	7	9	11	13	16	18	20	22	24	27	29	31	33	36	38	40	42	44	47	49	51	53	56	58	60	62	64	67	69	71	73	76	78	80	82	84	87	89	91	93	96	98	100					
46	2	4	7	9	11	13	15	17	20	22	24	26	28	30	33	35	37	39	41	43	46	48	50	52	54	57	59	61	63	65	67	70	72	74	76	78	80	83	85	87	89	91	93	96	98	100				
47	2	4	6	9	11	13	15	17	19	21	23	26	28	30	32	34	36	38	40	43	45	47	49	51	53	55	57	60	62	64	66	68	70	72	74	77	79	81	83	85	87	89	91	94	96	98	100			
48	2	4	6	8	10	13	15	17	19	21	23	25	27	29	31	33	35	38	40	42	44	46	48	50	52	54	56	58	60	63	65	67	69	71	73	75	77	79	81	83	85	88	90	92	94	96	98	100		
49	2	4	6	8	10	12	14	16	18	20	22	24	27	29	31	33	35	37	39	41	43	45	47	49	51	53	55	57	59	61	63	65	67	69	71	73	76	78	80	82	84	86	88	90	92	94	96	98	100	
50	2	4	6	8	10	12	14	16	18	20	22	24	26	28	30	32	34	36	38	40	42	44	46	48	50	52	54	56	58	60	62	64	66	68	70	72	74	76	78	80	82	84	86	88	90	92	94	96	98	100	
51	2	4	6	8	10	12	14	16	18	20	22	24	25	27	29	31	33	35	37	39	41	43	45	47	49	51	53	55	57	59	61	63	65	67	69	71	73	75	76	78	80	82	84	86	88	90	92	94	96	98	100	
52	2	4	6	8	10	12	13	15	17	19	21	23	25	27	29	31	33	35	37	38	40	42	44	46	48	50	52	54	56	58	60	62	63	65	67	69	71	73	75	77	79	81	83	85	87	88	90	92	94	96	98	100	
53	2	4	6	8	9	11	13	15	17	19	21	23	25	26	28	30	32	34	36	38	40	42	43	45	47	49	51	53	55	57	58	60	62	64	66	68	70	72	74	75	77	79	81	83	85	87	89	91	92	94	96	98	100